KS3 Maths

Practice Test Papers

Ages 11-14

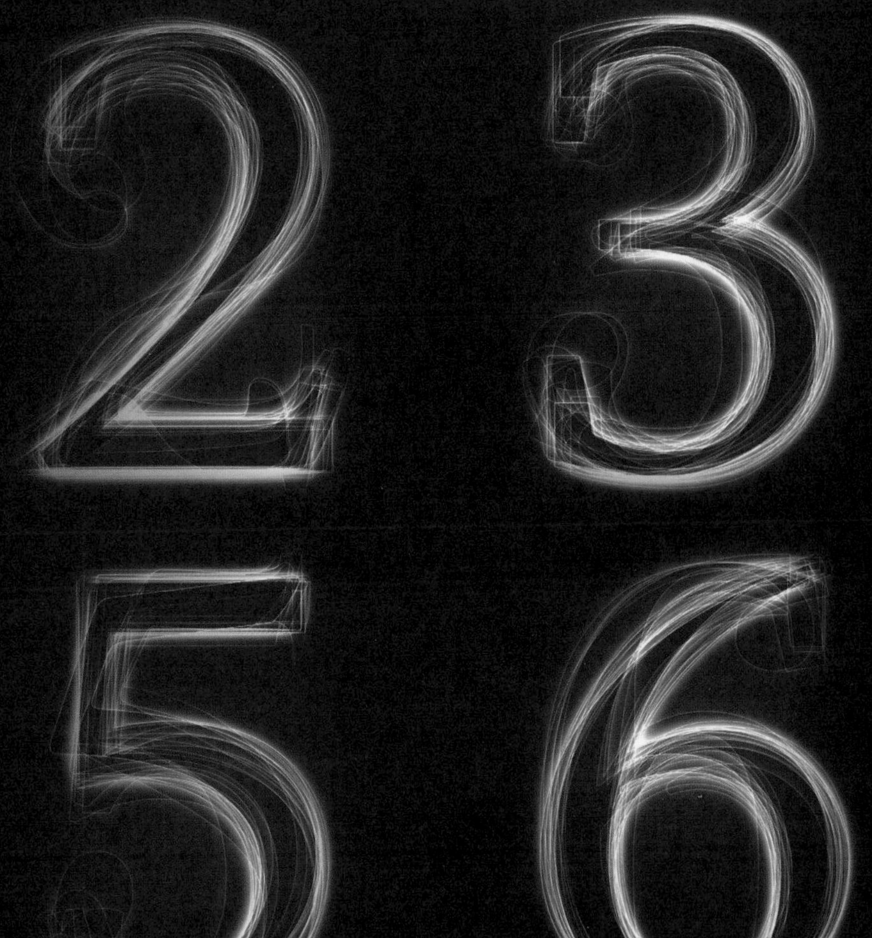

Mark Patmore and Brian Seager

Contents

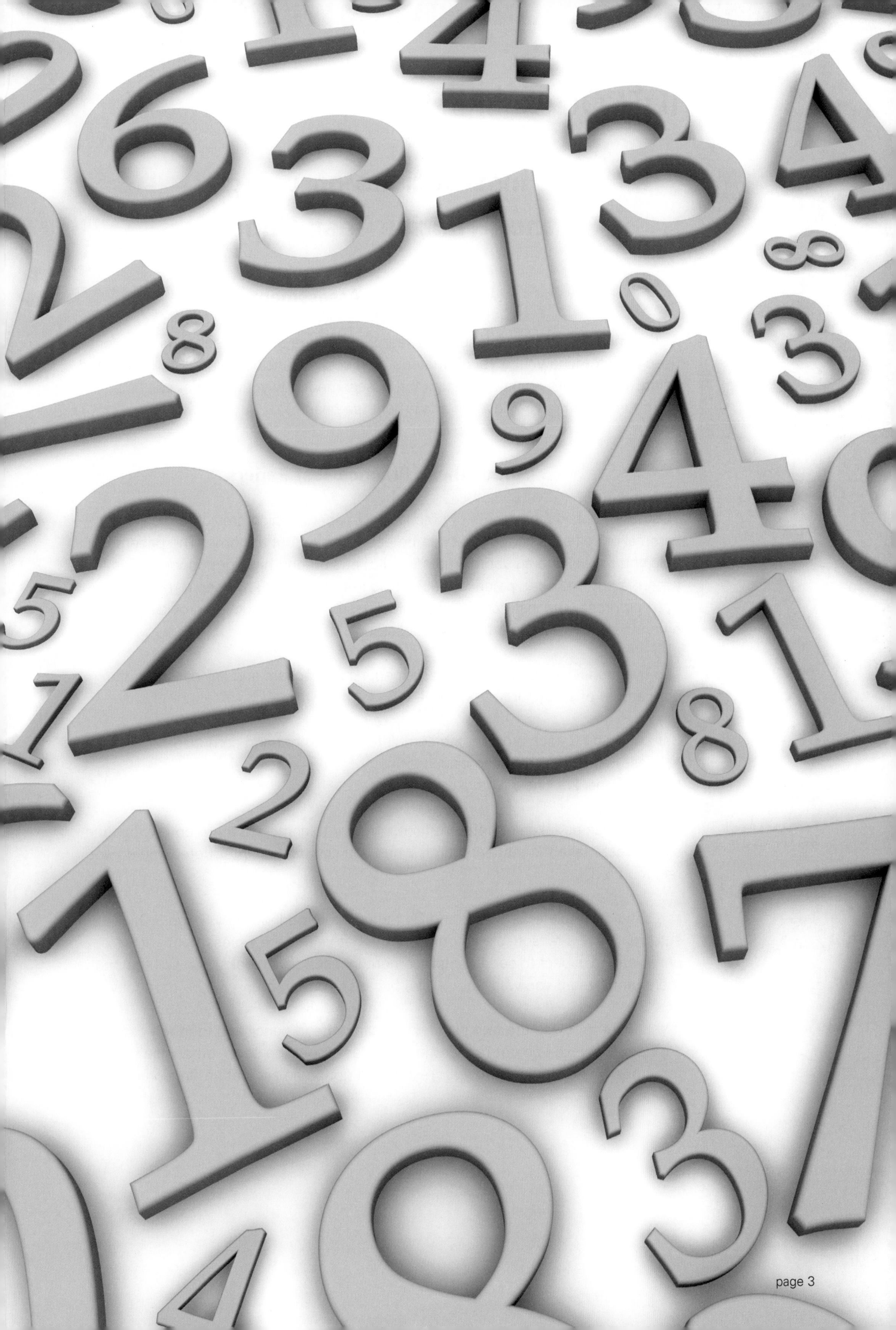

Introduction

Instructions on using the Practice Test Papers

Understanding Assessment

At the end of Key Stage 3 (usually in Year 9 at the age of 14), teacher assessment is used to determine your level of attainment in subjects including English, Maths and Science. There are no national tests but assessments by your teacher will help them to determine your level of attainment (see page 7).

About these Practice Test Papers

This book contains three sets of practice test papers, which provide a means of parental or self-assessment that can be easily carried out at home. The papers will help you to evaluate an approximate level of attainment, highlight opportunities for further study and skills practice that will aid improvement, and record results to track progress. The instructions and guidelines in this Introduction provide guidance on how to use the papers for self-assessment.

The questions have been written by experienced teachers and are based on the programme of study for Key Stage 3.

Sets A, B and C each provide one complete assessment and comprise:
- Test Paper 1 – 1 hour (no calculator)
- Test Paper 2 – 1 hour (with a calculator)

The tests can be taken at different times, but try to complete them both within the same week. Take the tests at a time when you can work uninterrupted and do not feel too tired.

You should complete Sets A, B and C at intervals throughout Key Stage 3. Make sure you leave a reasonable amount of time between each assessment – it is unrealistic to expect to see an improvement in just a few weeks. You will feel much more motivated if you wait for a while, because your progress will be more obvious.

If you want to re-use the test papers, you can write in pencil and then rub out your answers. However, do not repeat the same test paper too soon, otherwise you will remember the questions and your results will not be an accurate reflection of your abilities.

Before you start:

- find a suitable place to complete the papers – somewhere quiet, where you won't be disturbed
- make sure you have a pen, pencil, ruler, rubber and any other equipment stated on the front of the test paper (e.g. a protractor)
- make sure you have a clock or watch to time yourself
- turn off your mobile phone.

When completing the test papers:

- try to answer all of the questions and make sure you read them carefully
- write your answers in the spaces where you see the pencil icon 
- always show your working – it may get a mark
- keep an eye on the time – if you spend longer than an hour on the paper your results will not accurately reflect your abilities.

When you have finished:

- use the answers and marks provided in the pull-out Answers and Mark Scheme to mark the test paper
- read the top tips on how to improve your performance and remember the key points
- add up the total number of marks.

When you have taken the tests, they will be helpful to use to revise and prepare for actual assessments.

Tips for the Top

Make sure you have a suitable place to do the test and have a pen, pencil, ruler, rubber and any other equipment stated on the front of the test paper.

Try all of the questions and write your answers where you see the pencil:

The number of marks is shown for each part of the question.

Don't make silly mistakes. Remember to read the questions carefully.

Make your answers clearly legible. If you make a mistake, put a cross through it and write the correct answer clearly next to it. Use an eraser as little as possible.

Don't panic! These practice papers are meant to provide you with a guide to your progress and the level you are working at. They are not the be-all and end-all. If you cannot do a question, just go on to the next question and come back to it later if you have time.

Always show working. This may get a mark.

Using your Marks to Assess Levels

Record your test marks in the progress grid below:

	Week Beginning (Date)	Test Paper 1	Test Paper 2	Total	Level
Maximum Mark		60	60	120	8
Set A					
Set B					
Set C					

When you have completed both tests for each set, add the marks together to give a total mark out of 120.

The table below will give you an indication of your level based on your marks:

Below Level 6	Level 6	Level 7	Level 8
0–25	26–50	51–74	75–120

Remember that the level obtained in these tests may be different from the level that your teacher reports you are working at. This is because they can only test a limited range of skills and knowledge. Your teacher will have a better idea of your overall performance.

However, these tests will help you to identify areas of weakness that you can improve upon with a bit of hard work and extra study. This will help you to get a better mark on your next assessment test and progress at school.

Improving your Results and Making Progress

Go back through your test papers and make a note of all the questions that you got wrong. This will help you to identify topics that require further study.

If you want to improve your understanding and make progress, you need to be proactive! Use Study Guides and Workbooks for home study – they include lots of practice questions, which test your knowledge and reinforce what you have learned.

With a little bit of time and effort, when you take the next set of tests in the book you will achieve a higher mark. Remember to record the date alongside your marks in the grid above. This will allow you to track your progress over time and will help to build your confidence and a sense of achievement.

What do Levels Mean?

Attainment levels are used to measure your progress through Key Stages 1, 2 and 3. They are concerned with your knowledge, skills and understanding of a subject.

There are eight levels and they each have a description, which sets out the skills, knowledge and understanding that you are expected to demonstrate at that level. The descriptions for Levels 1 to 8 get increasingly difficult.

Although there are eight levels, at Key Stage 3 you are generally expected to work between Levels 3 and 7, where Level 7 represents excellent knowledge, skills and understanding.

The table below shows the expected National Curriculum levels for 14 year olds.

Level	Aged 14
Level 1	
Level 2 Level 2c Level 2b Level 2a	
Level 3	Below average
Level 4	Below average
Level 5	At level expected
Level 6	At level expected
Level 7	Excellent
Level 8	Exceptional

As you can see, it is expected that a majority of 14 year olds will achieve Level 5 or 6 by the end of Year 9. If you achieve Level 7, it is a real success. A 14 year old who achieves Level 8 is working at an exceptionally high level. For comparison, a student who gains a GCSE grade C has achieved Level 7.

Your teacher will carry out regular assessments to ensure that you are working at an appropriate level and progressing at the expected rate. The test papers in this book support this process. Provided you follow the instructions and address any potential problems that the tests highlight, they will help to ensure you are always working to the best of your abilities.

Set
A

KEY STAGE 3
Levels 6–8

Test Paper 1

Test Paper 1 (calculator **not** allowed)

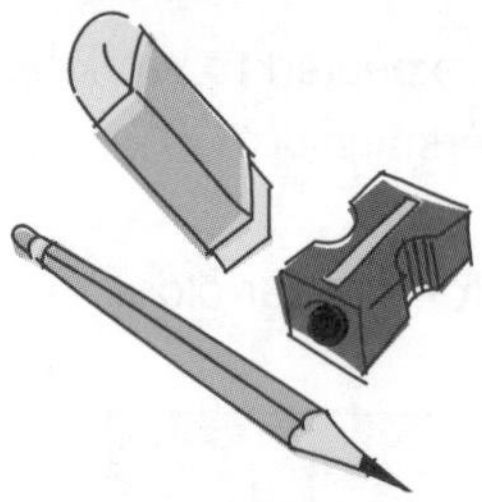

Instructions:

- find a quiet place where you can sit down and complete the test paper undisturbed
- make sure you have a pen, pencil, ruler, rubber and protractor
- read the questions carefully
- answer all the questions in this paper
- write your answers where you see this symbol 
- show all your working as marks may be awarded for this
- go through and check your answers when you have finished the test paper
- check how you have done using pages 97–98 of the Answers and Mark Scheme

Time:

This test paper is **1 hour** long.

Page	11	13	15	17	19	21	23	24	Max. Mark	**Actual Mark**
Score	....	....	....	....	....	....	....	....	60	....

First name ....

Last name ....

Test Paper 1 (calculator **not** allowed)

Formulae

Trapezium

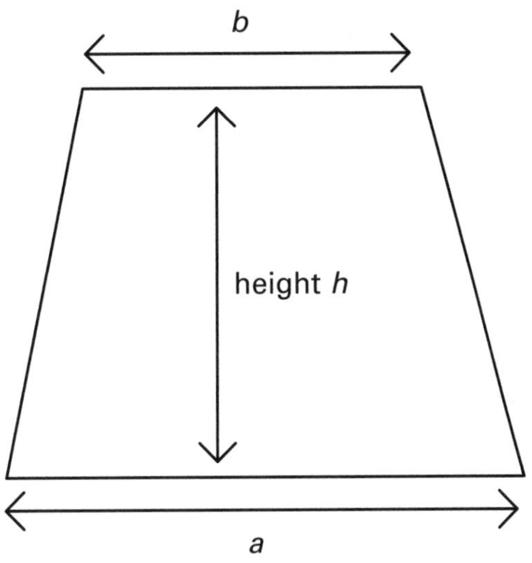

area $= \frac{1}{2}(a + b)h$

Prism

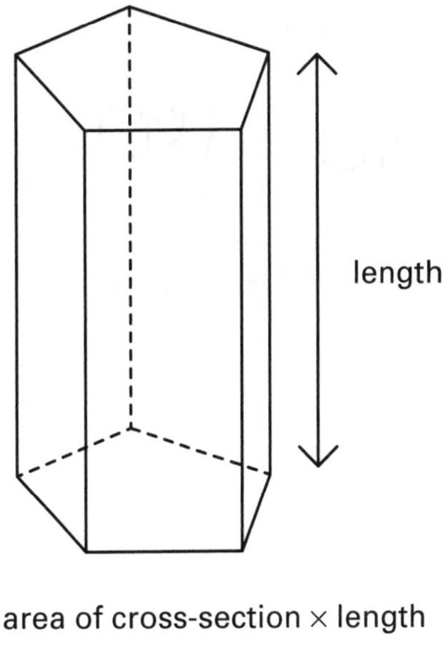

volume = area of cross-section × length

1 Amy finds out the following facts about a foreign country.

a) The population is roughly ninety million people.

Write this number in figures. *(1 mark)* Q1a

90,000,000.

b) It has roughly 600 doctors for every million people.

About how many doctors are in the country? *(1 mark)* Q1b

54,000.

2 The angles of a triangle are $x°$, $(2x + 10)°$ and $(3x + 20)°$.

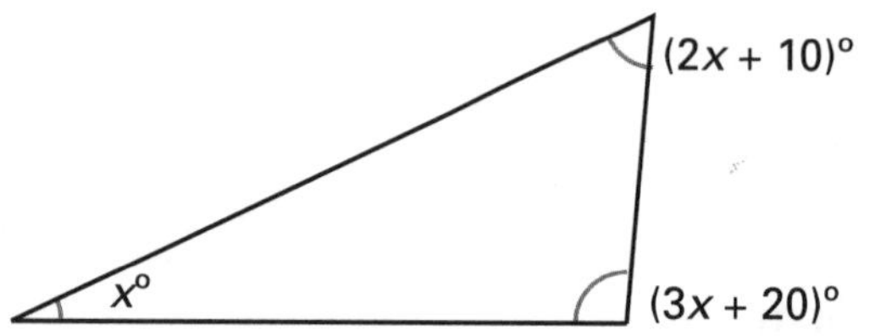

a) **Write down an equation in x.** *(1 mark)* Q2a

$6x + 30 = 180$.

b) **Solve your equation to find the 3 angles.** *(1 mark)* Q2b

25°
95°
60°

3 To change a speed in metres per second into speed in miles per hour a formula is:

$$V = \frac{11}{5} \times S$$

where V is speed in miles per hour and S is speed in metres per second.

a) A professional athlete could run at 10 metres per second.

What speed is this in miles per hour? *(1 mark)* Q3a

22mph.

b) Drag cars reach speeds of 100 metres per second.

What speed is this in miles per hour? *(1 mark)* Q3b

220mph.

4 A bag contains 20 beads: 6 are grey, 7 are black and the rest are white.

Diane takes a bead at random from the bag.

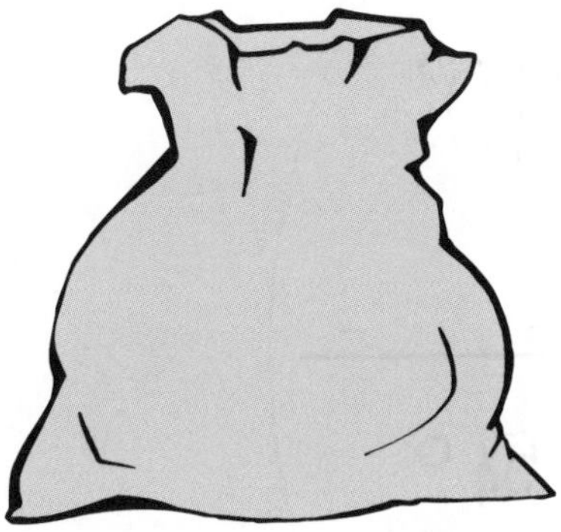

a) **What is the probability that it is black?** *(1 mark)* Q4a

7/20

b) **What is the probability that it is not grey?** *(1 mark)* Q4b

7/10

subtotal

5 The typical diet of a sportsman is given in the table below.

food type	**%**	**angle**
carbohydrate	60	216°
fat	25	90°
protein	15	54°

a) Calculate the angle of the sector that represents fat. *(1 mark)* Q5a

90°.

b) Draw the pie chart. *(2 marks)* Q5b

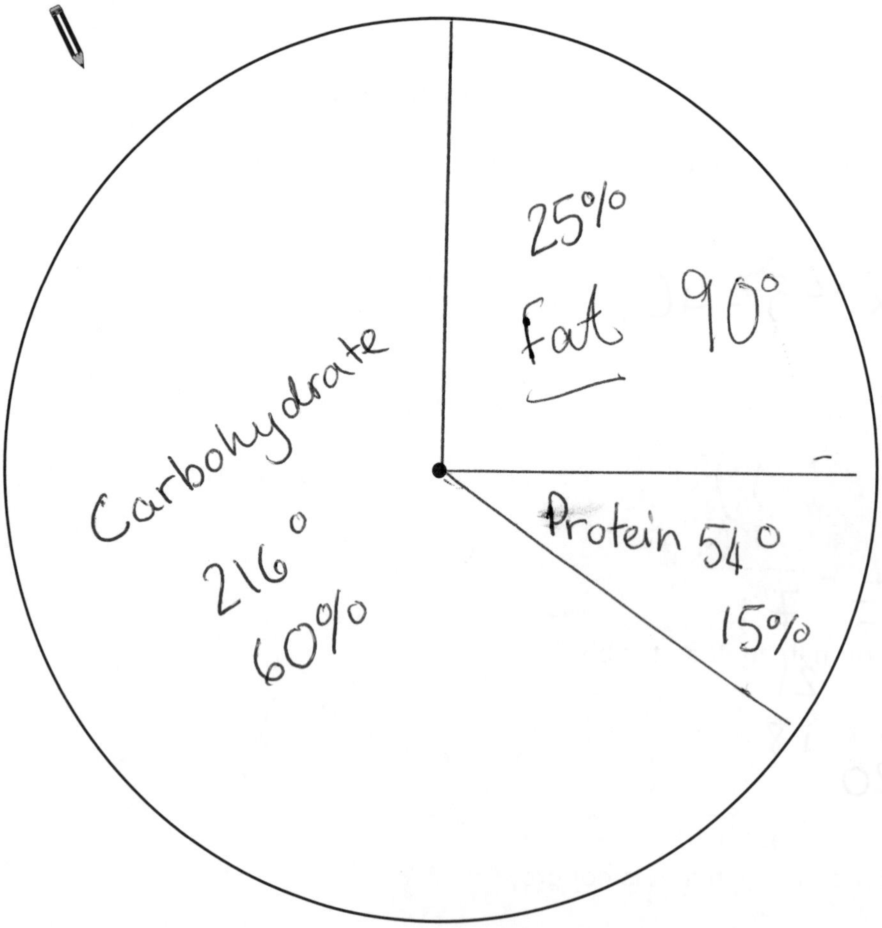

6 Bob thinks of a number puzzle.

"My first number is a prime number.

My second number is 3 times the first number.

My third number is 3 less than my second number."

a) **If the first number is *x*, write down in terms of *x* the second and third numbers.**

first number = x

i second number = $3x$ *(1 mark)* 1 Q6ai

ii third number = $3x-3$ *(1 mark)* 1 Q6aii

b) When these 3 numbers are added together they have a total of 46.

i **Write down an equation in *x*.** *(1 mark)* Q6bi

$7x - 3 = 46$.

ii **Use your equation to find the 3 numbers.** *(2 marks)* 2 Q6bii

$x = 7$

21

18.

subtotal

7 Janet is making a garden path using grey and white paving slabs.

One way of arranging them is shown below.

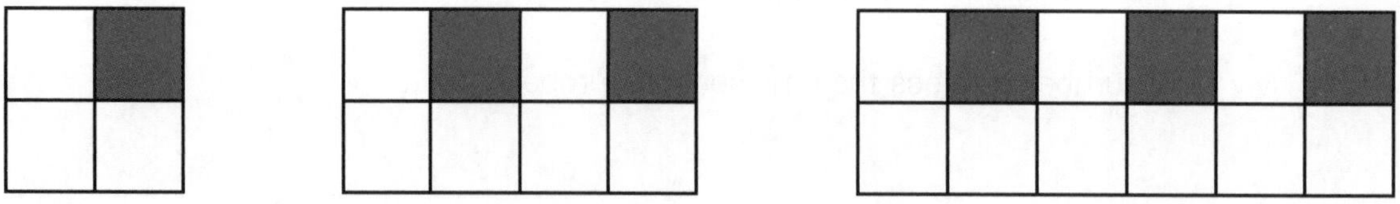

1 grey 2 grey 3 grey

g is the number of grey slabs.

w is the number of white slabs.

a) i **Write down a formula connecting g and w.** *(1 mark)* Q7ai

$w = 3g$

ii **How many grey slabs will be needed if 120 white slabs are used?** *(1 mark)* Q7aii

40

Another way of arranging the slabs to form a different pattern is shown below.

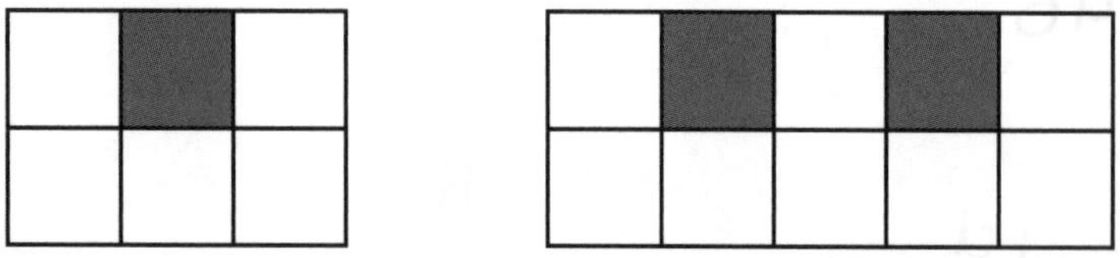

1 grey 2 grey

b) i **Write down a formula connecting g and w for this pattern.** *(1 mark)* Q7bi

$w = 3g + 2$.

ii **How many white slabs will be needed if 100 grey slabs are used?** *(1 mark)* Q7bii

302

8 The diagram shows 2 cards. One card is round, and the other is square. Both cards have numbers on the front and the back.

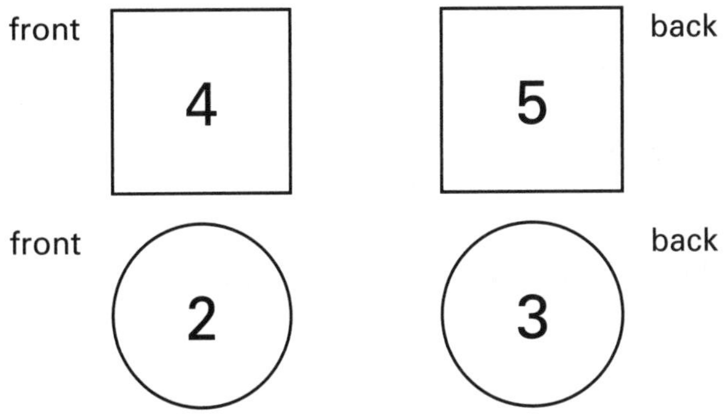

When the cards are dropped, either the front or the back can be seen.

Janet is investigating the numbers she can make when she drops the 2 cards. She drops both cards at the same time and looks at the 2 numbers she can see.

Mark on the probability line the likelihood of the following results.

The first one is done for you.

a) The two numbers add up to 10.

b) Both numbers are less than 6. *(1 mark)* Q8b

c) The two numbers add up to 8. *(1 mark)* Q8c

d) Only one of the two numbers is even. *(1 mark)* Q8d

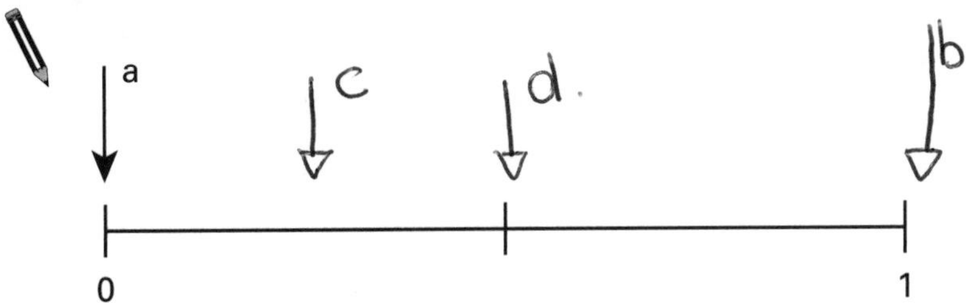

 subtotal

9 Look at these expressions.

A	B	C	D	E
$n - 3$	$3n$	n^3	$\frac{n}{3}$	$\frac{3}{n}$

Which of these statements is true when n has a value between 0 and 1? *(1 mark)* Q9

a) A > D

b) B = C

c) C > E

d) E > 1

Statement 'd'.

10 Jamie says, "I think of a number. I multiply it by 3 and add 5. The answer is a prime number between 20 and 30."

Which of the following is a possible answer? *(1 mark)* Q10

a) $3(n + 5) = 23$

b) $3(n + 5) = 29$

c) $3n + 5 = 29$

d) $3n + 5 = 27$

Write down your answer.

Statement 'c'.

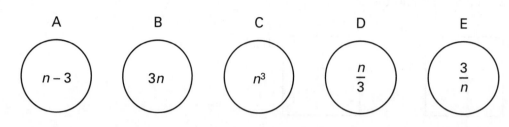

11 Michael saves shirt buttons in a tin, in case he loses one.

In the tin there are 12 white buttons, 6 green and 2 brown.

Michael takes a button from the tin without looking.

a) What is the probability that it is green? *(1 mark)* Q11a

3/10

b) What is the probability that it is either green or brown? *(1 mark)* Q11b

2/5.

Some of the buttons have 2 holes and all the others have 4 holes.

The probability of taking a button with 2 holes is 0.25.

c) What is the probability of taking a button with 4 holes? *(1 mark)* Q11c

0.75.

12 Here is a number pattern made with crosses.

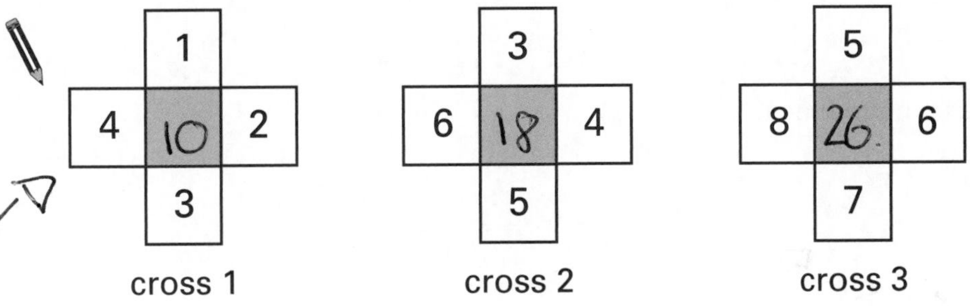

The number in the shaded centre of each cross is found by adding the numbers in each square.

a) Write the missing numbers in each shaded square. *(1 mark)* Q12a

subtotal

b) Cross n is shown below.

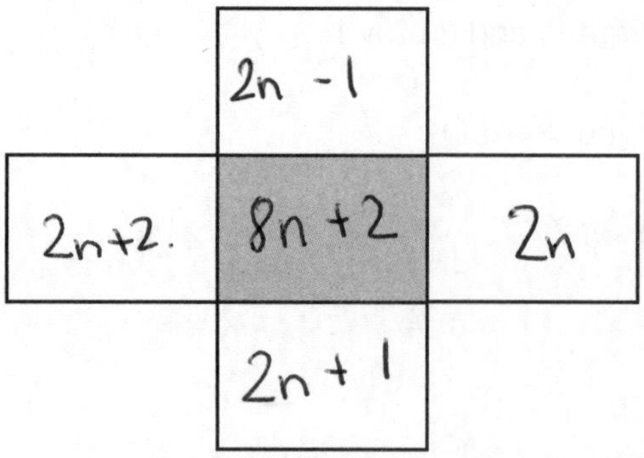

Cross n

Write the correct expressions in each of the squares for the nth shape. *(2 marks)* Q12b

13 Solve these equations.

a) i $3x + 2 = 17$ *(1 mark)* Q13ai

$x = 5.$

ii $\frac{1}{2}x - 1 = 7$ *(1 mark)* Q13aii

$x = 16.$

b) Solve these inequalities.

i $3x + 2 < 17$ *(1 mark)* Q13bi

$x < 5.$

ii $2 - x \leq 5$ *(1 mark)* Q13bii

$x \geq -3$

14 These straight line graphs all pass through the point (12, 12).

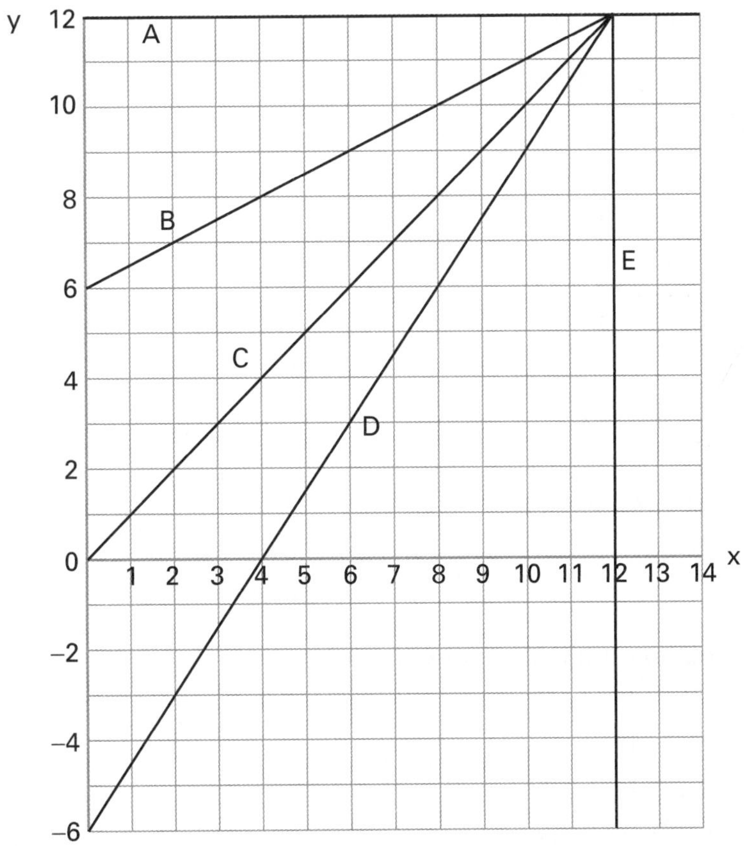

Answer the following by writing in the appropriate letter. *(3 marks)*

3 Q14

a) line E has equation $x = 12$

b) line A has equation $y = 12$

c) line C has equation $y = x$

d) line D has equation $y = \frac{3}{2}x - 6$

e) line B has equation $y = \frac{1}{2}x + 6$

subtotal

15 Which of these triangles is congruent to triangle A?

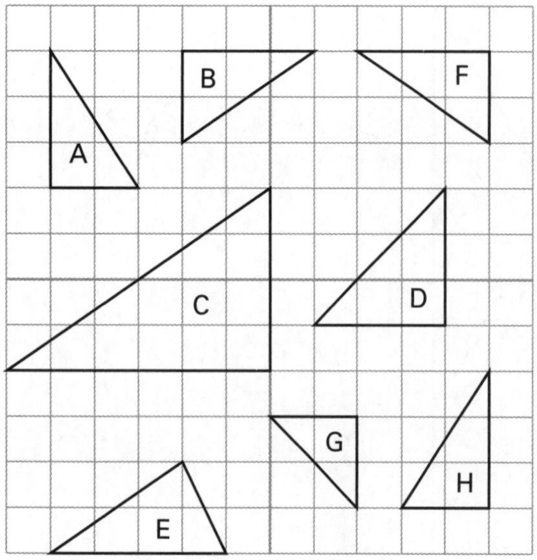

Put a tick next to the statement you think is correct. *(1 mark)* Q15

a) Only B and F ☐

b) Only D and H ☐

c) Only E and B ☐

d) Only B, F and H ☑

16 The length of the line BC is 8 cm.

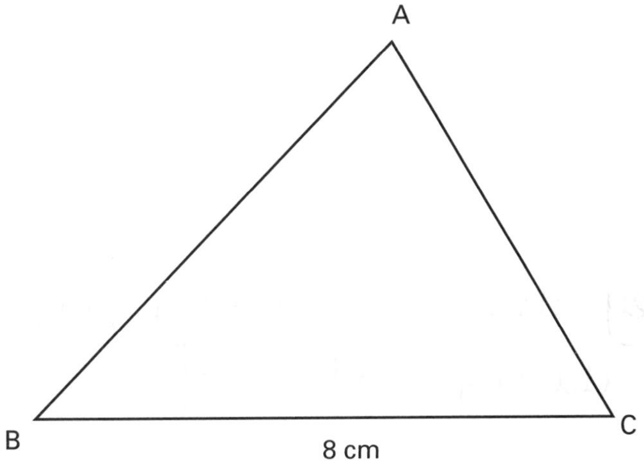

What is the locus of the point A which moves so that the area of triangle ABC is always 16 cm^2? *(2 marks)* 2 Q16

A line which is parallel to BC (the line) and passes through A.

17 What might be the values of a and b in this trapezium if the area is 8 cm^2? *(2 marks)* Q17

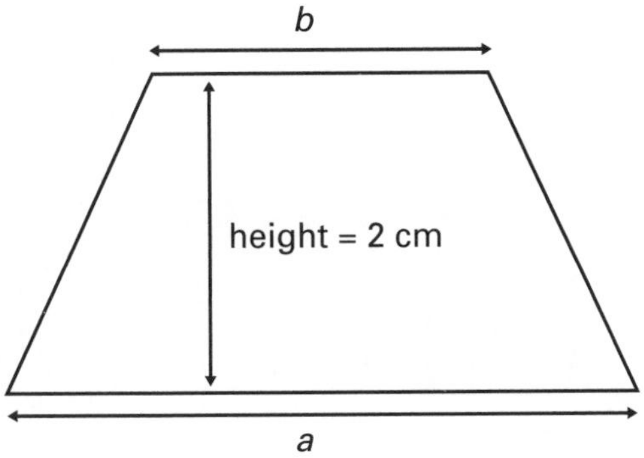

Circle your answer.

a) $a = 1 \quad b = 3$

b) $a = 3 \quad b = 1$

c) $a = 1 \quad b = 7$

d) $a = 7 \quad b = 1$

subtotal

18 Alfred's dad owns a cake shop. The shop is not selling many cakes. Alfred thinks it is because the cakes in his father's shop are too expensive.

Alfred conducts a survey to test this.

He asks the customers in his father's shop on a Saturday morning about the prices.

a) **Why will this not give a fair result? Give one reason.** *(1 mark)* Q18a

Because they are not asking people who shop during the week.

Here are two of the questions he asked.

Question 1: "Why do you buy cakes from my father's shop when they are much cheaper elsewhere?"

Question 2: "Do you think the cakes from this shop represent good value?"

b) **Do you think either of these questions is suitable? Explain.** *(1 mark)* Q18b

The costomers maybe are not 100% honest with Alfred

19 The graph shows the speed of a car on the switchback ride at a fair.

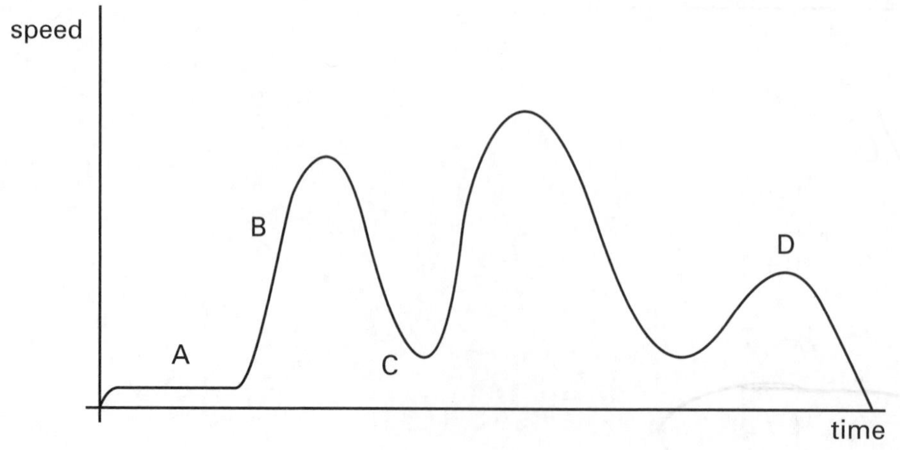

Describe what is happening at: *(3 marks)* Q19

A a steady constant speed.

B acceleration.

C car reaches top.

D car reaches bottom.

20 Amy plays bingo. This is the card she was given for a game.

3	12	24					72	83
	14		33	42	56		88	
	16	9		59		66		90

The caller picked out a number from 1 to 90 from a bag. The number was not replaced.

a) What was the probability that the first number called out was on Amy's card? *(1 mark)* Q20a

1/6.

b) What was the probability that the first number called out was not on the card? *(1 mark)* Q20b

5/6

Later in the game there were only 20 numbers left in the bag.

To win, Amy needed the number "59" to be called out.

c) What was the probability that the number "59" was the next number called out? *(1 mark)* Q20c

1/20.

subtotal

21 This is an addition number tower.
It has 3 rows.

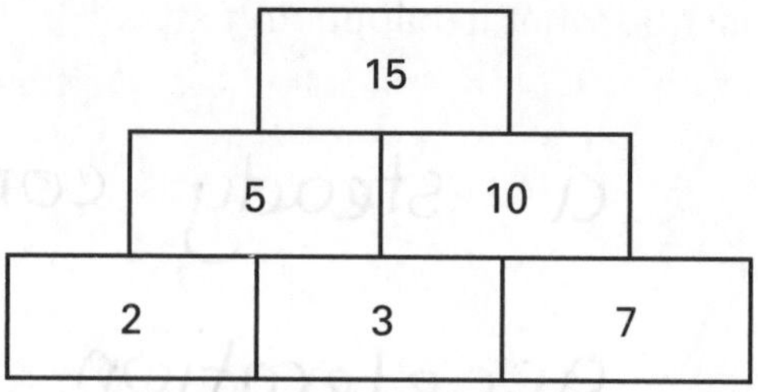

In this tower, each number is the sum of the 2 numbers just below it.

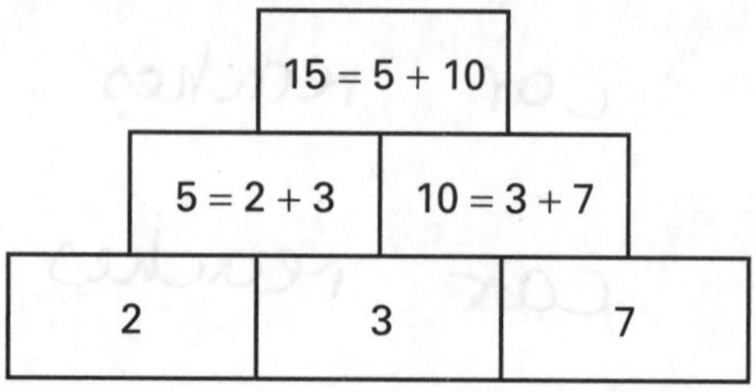

This is a 4 row number tower.

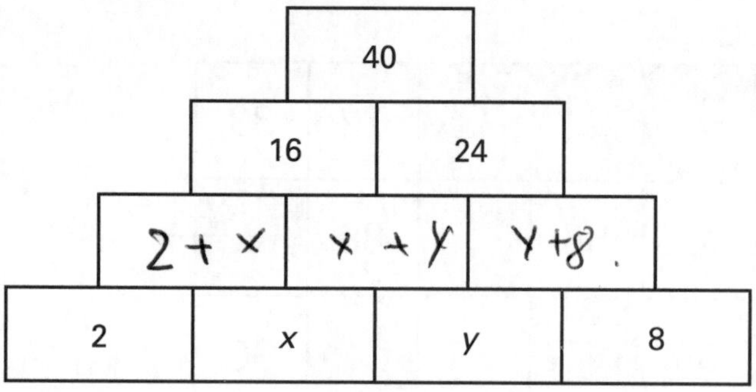

a) Write the appropriate algebraic expressions in each space. *(2 marks)* Q21a

b) Show that $2x + y = 14$ and $x + 2y = 16$. *(4 marks)* Q21b

$x + 2y = 16.$

c) Solve these 2 simultaneous equations to find the values of x and y. *(3 marks)* Q21c

$x = 4$
$y = 6.$

END OF TEST

subtotal

Test Paper 2 (calculator allowed)

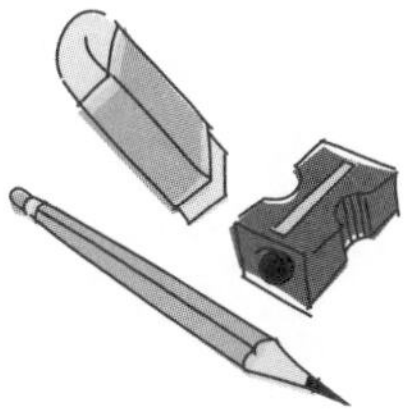

Instructions:

- find a quiet place where you can sit down and complete the test paper undisturbed
- make sure you have a pen, pencil, ruler, rubber and calculator
- read the questions carefully
- answer all the questions in this paper
- write your answers where you see this symbol
- show all your working as marks may be awarded for this
- go through and check your answers when you have finished the test paper
- check how you have done using pages 98–99 of the Answers and Mark Scheme

Time:

This test paper is **1 hour** long.

Page	27	29	31	33	35	37	39	Max. Mark	**Actual Mark**
Score	....	....	....	....	....	....	....	60	....

First name ....

Last name ....

Set A

KEY STAGE 3
Levels 6–8

Test Paper 2

Maths

Test Paper 2 (calculator allowed)

Formulae

Trapezium

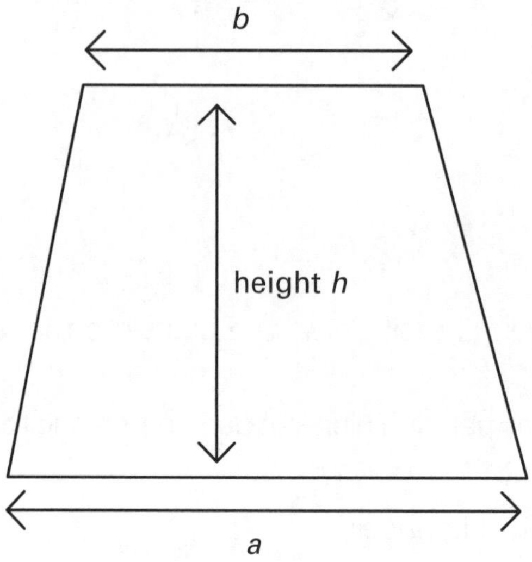

area $= \frac{1}{2}(a + b)h$

Prism

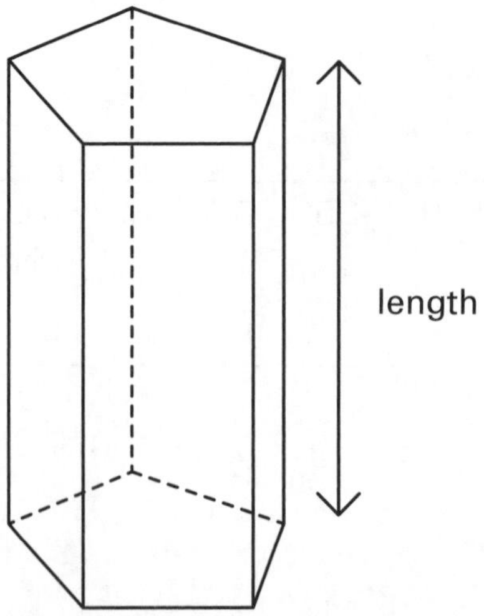

volume = area of cross-section × length

1 Tree Tea tea bags cost £1.45 for a box of 80 and 95p for a box of 50.

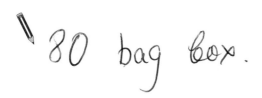

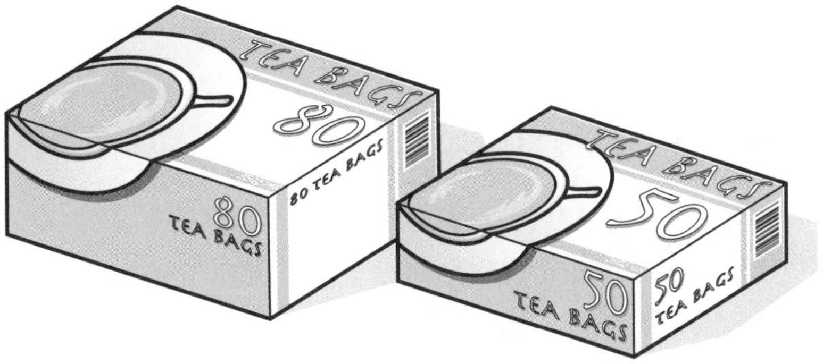

Which represents the best value? Show your working. *(2 marks)* Q1

80 bag box.

2 **Use your calculator to work out:**

a) $\dfrac{5.72 \times 4.92}{3.75 - 1.49}$ *(1 mark)* Q2a

12·45 (Rounded).

b) $\dfrac{3 \times 4.6 \times 5.4^2}{4.6 + 5.4}$ *(1 mark)* Q2b

40·24 (rounded.

subtotal

3 Use all of the digits 1, 3, 5 and 7 to make two decimal numbers so that:

- the difference between these two numbers is less than 2.0

and

- the product of these two numbers is less than 6.0

Write the digits in the correct places in the boxes. *(2 marks)* Q3

1 . 7 and 3 . 5

4 A bag contains some yellow balls and some red balls.

The ratio of the yellow balls to the red balls is 5:6.

a) **What is the minimum total number of balls in the bag?** *(1 mark)* Q4a

11

b) There are actually 20 yellow balls.

How many red balls are there? *(1 mark)* Q4b

24

Michelle puts yellow and red balls in a different bag. She says to Ruth, "The ratio of yellow balls to red balls is still 5:6, but there are 5 more red balls than yellow balls."

c) **What number of each colour could there be?** *(1 mark)* Q4c

25 yellow

30 red.

5 Percy is a gardener. He uses a heated greenhouse in winter to grow his summer bedding plants. The temperature in the greenhouse has to be kept at a constant 15°C.

a) If the temperature outside is –7°C what is the difference between this temperature and the temperature in the greenhouse? *(1 mark)* Q5a

22°

Percy will arrange the bedding plants round the edge of a circular flowerbed in a park. The flowerbed has a radius of 5 m. The plants have to be set 25 cm apart.

b) About how many plants will he need? *(2 marks)* Q5b

126.

6 Amy and Tom are given this number puzzle:

"Find 2 numbers which add up to 20 and make 30 when multiplied together."

Amy guesses 15 and 5.	Tom guesses 17.3 and 2.7
$15 + 5 = 20$	$17.3 + 2.7 = 20$
$15 \times 5 = 75$	$17.3 \times 2.7 = 46.71$

Use the method of trial and improvement to find the two numbers as accurately as you can.

Write down all your trials. *(3 marks)* Q6

18·36

1·634.

subtotal

7 Sabrina is using a recipe for strawberry ice-cream.

The recipe is for 6 people.

Strawberry ice-cream – to serve 6 people
600 g strawberries
250 g sugar
200 ml cream
100 ml water

a) What weight of strawberries will Sabrina need to make ice-cream for 10 people?

(1 mark) Q7a

1000g

b) How much sugar will she need for 10 people? *(1 mark)* Q7b

417g

8 **Calculate the volume of concrete needed to make these garden steps.** *(3 marks)* Q8

All 3 steps are the same size.

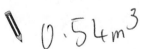

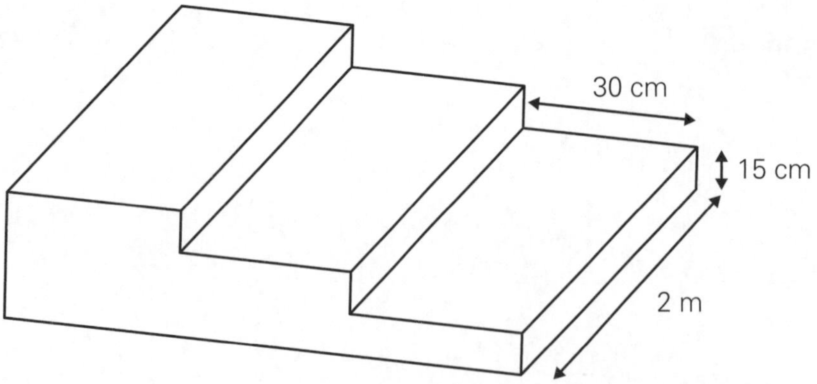

0.54m³

9 Sodapops make canned drinks. Each can contains 440 ml. A new can is made to hold 500 ml.

a) What is the percentage increase in the size of can? *(1 mark)* Q9a

13.6 % (Rounded).

On top of the new can is printed "13.5% more".

b) Is this correct? Explain your answer. *(1 mark)* Q9b

499 ml.

The measurement 440 ml is correct to the nearest millilitre.

c) What is the least amount the can could contain? *(1 mark)* Q9c

~~499~~ 439.5ml.

10 Marker buoys A, B, C and D are placed in the shape of a triangle on the sea to mark the turning points for a speedboat race. A is the start, B is 50 km east of A, C is 35 km north of A, and D is west of A and 40 km from C.

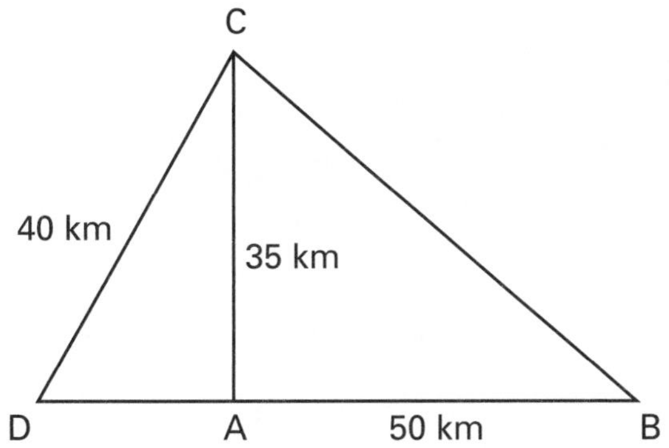

subtotal

a) Use Pythagoras' theorem to calculate the total distance round the course from A to B, C, D and back to A. *(5 marks)* ☐ Q10a

Show your working.

CB = 61 km.
DA = 19.4 km.

b) Calculate the time for a speedboat to complete the course at an average speed of 40 km per hour. *(1 mark)* ☐ Q10b

Distance = 17.4 km
Time: 4hr 16mins

11 These are familiar logos.

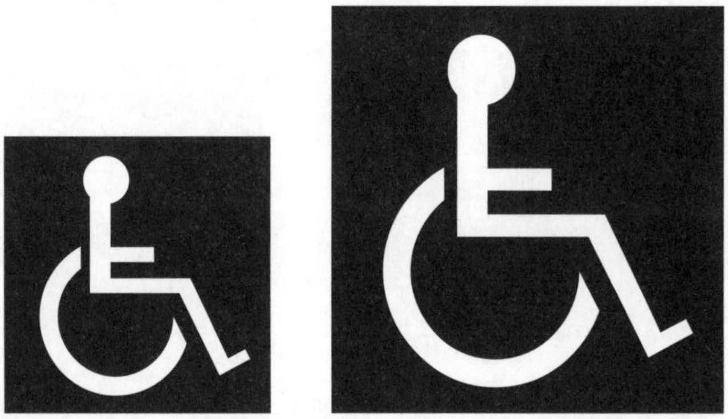

The two logos are mathematically similar. The width of the smaller logo is 3.2 cm. The scale factor of the enlargement is 1.5.

a) How wide is the larger logo? *(1 mark)* ☐ Q11a

4.8 cm.

The height of the larger logo is 4.7 cm.

b) How high is the smaller logo? *(1 mark)* ☐ Q11b

3.13 cm

12 Find, by trial and improvement, a solution to the following equation. *(3 marks)* Q12

$x(x - 3) = 11$

Use the table to help you.

x	$(x - 3)$	$x(x - 3)$	small/large
6	3	18	too large

Give your answer to 2 decimal places.

5·14 2·14.

13 In a school, the Year 9 pupils were asked to choose either swimming or tennis. Their choices are shown in the table.

	swimming	tennis
girls	27	33
boys	42	28

a) **What percentage of the girls chose swimming?** *(1 mark)* Q13a

$\frac{27}{60} = 45\%$

b) **What percentage of the boys chose tennis?** *(1 mark)* Q13b

$\frac{28}{70} = 40\%$

c) **What was the total percentage of pupils who chose swimming?** *(1 mark)* Q13c

$\frac{69}{130} = 53\%.$

subtotal

14 Here is a Fibonacci-style sequence.

Each number is made by adding together the 2 preceding numbers as shown.

5	7	12	19	31
		↑	↑	↑
		5 + 7	7 + 12	12 + 19

Here is another Fibonacci-style sequence.

6	a	A	B	36

a) Write down the expressions which would go in box A and box B.

i Box A *(1 mark)* Q14ai

6 + a.

ii Box B *(1 mark)* Q14aii

6 + 2a.

b) Use the rule for generating a Fibonacci sequence to derive an equation which is equal to 36. *(1 mark)* Q14b

12 + 3a = 36.

c) Solve this equation to find the value of *a*. *(1 mark)* Q14c

a = 8

15 The formula $A = \pi R\ (R+L)$ is used to find the surface area of a cone.

(R = radius of base and L = length of slant height.)

a) Find the surface area of a cone with radius 4 cm and slant height 10 cm. *(1 mark)* Q15a

176 cm²

b) John estimates the surface area of a cone with radius 14.4 cm and slant height 28.2 cm to be 1800 cm². By using suitable approximations show whether he is right. *(1 mark)* Q15b

A = 3 × 14 × (14 + 28)
= 42 × 42
= 1764 cm²

16 Simon and Jayne are exploring number sequences.

a) Simon writes down 2, 4, 8, 16.

i Write down the next 3 terms of his sequence. *(1 mark)* Q16ai

32, 64, 128.

ii Write an expression for the nth term of his sequence. *(1 mark)* Q16aii

2^n.

b) Jayne writes down the first numbers of a different sequence: 1, 3, 7, 15 …

i Write down the next 3 terms of Jayne's sequence. *(1 mark)* Q16bi

31, 63, 127.

ii Use your answer to a) ii to write an expression for the nth term of this sequence. *(1 mark)* Q16bii

2n − 1

subtotal

17 The formula for the population, P, of a country with a growth rate of $r\%$ per year in time t years is given by the formula

$$P = P_0\left(1 + \frac{r}{100}\right)^t$$ where P_0 is the population this year.

The population of a country is 55.4 million.

If the growth rate is 4% per year, calculate the population in 5 years' time. *(2 marks)* Q17

67.4 million.

18 The diagram shows a circle and a square.

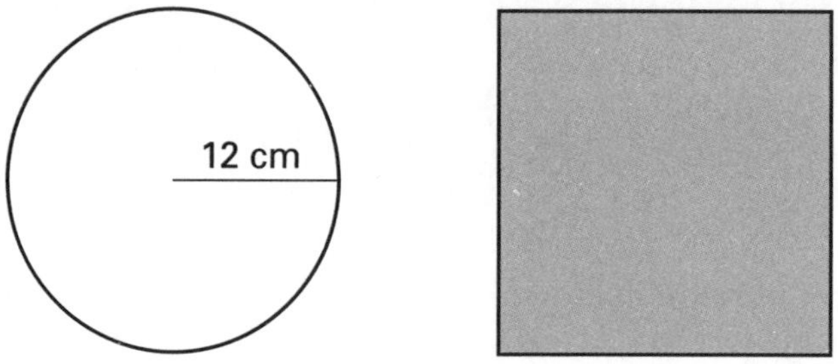

a) The radius of the circle is 12 cm.

What is the circumference of the circle? Take $\pi = 3$. *(1 mark)* Q18a

72cm

b) The ratio of the circumference of the circle to the perimeter of the square is 1:2.

i **What is the perimeter of the square?** *(1 mark)* Q18bi

144cm.

ii **What is the length of a side of the square?** *(1 mark)* Q18bii

36cm

c) A triangle is drawn that just fits inside the square.

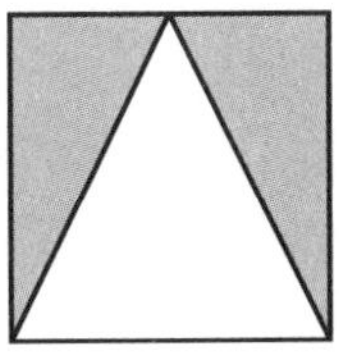

What is the area of the triangle? *(1 mark)* Q18c

648cm²

19 Here is a rule to work out the squares of some mixed numbers.

To work out $\left(2\frac{1}{2}\right)^2$ calculate $(2 \times 3) + \frac{1}{4} = 6\frac{1}{4}$

To work out $\left(3\frac{1}{2}\right)^2$ calculate $(3 \times 4) + \frac{1}{4} = 12\frac{1}{4}$

To work out $\left(4\frac{1}{2}\right)^2$ calculate $(4 \times 5) + \frac{1}{4} = 20\frac{1}{4}$

a) **Check that the rule works by calculating** $3\frac{1}{2} \times 3\frac{1}{2}$ *(1 mark)* Q19a

Show your working.

12·25

The rule can be written as $\left(n + \frac{1}{2}\right)^2 = (n \times (n + 1)) + \frac{1}{4}$

b) **Show that** $\left(n + \frac{1}{2}\right)^2 = n(n + 1) + \frac{1}{4}$ *(1 mark)* Q19b

2n + n + 1/4

subtotal

c) What number has a square of 3782.25? *(1 mark)*

Q19c

$(61\frac{1}{2})^2$

20 Mr Smith set a reasoning test for the pupils in Year 7.

The graph shows the number of questions answered correctly by the 200 pupils in Year 7.

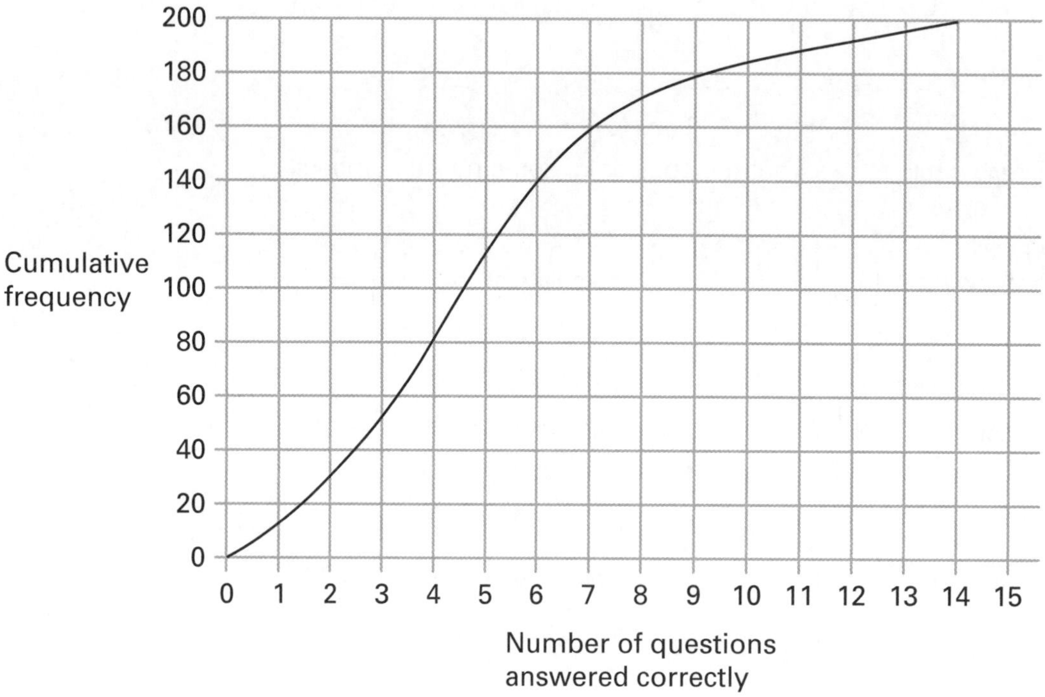

a) Estimate how many pupils answered **more** than 4 questions correctly. *(1 mark)*

Q20a

120

b) Estimate how many pupils answered **fewer** than 7 questions correctly. *(1 mark)*

Q20b

140

21 Phillipa says it is impossible to draw a right-angled triangle with edges of 8 cm, 12 cm and 18 cm.

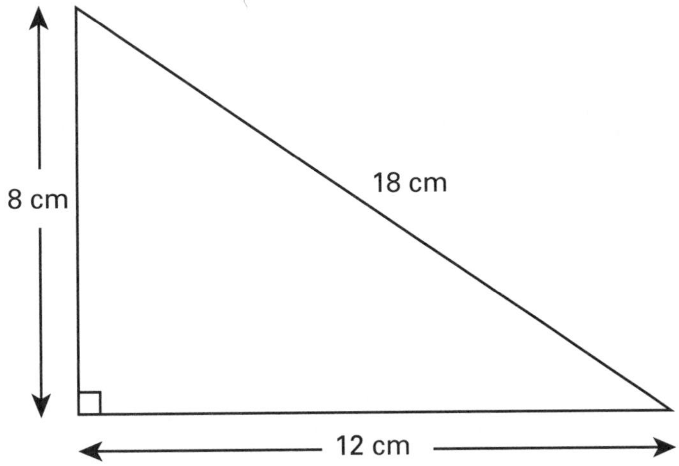

Irene says it is possible.

a) Who is correct? *(1 mark)* Q21a

Phillipa.

Irene also says it is possible to draw a right-angled triangle with the measurements shown in this diagram.

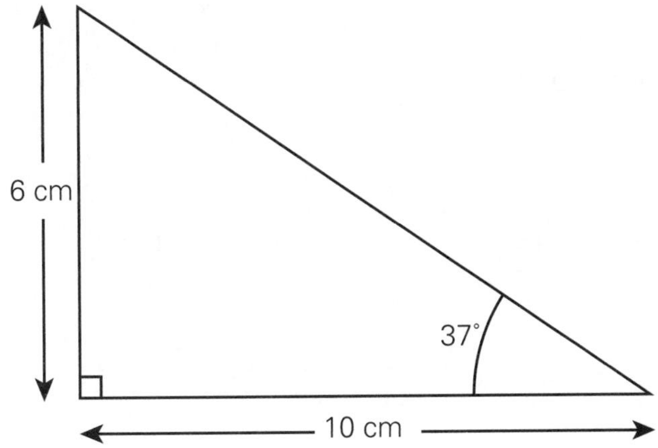

b) Is Irene correct? *(1 mark)* Q21b

Show all your working.

30.96 Irene is incorrect.

END OF TEST

subtotal

Set
B

KEY STAGE 3
Levels 6–8

Test Paper 1

Maths

Test Paper 1 (calculator **not** allowed)

Test Paper 1 (calculator **not** allowed)

Instructions:

- find a quiet place where you can sit down and complete the test paper undisturbed
- make sure you have a pen, pencil, ruler, rubber and a pair of compasses
- read the questions carefully
- answer all the questions in this paper
- write your answers where you see this symbol 
- show all your working as marks may be awarded for this
- go through and check your answers when you have finished the test paper
- check how you have done using pages 99–100 of the Answers and Mark Scheme

Time:

This test paper is **1 hour** long.

Page	43	45	47	49	51	53	Max. Mark	**Actual Mark**
Score	....	....	....	....	....	....	60	....

First name ____________________

Last name ____________________

Formulae

Trapezium

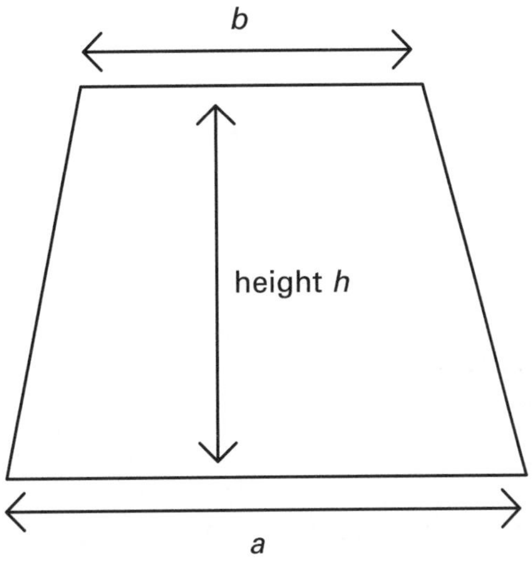

area $= \frac{1}{2}(a + b)h$

Prism

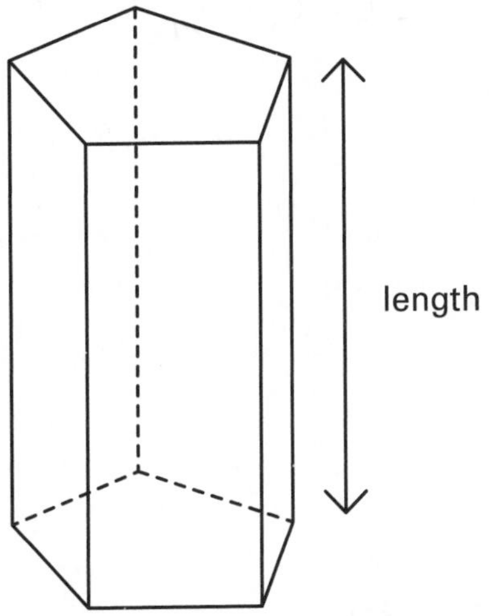

volume = area of cross-section × length

1 Fill in the missing numbers.

a) -8 − −5 = −3 *(1 mark)* Q1a

b) −5 − -2 = −3 *(1 mark)* Q1b

2 A quadrilateral has only one line of symmetry.

a) Two sides are parallel. Name this shape and describe its properties. *(2 marks)* Q2a

Trapezium.

b) No sides are parallel. Name this shape and describe its properties. *(2 marks)* Q2b

Kite.

c) What can you say about the symmetry if two pairs of sides are parallel? *(1 mark)* Q2c

No line of symmetry.

3 Solve the equation $3x + 7 = 25 - x$ *(2 marks)* Q3

Show each step of your working.

4x+7= 25

x=4 5

$x =$ ☐

4 ABCD is a rectangle.

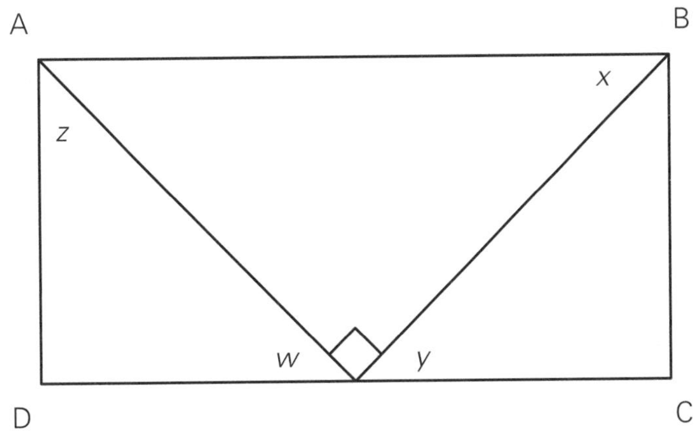

a) Explain why $x = y$ (1 mark) Q4a

Alterate angles.
AB parallel to DC.

b) Explain why $y = z$ (2 marks) Q4b

$w + y + 90 = 180$
$w + z + 90 = 180$
$y = z$.

5 Add $\frac{1}{12} + \frac{1}{4} + \frac{1}{6}$

Write your answer as simply as possible. (2 marks) Q5

$1/2$.

subtotal

6 a) Match the lines shown in the diagram to their equations.

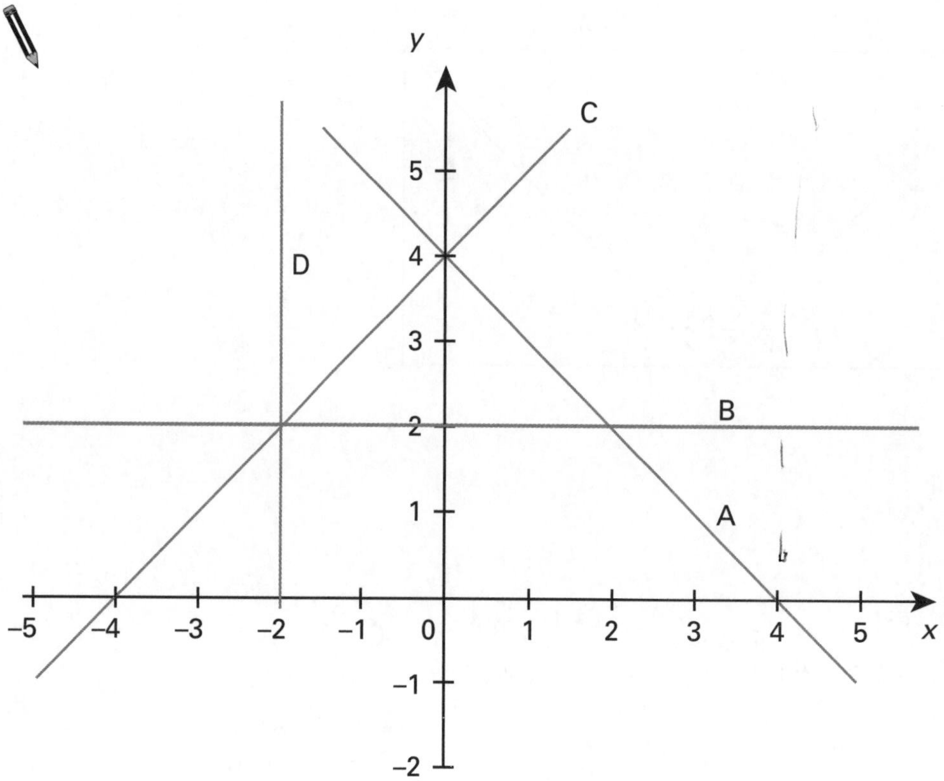

Graph [B] is $y = 2$

Graph [D] is $x + 2 = 0$

Graph [C] is $y = x + 4$

Graph [A] is $x + y = 4$ *(3 marks)* Q6a

b) On the grid, draw the line $x = 4$. *(1 mark)* Q6b

7 a) If n is an integer, explain why $2n$ is an even number. *(1 mark)* Q7a

Integer ×2 is even.

b) Write down, in terms of n, an expression for an odd number. *(1 mark)* Q7b

$2n+1$.

8 Michael has collected data on the age and value of some cars, all 2 litre Astreos. His results are shown on the scattergraph.

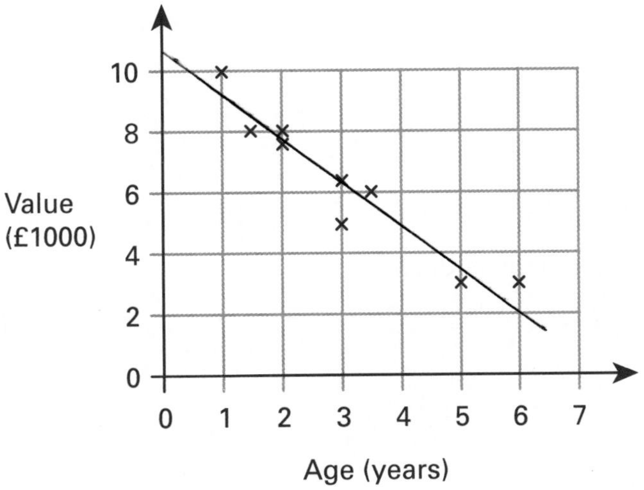

a) Describe the correlation. *(1 mark)* Q8a

Negative.

b) Draw a line of best fit. *(1 mark)* Q8b

subtotal

c) What value would you expect a 4-year-old 2 litre Astreo to have? *(1 mark)* Q8c

£5000.

d) Peter tells Michael that he has seen a 2-year-old Astreo for sale for £4000.
Do you think this is a 2 litre Astreo? *(1 mark)* Q8d

Yes ☑ No ☐

Explain.

It is too far from other data.

9 $M = 10(a + 2b)$

Rearrange this formula to make b the subject. *(2 marks)* Q9

$20b = M - 10a$.

$b = \frac{1}{20}(M - 10a)$

10 Here is an accurate plan of my garden.

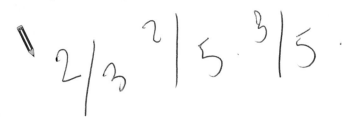

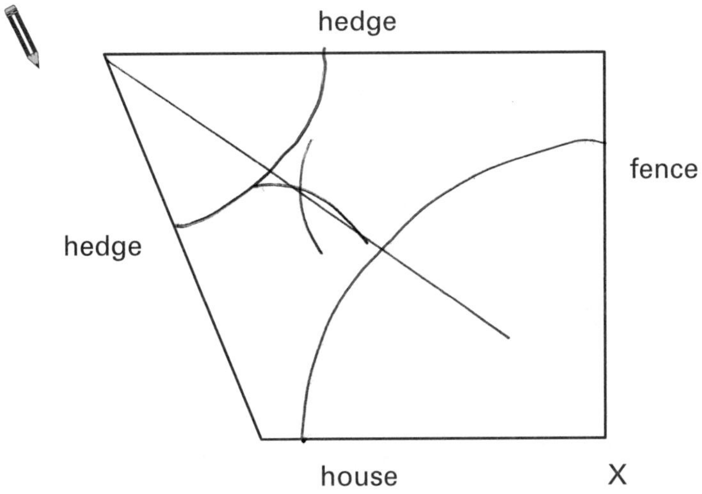

a) There is a path across the garden from where the hedges meet. It is the same distance from each of the hedges.

Using a straight edge and a pair of compasses only, draw the line of the path. Leave in all your construction lines. *(2 marks)*

Q10a

b) An electric lawnmower is plugged in at X. Its cable is 10 m long.

Shade the part of the garden that the lawnmower will reach. *(2 marks)*

Q10b

11 Prices in a store are reduced by 40% in a sale. These sale prices are then further reduced by a third.

By what fraction in total have the prices been reduced? *(3 marks)*

Q11

Show your working.

2/3 2/5 3/5

subtotal

12 The graph shows Paul's journey to school.

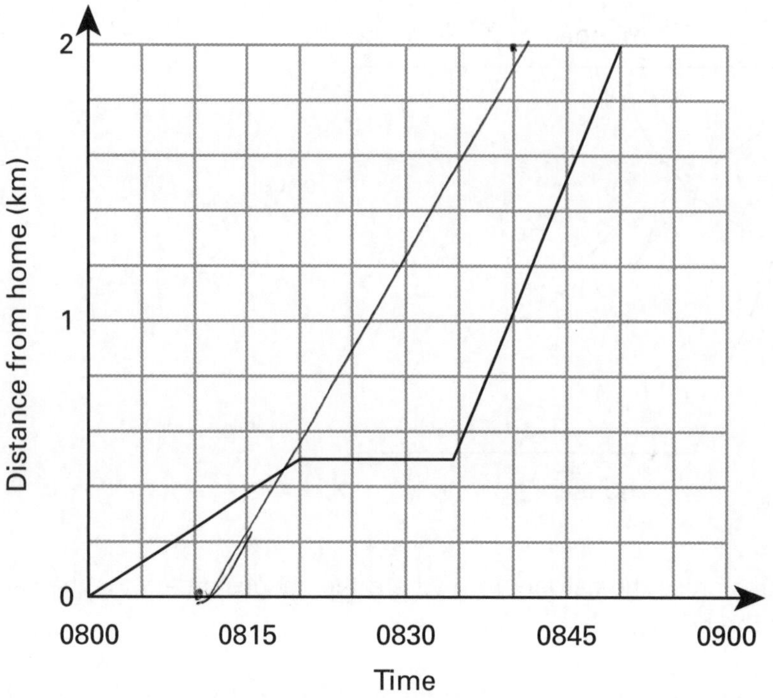

a) Work out Paul's speed, in km/hour, for the first 500 m. *(2 marks)* Q12a

½ km 20 mins.

b) Paul's sister left to walk to school at 0810. She walked steadily at 4 km/hour.

Show this on the graph. *(2 marks)* Q12b

13 I roll 2 ordinary dice, each numbered 1, 2, 3, 4, 5, 6. I subtract the 2 numbers to find the difference.

What is the probability that the difference is 2? Show how you worked it out. *(3 marks)* Q13

36.

6-4.
5-3.
4-2.
3-1.

2/9.

14 The rectangle and the right-angled triangle each have the same area.

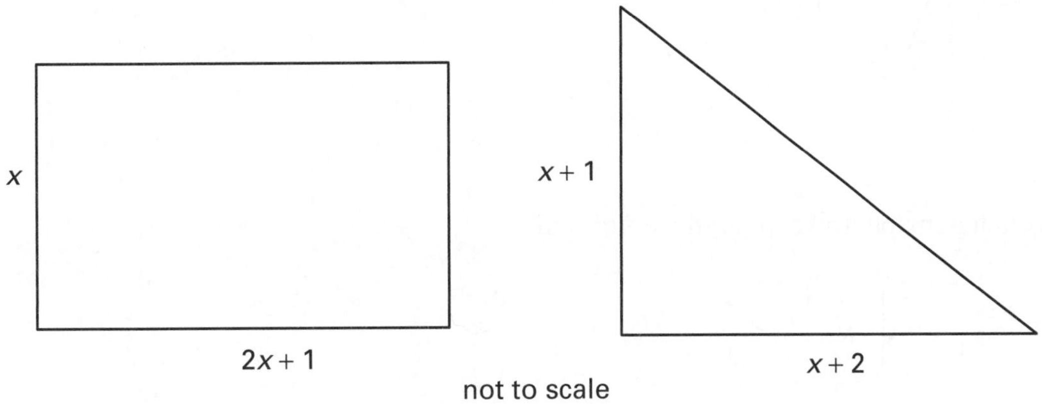

not to scale

a) **Show that $3x^2 - x - 2 = 0$** *(3 marks)* Q14a

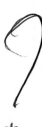

?

subtotal

b) Solve the equation $3x^2 - x - 2 = 0$ and write down the dimensions of the shapes. *(3 marks)* Q14b

Rectangle ______________________ Triangle ______________________

15 Geologists believe the Moon was formed about 4.6×10^9 years ago and the ice cap on Antarctica some 7.5×10^7 years ago.

a) How many years are there between these events?

Leave all the figures in your answer and give it in standard form. *(1 mark)* Q15a

4.525 x 10⁹

b) Is it sensible to keep all these figures? *(1 mark)* Q15b

Yes ☐ No ☑

Explain.

Only 2 significant figures

16 Write these expressions as simply as possible, using indices.

a) $4 \times 2^5 \div 8$ *(1 mark)* Q16a

2^4.

b) $\dfrac{a^2b^3}{a^3b^2}$ *(1 mark)* Q16b

$\dfrac{B}{a}$.

subtotal

17 How long two brands of battery lasted were compared. The two box plots summarise the results.

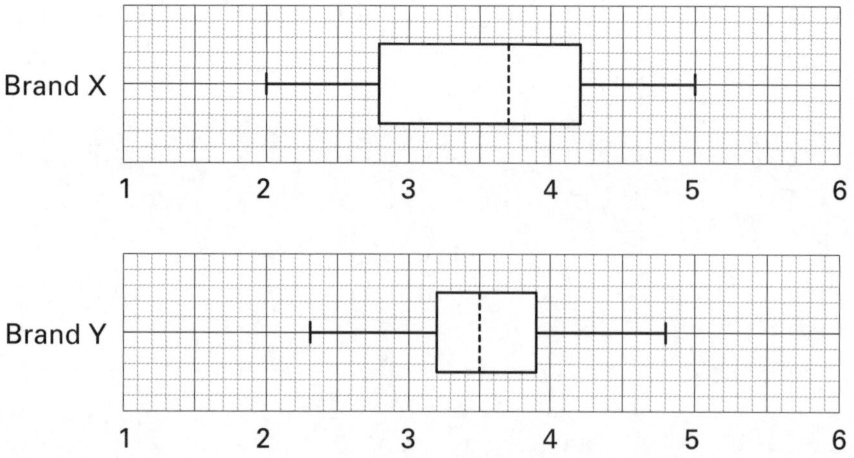

a) Give two statistics that support Brand X as a better buy. *(2 marks)* Q17a

Higher median.

b) Give two statistics that support Brand Y as a better buy. *(2 marks)* Q17b

Lower Inter quartile

c) Which would you choose, and why? *(1 mark)* Q17c

Y less variation.

18 ABCDE is a regular pentagon.

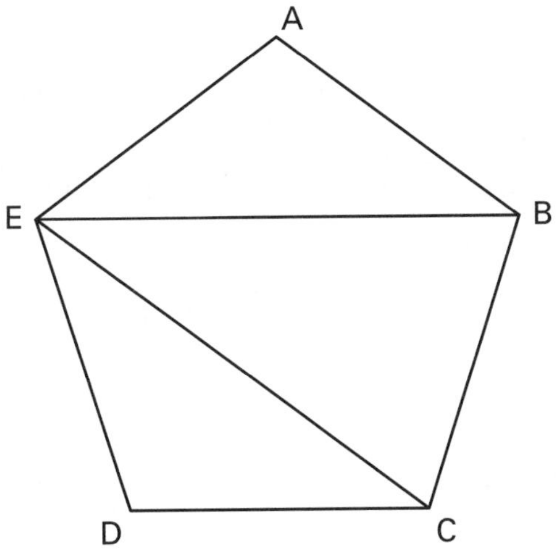

not to scale

a) Prove that angle EBC = 72°. *(2 marks)* Q18a

108°.

b) Prove that angle AED is trisected (divided equally in 3) by BE and CE. *(3 marks)* Q18b

36°.

END OF TEST

subtotal

Set
B

KEY STAGE 3
Levels 6–8

Test Paper 2

Maths

Test Paper 2 (calculator allowed)

Test Paper 2 (calculator allowed)

Instructions:

- find a quiet place where you can sit down and complete the test paper undisturbed
- make sure you have a pen, pencil, ruler, rubber, protractor and calculator
- read the questions carefully
- answer all the questions in this paper
- write your answers where you see this symbol
- show all your working as marks may be awarded for this
- go through and check your answers when you have finished the test paper
- check how you have done using pages 100–101 of the Answers and Mark Scheme

Time:

This test paper is **1 hour** long.

Page	57	59	61	63	65	67	68	Max. Mark	**Actual Mark**
Score	....	....	....	....	....	....	....	60	....

First name ....

Last name ....

Formulae

Trapezium

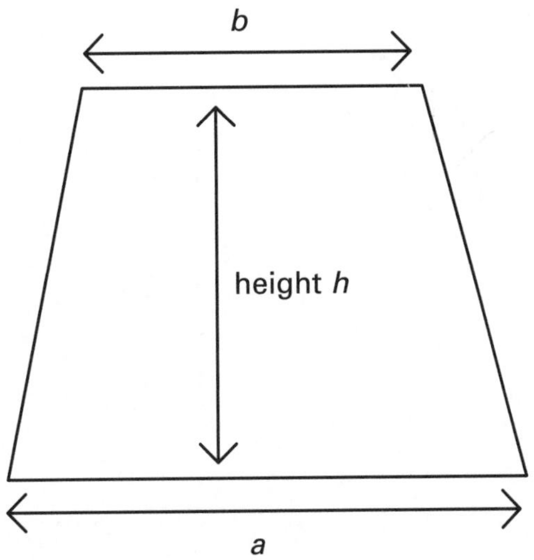

$$\text{area} = \frac{1}{2}(a + b)h$$

Prism

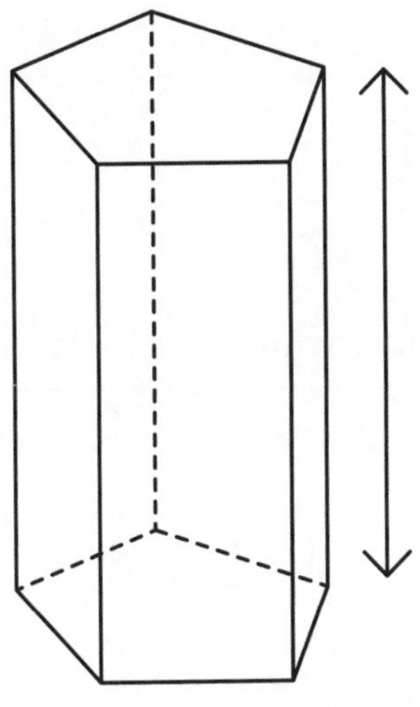

volume = area of cross-section × length

1 Errol weighs 85 kg.

He wants to slim and lose 12 kg.

What percentage reduction is this? *(2 marks)* Q1

Show your working.

$\frac{12}{85} \times 100$

14 %

2 This formula gives the surface area of a cylinder, radius *r* and height *h*.

$S = 2\pi r(r + h)$

a) Find *S* when $r = 4.7$ cm, $h = 15.2$ cm. *(2 marks)* Q2a

588 cm²

b) Find the height of a cylinder with surface area 1000 cm² and radius 7.5 cm. *(2 marks)* Q2b

$\frac{100}{2 \times \pi \times 7.5} - 7.5$

13.7 cm

3 Here are the nets of two cuboids.

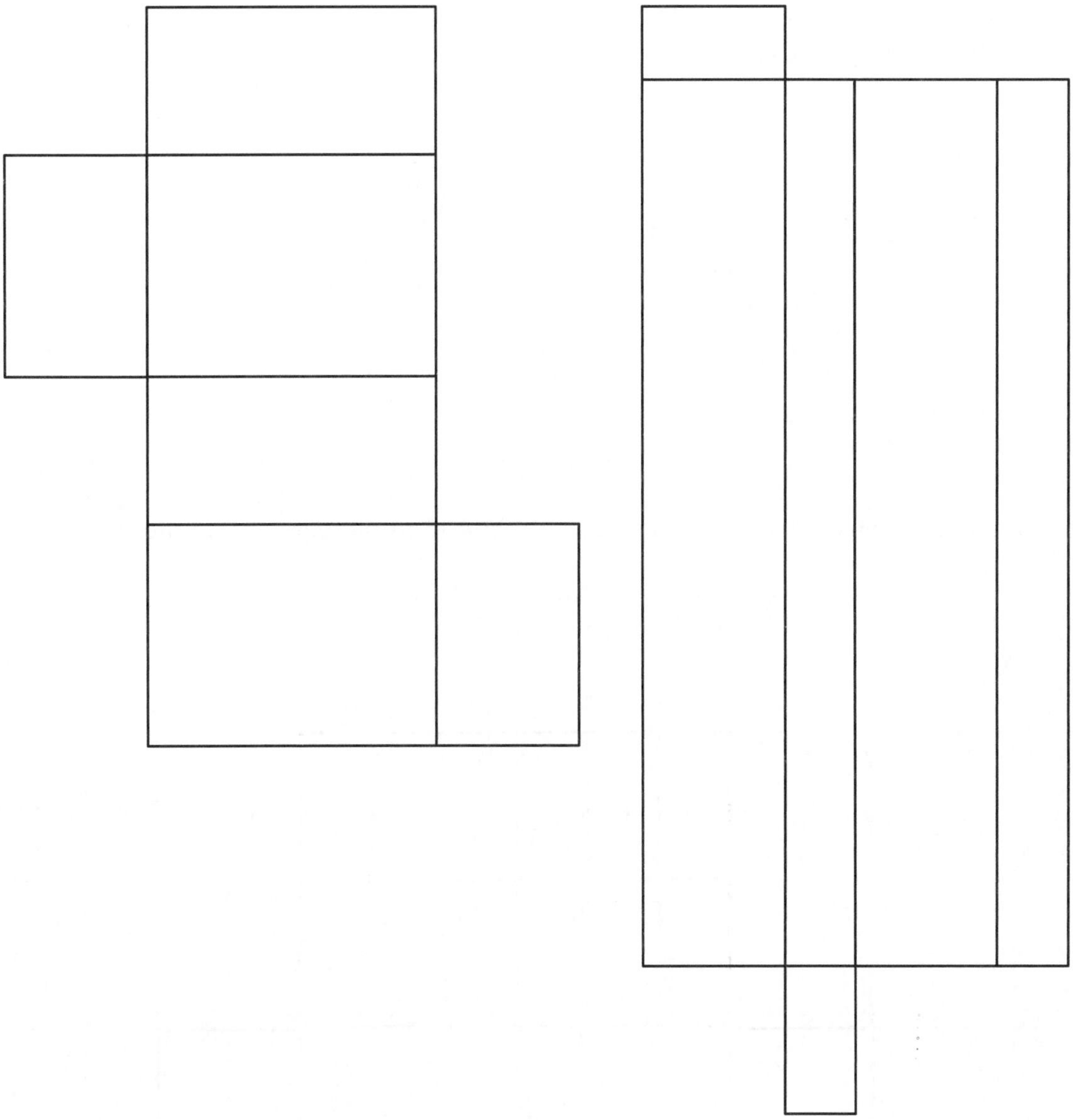

a) Which has the greater volume?

A ☐ B ☐ Same ☑

Show how you decide. *(2 marks)* ☐ Q3a

Both 24cm³

subtotal ☐

b) Which has the greater surface area?

A ☐ B ☑ Same ☐

Show how you decide. *(2 marks)* ☐ Q3b

B = 76 cm²
A = 52 cm²

c) Cuboid C has the same volume as cuboid A. Complete its net on the grid. *(3 marks)* ☐ Q3c

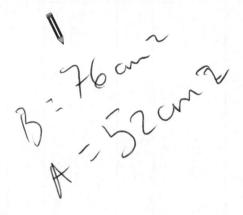

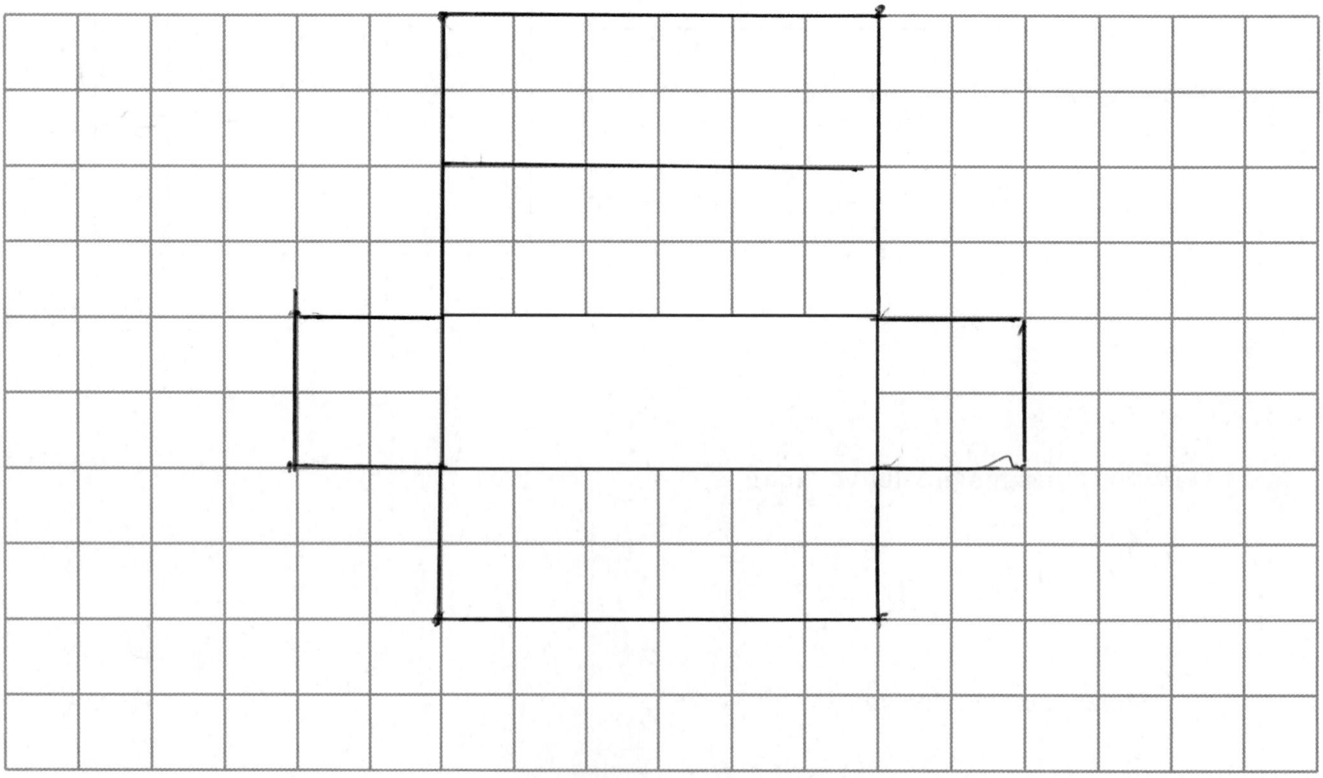

4 The pie chart shows the distribution of the world's population across continents.

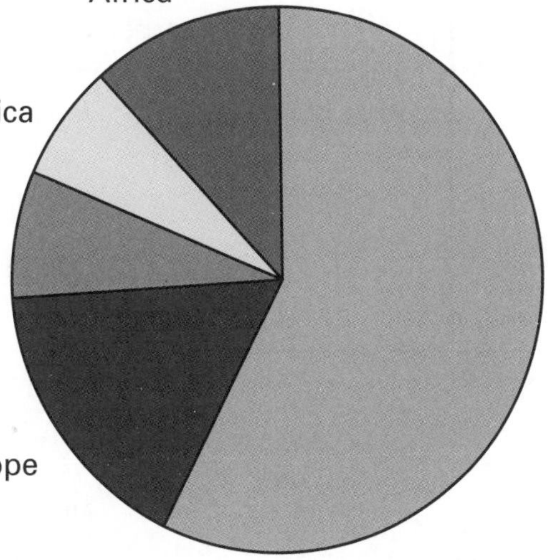

Taking the world total population to be 5000 million, calculate the population of Asia. *(3 marks)*

Q4

Show your method clearly.

208 - 210° x 5000 ÷ 360

2900 million.

2900 million

subtotal

5 Is digital photography cheaper?

ordinary camera (24 prints)		digital camera	
film	£2.66	paper (20 sheets)	£6.99
printing	£2.50	ink (500 prints)	£29.99
postage	£1.30		

a) Compare the costs. *(2 marks)* Q5a

Normal

(2.66 + 2.50 + 1.30) ÷ 24 = 26.9p per print.

Digital

6.99 ÷ 20 + 29.99 ÷ 500 = 40.95p per print.

b) If only half the pictures are worth printing, how does this change the answer? *(1 mark)* Q5b

Digital now cheaper.

6 The capacity of a sample of 1 litre bottles was measured. The results are summarised in the table.

capacity (ml)	number of bottles
995 – 997	94
997 – 999	49
999 – 1001	13
1001 – 1003	11
1003 – 1005	8

a) Find the interval which includes the median capacity. *(1 mark)* Q6a

995 - 997.

995 - 997 ml

b) Calculate an estimate of the mean capacity. *(3 marks)* Q6b

Show your working.

996×94+998 × 49 + 174580 ÷175.

997 ml .6.

 subtotal

7 This circle has radius 3.5 cm.

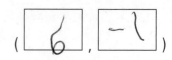

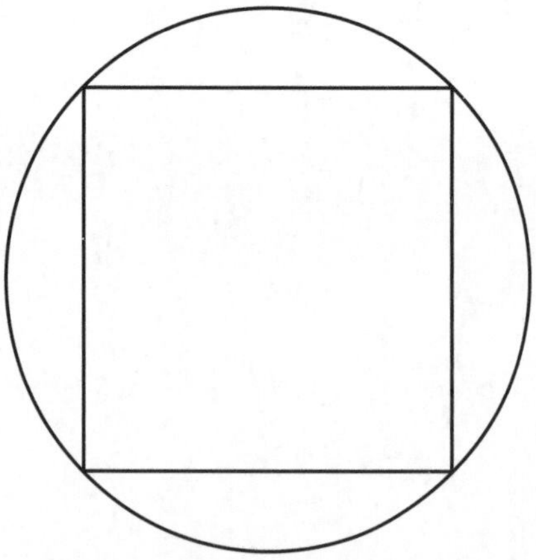

A square is drawn in the circle, with vertices on the circumference.

What percentage of the area of the circle is outside the square? *(3 marks)* Q7

Area of square = 2 × 3.5²
Area of circle = π × 3.5²

$\frac{\pi \times 3.5^2 - 2 \times 3.5^2}{\pi \times 3.5^2} \times 100$

36.3 %

8 Two straight lines have equations.

$x + 2y = 4$

$2x - y = 13$

Use an algebraic method to find the point where they meet. *(3 marks)* Q8

5y = -5.

(6 , -1)

9 The ages of three friends are in the ratio 3:5:6.

a) The oldest is 30. How old is the youngest? *(1 mark)* Q9a

15.

b) When the middle friend reaches 30, how old will the others be? *(2 marks)* Q9b

20, ~~25~~, 35.

10 Solve these inequalities.

a) $2x + 3 < 4 - x$ *(1 mark)* Q10a

$3x < 1$, $x < 1/3$

b) $3(x - 2) \leq 7x + 2$ *(2 marks)* Q10b

$3x - 6 \leq 7x + 2$

subtotal

11 A ramp is made by placing a board on some steps. The steps are all the same size and the lengths are in centimetres.

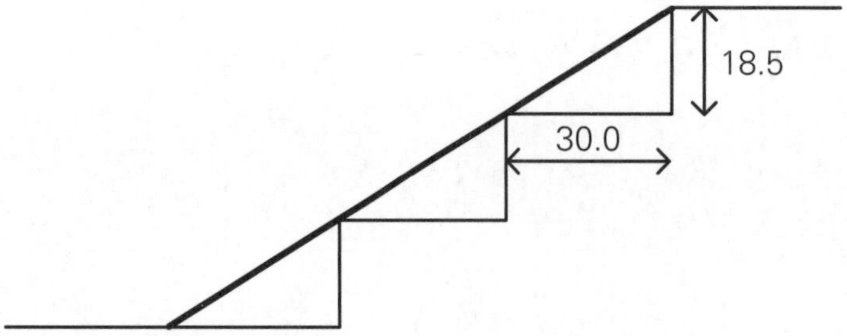

a) Calculate the length of the board. *(3 marks)*

Q11a

35.2 x 3.

106 cm

A longer board is now used from the top step. This makes an angle of 24° with the horizontal ground.

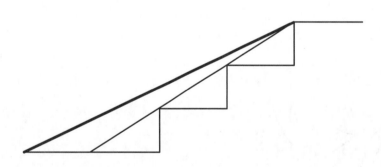

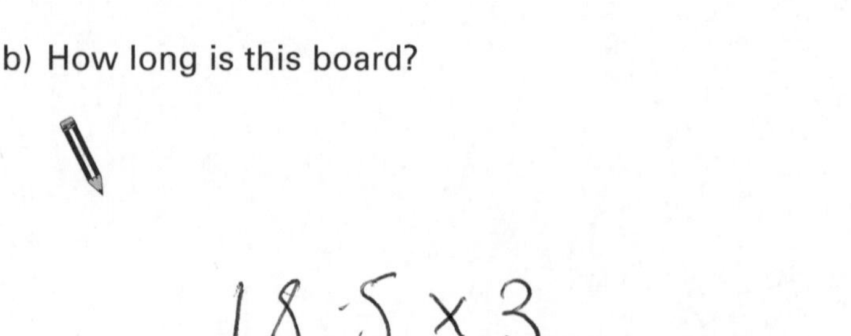

b) How long is this board? *(3 marks)*

Q11b

18.5 x 3.

136.4 cm

12

Special offer!!

We pay the VAT (20%)

a) Explain why dividing the price you pay by 1.2 gives the price before VAT is added. *(1 mark)* Q12a

$\frac{1}{1.2} = 0.833$

17%.

b) Find the percentage discount represented by this offer. *(2 marks)* Q12b

Multiplying by 1.2 give the price (including the MOT.)

13 A builder has a plot of land in the shape of a trapezium ABCD.

The lengths on the diagram are in metres.

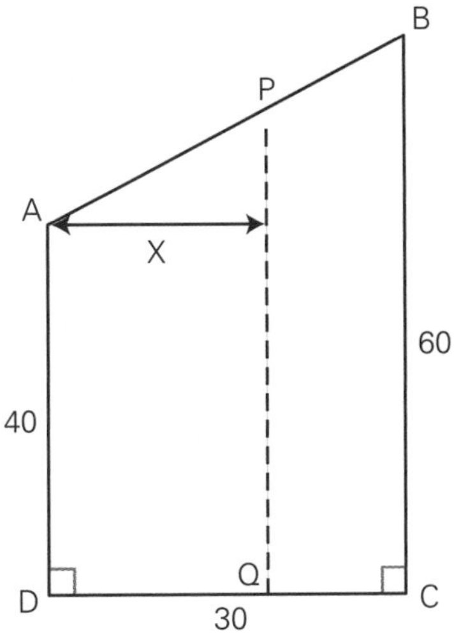

subtotal

a) Calculate the area of the plot. *(1 mark)* Q13a

1500 m^2

m²

The builder wants to divide the plot in two. The part APQD has width *x* metres.

b) Show that $PQ = \frac{1}{3}(120 + 2x)$. *(2 marks)* Q13b

$PQ = 40 + \frac{x}{30} \times 20$

c) Find the area of APQD in terms of *x*, simplifying your answer. *(2 marks)* Q13c

$\frac{x}{2}\left(40 + 40 + \frac{2x}{3}\right) = x\left(40 + \frac{x}{3}\right)$

d) The two plots are to be equal in area. Show that $x \approx 16.5$. *(2 marks)* Q13d

$x\left(40 + \frac{x}{3}\right) = 750$

$16.5^2 + 120 \times 16.6 - 2250 = 2.25$

14 p $\frac{1}{p}$ $\sqrt{p}$ p^2

Arrange these functions in ascending order when:

a) $p > 1$ *(1 mark)* Q14a

$\frac{1}{p}$, $\sqrt{p}$, p, p^2.

b) $0 < p < 1$ *(2 marks)* Q14b

p^2, p.

$\sqrt{p}$, $\frac{1}{p}$.

15 The probability of winning the Lottery next Saturday with one ticket is:

$\frac{1}{13\ 983\ 816}$

a) Write this in standard form, correct to 3 significant figures. *(1 mark)* Q15a

7.15×10^{-8}.

b) What is the probability of winning the Lottery with one ticket this Saturday and next Saturday? *(2 marks)* Q15b

$(7.15 \times 10^{-8})^2$

5.11×10^{-15}.

subtotal

16 The digits of a number are *a*, *b*, *c*.

a) Explain why the number may be written $100a + 10b + c$. *(1 mark)* Q16a

a is a hundreds digit. b is a tens digit

b) Write down an expression for the difference between the number and the sum of its digits. *(1 mark)* Q16b

99a + 9b.

c) Prove that, if the sum of the digits is divisible by 3, then so is the number. *(1 mark)* Q16c

a + b + c has a factor of 3.

END OF TEST

subtotal

Set
C

KEY STAGE 3
Levels 6–8

Test Paper 1

Maths

Test Paper 1 (calculator **not** allowed)

Instructions:

- find a quiet place where you can sit down and complete the test paper undisturbed
- make sure you have a pen, pencil, ruler, rubber and a pair of compasses
- read the questions carefully
- answer all the questions in this paper
- write your answers where you see this symbol
- show all your working as marks may be awarded for this
- go through and check your answers when you have finished the test paper
- check how you have done using pages 102–103 of the Answers and Mark Scheme

Time:

This test paper is **1 hour** long.

Page	71	73	75	77	79	81	82	Max. Mark	**Actual Mark**
Score	....	....	....	....	....	....	....	60	....

First name ....

Last name ....

Test Paper 1 (calculator **not** allowed)

Formulae

Trapezium

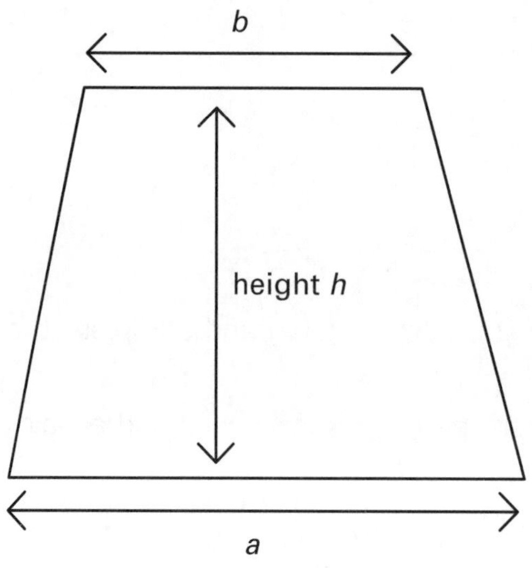

$$\text{area} = \frac{1}{2}(a + b)h$$

Prism

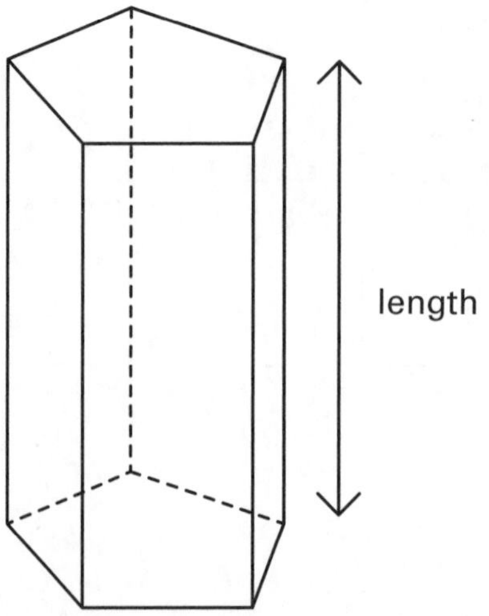

volume = area of cross-section × length

1 The stem and leaf diagram shows the yields (in kilograms) of a sample of tomato plants.

1	1	7							
2	0	0	1	3	4	8			
3	0	4	4	5	7	8	9	9	9
4	0	1	1	2	3	5	6	8	

1 | 1 means 1.1

a) How many tomato plants were there in the sample? *(1 mark)* Q1a

25

b) Write down the mode. *(1 mark)* Q1b

3.9

c) Find the median yield. *(2 marks)* Q1c

Show how you found it.

13th 3.7

subtotal

2 a) Add $\frac{3}{5} + \frac{4}{15}$ *(1 mark)* Q2a

$\frac{13}{15}$

b) Calculate $\frac{3}{5} \times \frac{4}{15}$

Show your working and give your answer in its simplest form. *(2 marks)* Q2b

$\frac{12}{75}$ $\frac{4}{25}$.

3 Solve the equations.

a) $4x + 5 = 2 - x$ *(2 marks)* Q3a

$5x = -3$

$x = -\frac{3}{5}$

b) $5(2x - 1) = x + 4$ *(2 marks)* Q3b

$10x - 5 = x + 4$

$x = 1$.

4 ABCD is a trapezium.

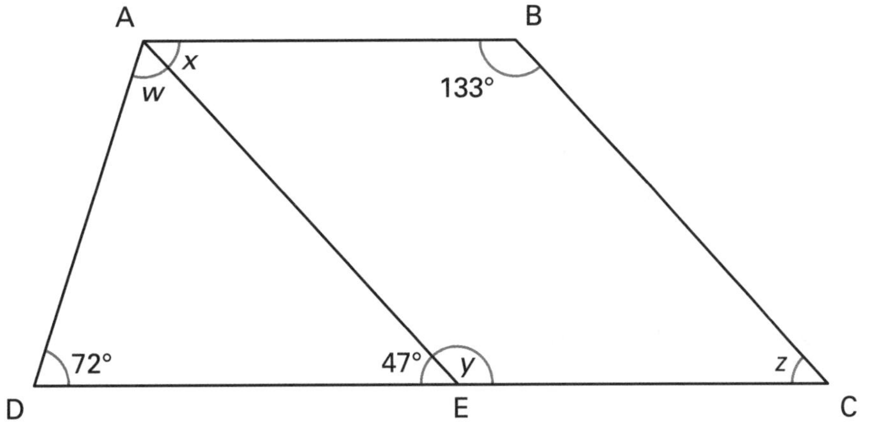

a) Work out the sizes of *w*, *x*, *y* and *z*. In each case, give a reason.

i *w* = 61° Reason All the angles in a triangle have to add up to 180°. *(1 mark)* Q4ai

ii *x* = 47° Reason Alternate angles AB are parallel to DC *(1 mark)* Q4aii

iii *y* = 133° Reason All the angles on a straight line add up to 180°. *(1 mark)* Q4aiii

iv *z* = 47° Reason AB is parralel to DC. *(1 mark)* Q4aiv

b) What sort of quadrilateral is ABCE? Justify your answer. *(1 mark)* Q4b

Angles BCE = angle AED.

 subtotal

5 Rearrange this equation to make *p* the subject. *(2 marks)*

Q5

$2(1 + 3p) = at$

$2 + 6p = at.$

$p = \frac{1}{6}(at - 2)$

6 Draw a triangle the same area as this kite. *(2 marks)*

Q6

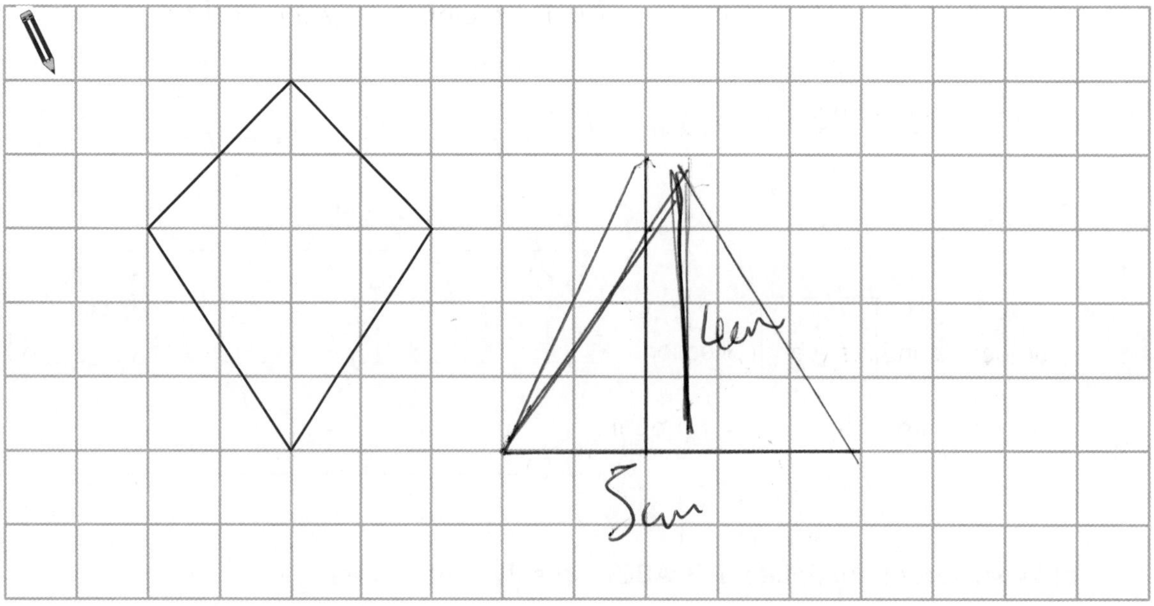

7 a) Using a pair of compasses and a straight edge only, construct the perpendicular bisector of the line segment AB below. *(2 marks)* Q7a

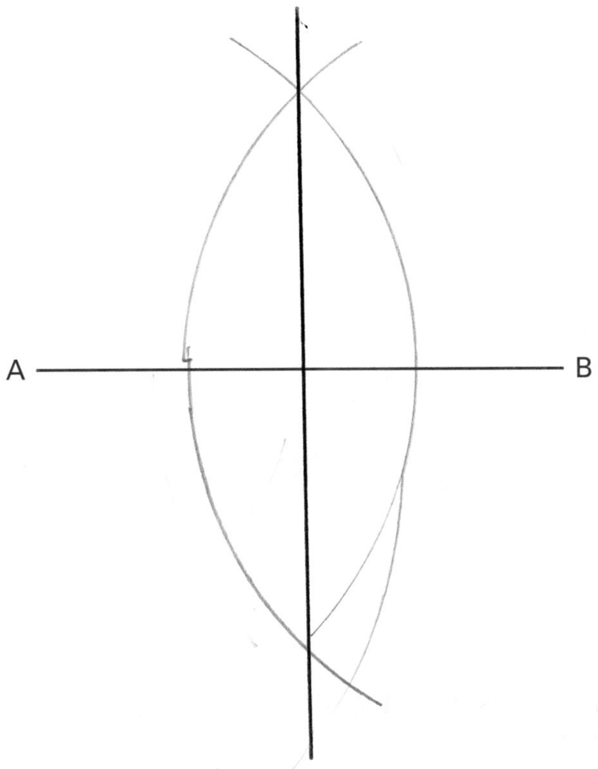

b) Mark any point P on the perpendicular bisector. What is the relationship between P and the points A and B? *(1 mark)* Q7b

AP = PB.

8 Numbers *a* and *b* are both prime.

Is $a^2 + b^2$ an odd or an even number? *(2 marks)* Q8

odd ☐ even ☐ either ☑

Justify your answer.

a and b are both odd. $a^2 + b^2$ is even

subtotal

9 At a theatre, customers leave their coats in a cloakroom. Each customer is given a ticket to claim the coat at the end of the evening. The tickets are blue, yellow or pink.

At the end of the evening, 279 tickets have been taken.

Blue: 1 – 76 Yellow: 1 – 112 Pink: 1 – 91

a) **Work out the probability that the first person to collect their coat has a blue ticket.**

(1 mark) Q9a

$\frac{76}{279}$.

b) **The first person to collect their coat has a blue ticket. What is the probability that it is 69?**

(1 mark) Q9b

$1/76$

c) **The first person actually has ticket 69. What is the probability that it is pink?** *(1 mark)* Q9c

$1/3$.

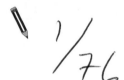

10 Here is an old recipe for gruel.

Gruel (enough for 2)	
$1\frac{1}{2}$ oz	oatmeal
$\frac{3}{4}$ pint	water
$\frac{1}{6}$ teaspoon	salt

Complete the table to show the quantities for 3. *(3 marks)* Q10

Gruel (enough for 3)	
$2\frac{1}{4}$ oz	oatmeal
$1\frac{1}{8}$ pint	water
$1/4$ teaspoon	salt

11 The graph labelled A has the equation $y = 2x + 2$.

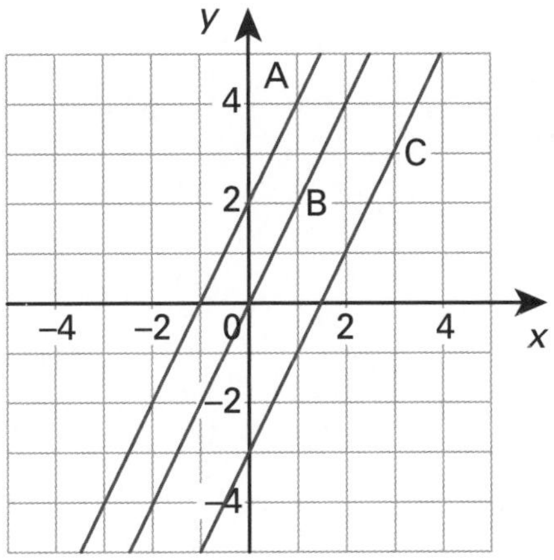

Write down the equations of the lines B and C.

a) B: $y = 2x$. *(1 mark)* Q11a

b) C: $y = 2x - 3$ *(1 mark)* Q11b

subtotal

12 My journey to work is in two parts. From home to the bypass is 12 miles and takes 20 minutes.

a) **Work out the average speed for this part of the journey.** *(1 mark)* Q12a

36 miles/hour

From the bypass to my office is 3 miles and takes 10 minutes.

b) **Work out the average speed for this part of the journey.** *(1 mark)* Q12b

18 miles/hour

c) **Work out the average speed for the whole of the journey.** *(1 mark)* Q12c

30 miles/hour

13 A regular polygon has exterior angle 20°.

How many sides does it have? *(2 marks)* Q13

Show how you worked it out.

Average speed

distance

14 a) Solve the inequality $3x - 2 > 4$ *(1 mark)* Q14a

$x > 2$.

b) Mark the solution on the number line. *(1 mark)* Q14b

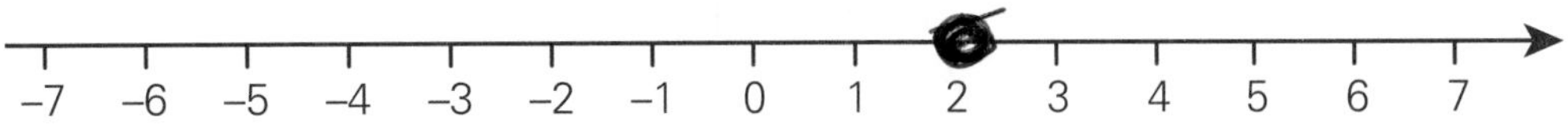

15 Work out:

a) $(2^3)^2 \times 3$ *(1 mark)* Q15a

192.

b) $\dfrac{2^4 \times 3^2 \times 5}{2 \times 3^2}$ *(1 mark)* Q15b

40

c) the highest factor common to 24 and 60. *(1 mark)* Q15c

12

 subtotal

16 The cumulative frequency graph shows the percentage by age of the male population in 1881.

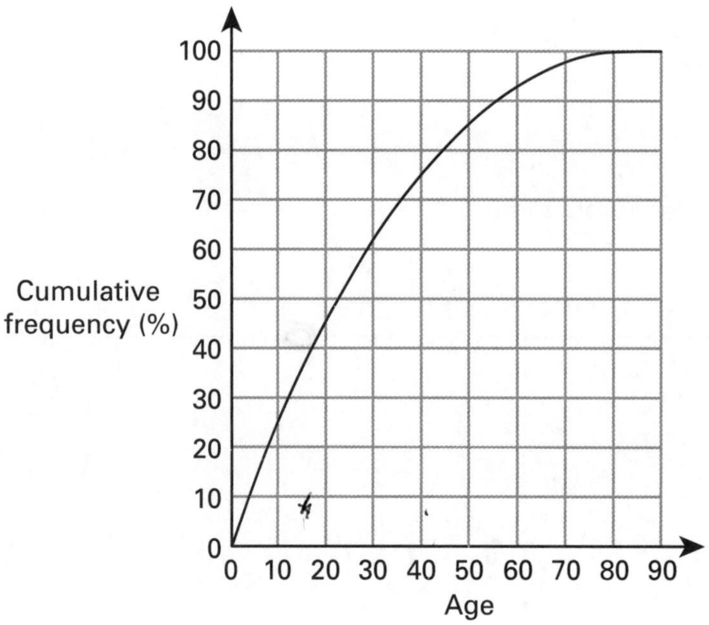

a) Find the median. *(1 mark)* Q16a

23 years.

b) What percentage of this population was over 65? *(1 mark)* Q16b

4 %.

This table shows similar data for 1951.

age	under 15	15 and under 30	30 and under 45	45 and under 60	60 and under 75	75 and over
percentage	19.9	21.8	24.3	19.5	11.7	2.8

c) Work out the cumulative frequencies and plot a graph on the same grid. *(2 marks)* Q16c

19.9, 41.7. 66.0, 85.5.
97.2, 100.

d) Make three comparisons between the age distribution of males in 1881 and 1951. *(3 marks)* Q16d

The average age is much higer in 1951.

17 a) Expand the brackets and write as simply as possible. *(2 marks)* Q17a

$(x + 4)(x - 3)$

$x^2 + 4x - 3x - 12.$

$x^2 + x - 12.$

b) Solve the equation. *(3 marks)* Q17b

$$\frac{2x-3}{4} - \frac{x-1}{3} = \frac{5}{2}$$

$3(2x - 3) - 4(x - 1) = 30$

$2x = 35$

$x = 17\frac{1}{2}.$

subtotal

18 ABC is a right-angled triangle. PQRB is a square. Two areas are marked on the diagram.

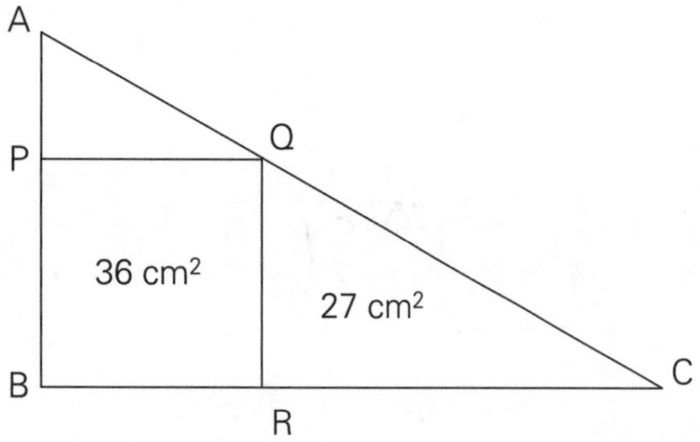

Work out the area of triangle APQ. *(3 marks)* Q18

QR = 6
RC = 9
PQ = 6 × $\frac{6}{9}$ = 4.
AP = 6

12 cm²

19 Here are sketches of the graphs of 4 functions.

Match each function to a graph.

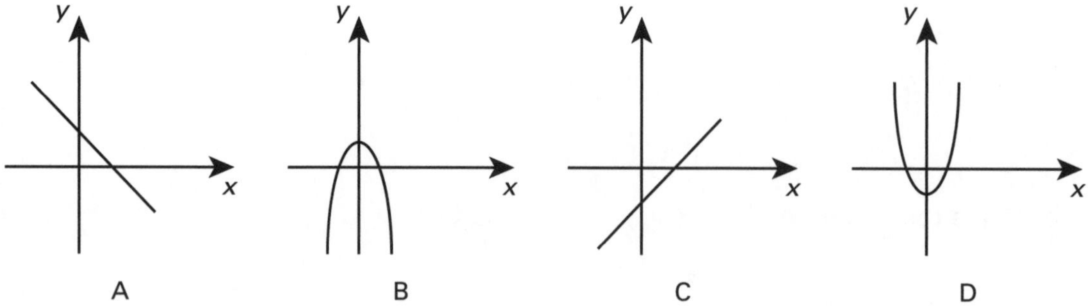

$y = x^2 - 2$ D *(2 marks)* Q19

$y = x - 2$ C

$y = 2 - x$ A

END OF TEST

subtotal

Test Paper 2 (calculator allowed)

Instructions:

- find a quiet place where you can sit down and complete the test paper undisturbed
- make sure you have a pen, pencil, ruler, rubber, protractor and calculator
- read the questions carefully
- answer all the questions in this paper
- write your answers where you see this symbol
- show all your working as marks may be awarded for this
- go through and check your answers when you have finished the test paper
- check how you have done using pages 103–104 of the Answers and Mark Scheme

Time:

This test paper is **1 hour** long.

Page	85	87	89	91	93	95	96	Max. Mark	**Actual Mark**
Score	....	....	....	....	....	....	....	60	....

First name ....

Last name ....

Set C

KEY STAGE 3
Levels 6–8

Test Paper 2

Maths

Test Paper 2 (calculator allowed)

Formulae

Trapezium

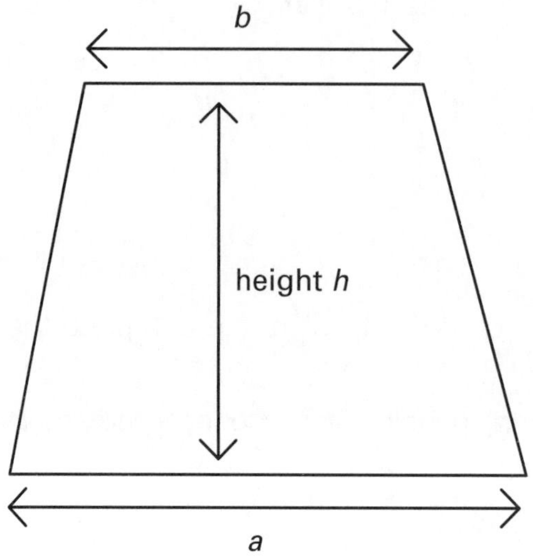

area $= \frac{1}{2}(a + b)h$

Prism

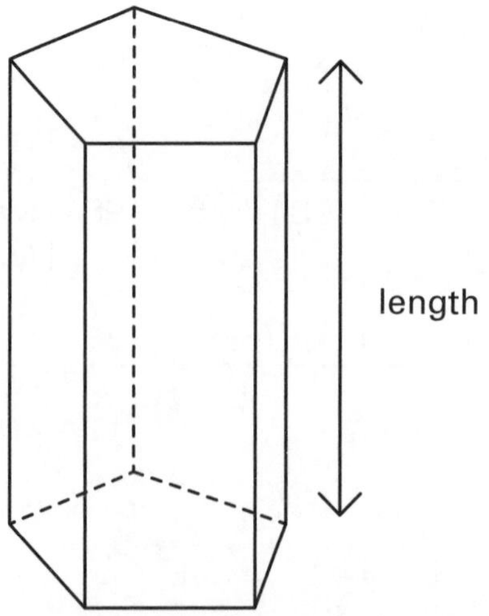

volume = area of cross-section × length

1

£1 = \$1.80
£1 = €1.50

An American bought a shirt in London for £49.

a) Work out how much that is in dollars. *(2 marks)* Q1a

49 × 1.8

\$ 88.20

b) How much is €1 worth in pounds? Give your answer to the nearest penny. *(2 marks)* Q1b

÷ 1.5

£ 0.67

c) I have €200. How many dollars is that? *(2 marks)* Q1c

(200 ÷ 1.5) 1.8

\$ 240

subtotal

2 Solve these equations.

a) $\frac{x}{4} = \frac{5}{6}$

$x = \frac{10}{3}$

(1 mark) Q2a

b) $\frac{1}{2}x - 3 = 3 - x$

$\frac{3x}{2} = 6$.

(2 marks) Q2b

3 Look at these expressions. The value of the first is given.

Complete the boxes to show the values of the other expressions.

	$n + 2$	**5**
a)	$n - 2$	1
b)	$2n - 2$	4
c)	$2n + 1$	7.

a) *(1 mark)* Q3a

b) *(1 mark)* Q3b

c) *(1 mark)* Q3c

4 The table shows how a small child spends a day.

activity	hours
sleeping	14
eating	2
playing with others	5
playing on own	3

210°
15°
45°
30°

Draw a pie chart to represent the data. *(4 marks)* Q4

Show your method clearly.

subtotal

5 Rashid is measuring some tins.

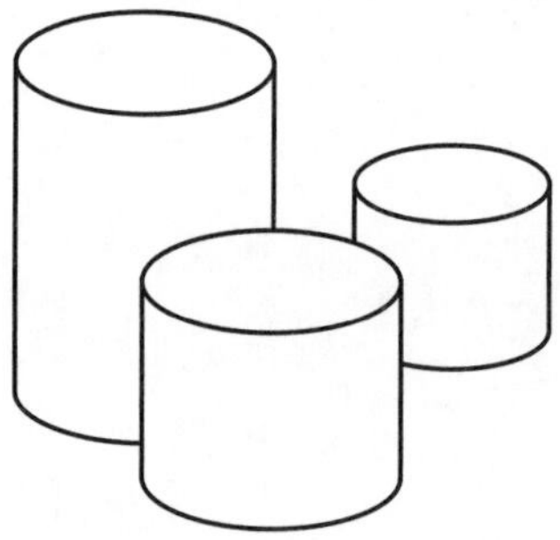

The top of a tin of pineapple cubes has diameter 8.5 cm.

a) Calculate its area. *(2 marks)* Q5a

56·7

56·7 cm²

Rashid wraps a piece of string around another tin to find the circumference.
It measures 160 mm.

b) Calculate the diameter of the tin. *(2 marks)* Q5b

160 ÷ π

51. mm

Now he wraps the string around a tin of bean sprouts, as shown in the diagram.
One end of the string is at the top of the tin and the other at the bottom directly below.

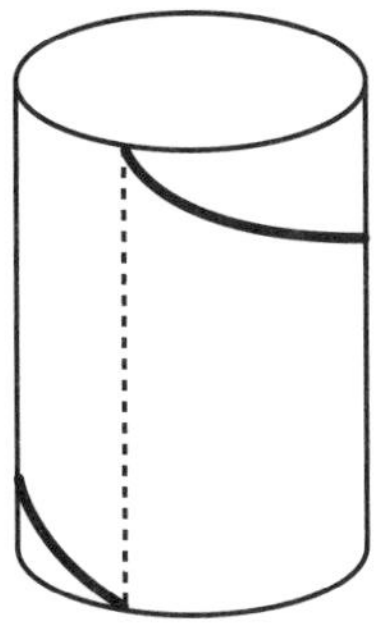

The tin has radius 3.6 cm and height 11.0 cm.

c) Calculate the length of the string. *(4 marks)* Q5c

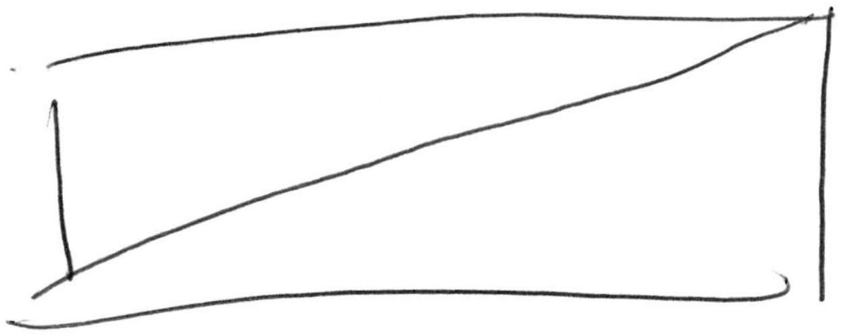

22.6

25.15 cm

6 There are 60 members in a club. The mean age is 55 years and the range 45 years.

a) If no members leave or join, what will be the mean and range in 1 year's time?

i 56 Mean *(1 mark)* Q6ai

ii 45 Range *(1 mark)* Q6aii

 subtotal

The mean age is reduced by a year when 5 new members join.

b) Work out the mean age of the 5 new members. *(4 marks)* Q6b

6 5x54

-60x55

÷5

[38x9] mean

42.

7 This formula gives the height, *h* cm, of a solid with volume *V* cm^3 and radius *r* cm.

$$h = \frac{V}{\pi r^2} + \frac{r}{3}$$

a) Find *h* when *V* = 1600 and *r* = 6. *(1 mark)* Q7a

$h =$ [16.1]

b) Calculate the value of *V* when *h* = 6.75 and *r* = 2.5. *(2 marks)* Q7b

$V =$ [116] cm^3

8 The diagram shows a regular octagon.

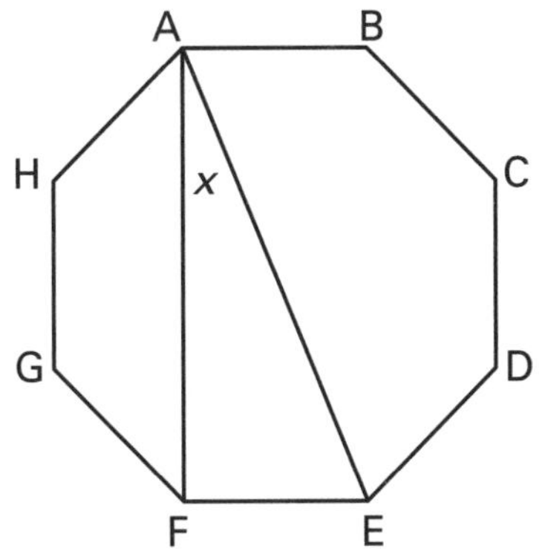

a) **Explain why the interior angle of a regular octagon is 135°.** *(2 marks)* Q8a

180 - 45 = 135°.

b) **Calculate the size of angle AFG.**

Give reasons for your answer. *(2 marks)* Q8b

AFGH is an isosoles trapezium.

c) **Prove that angle x is $22\frac{1}{2}$°.** *(3 marks)* Q8c

Done on Scrap.

 subtotal

9

SALE
35% off everything

In a sale, all prices are reduced by 35%.

A teapot was priced at £68 before the sale.

a) Which calculation gives the sale price? Tick the correct one. *(1 mark)* Q9a

- [ ] 68×0.35
- [x] 68×0.65
- [ ] 68×1.35
- [ ] 68×1.65

The sale price of a washing machine is £195.

b) Find the price before the sale. *(2 marks)* Q9b

195 ÷ 0.65

£ 300

10 The graph shows three inequalities.

Two of the inequalities are $x \geq 0$ and $y \geq 0$.

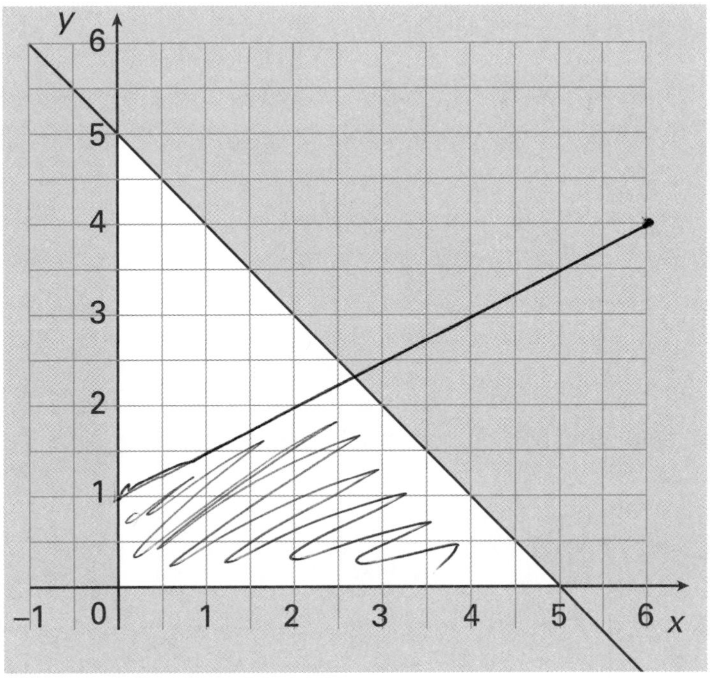

a) Find the third inequality. *(2 marks)* Q10a

$x + y = 5.$

$x + y \leq = 5.$

b) Show the inequality $2y - x \geq 2$ on the same axes. *(2 marks)* Q10b

c) What is the largest value of x to satisfy all the inequalities? *(1 mark)* Q10c

2.7.

subtotal

11 **Simplify the expression:** *(2 marks)* Q11

$$\frac{(x-y)^2}{x^2-y^2}$$

$$\frac{(x-y)(x+y)}{x-y}$$

$$x+y$$

12 The diagram shows the side of a shed on horizontal ground. The dimensions are in metres.

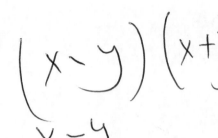

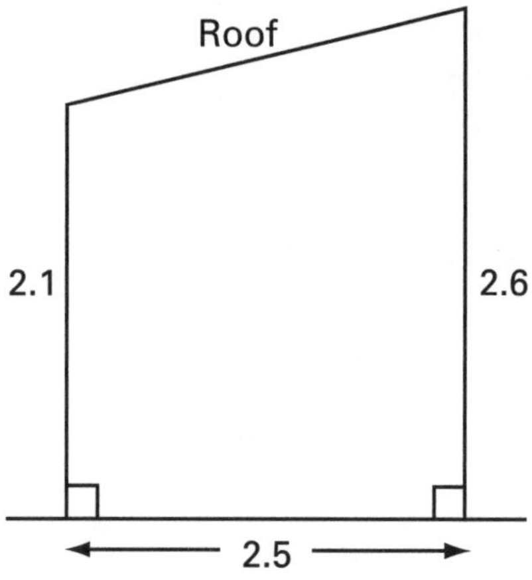

Calculate the angle made by the roof with the horizontal. *(3 marks)* Q12

$$\tan = \frac{0.5}{2.5}$$

11.3.

°

13 A child's toy is programmed to move along the lines on a square grid.

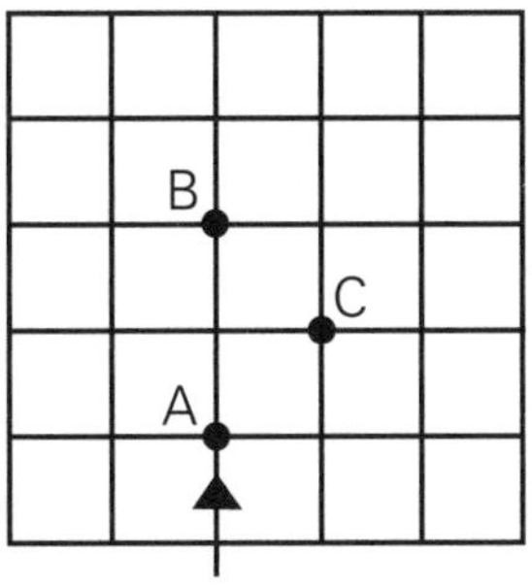

At each intersection, it is equally likely to go straight on or turn. If it turns, it is equally likely to turn left or turn right. It arrives at A in the direction of the arrow.

a) Write down the probabilities of it: *(1 mark)* Q13a

going straight on	1/2
turning left	1/4
turning right	1/4.

b) Show that the probability that it is at B after 2 steps is $\frac{1}{4}$. *(1 mark)* Q13b

1/4

c) Work out the probability that it is at C after just 2 steps. *(2 marks)* Q13c

1/4 + 1/4 × 1/4 + 1/4

$\frac{3}{16}$

subtotal

14 The speed of light is about 1.08×10^9 km/hour.

1 mile ≈ 1.6 km. 1 mile = 5280 feet.

Calculate the speed of light in feet/second. *(3 marks)*

Q14

9·9 × 10[8]	feet/second

END OF TEST

subtota

Answers and Mark Scheme

Maths Set A Test Paper 1 Answers

1) a) 90 000 000 *(1 mark)*
b) 54 000 *(1 mark)*
Examiner's tip *In part b) the question has 90 million people so it is 90 × 600.*

2) a) $6x + 30 = 180$ *(1 mark)*
b) 25°; 60°; 95° *(1 mark)*

3) a) 22 m/h *(1 mark)*
b) 220 m/h *(1 mark)*

4) a) $\frac{7}{20}$ *(1 mark)*
b) $\frac{14}{20}$ or $\frac{7}{10}$ *(1 mark)*
Examiner's tip *You should write fractions as simply as possible.*

5) a) 90° *(1 mark)*
b) Check drawing.
Protein = 54°, fat = 90° *(2 marks)*

6) a) i $3x$ *(1 mark)*
ii $3x - 3$ *(1 mark)*
b) i $7x = 49$ or $7x - 3 = 46$ *(1 mark)*
ii $x = 7$, 21, 18 *(2 marks)*
Examiner's tip *Your answer should be a whole number. Use this fact to check you have solved the equation correctly.*

7) a) i $w = 3g$ *(1 mark)*
ii 40 *(1 mark)*
b) i $w = 3g + 2$ *(1 mark)*
ii 302 *(1 mark)*
Examiner's tip *In part a) take care – at first sight the formula would seem to be $g = 3w$ but check. The first picture has 3 white and 1 grey – $g = 3w$ would give 9 grey.*

8) b) indicated at 1 *(1 mark)*
c) at 0.25 *(1 mark)*
d) at 0.5 *(1 mark)*

9) Statement d, i.e. E > 1 *(1 mark)*

10) Statement c, i.e. $3n + 5 = 29$ *(1 mark)*
Examiner's tip *To check, use a value of n less than 1 – e.g. 0.5*

11) a) $\frac{6}{20}$ or $\frac{3}{10}$ *(1 mark)*
b) $\frac{8}{20}$ or $\frac{4}{10}$ or $\frac{2}{5}$ *(1 mark)*
c) 0.75 *(1 mark)*

12) a) 10, 18, 26 *(1 mark)*
b) *(2 marks)*

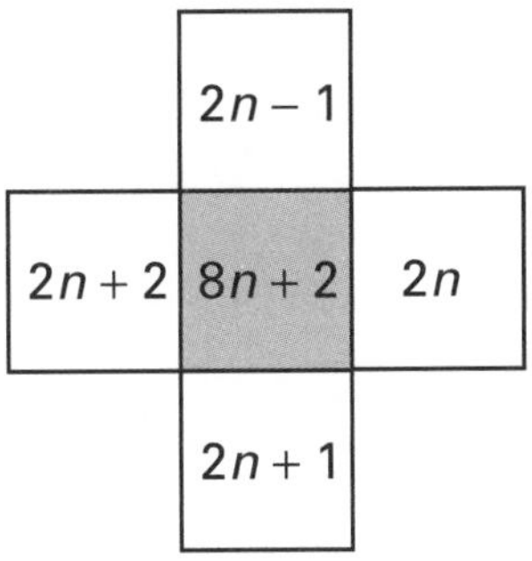

2 marks all correct
1 mark 2 or 3 correct
Examiner's tip *Start with the number at the top of the cross. This is an odd number, so given by $2n - 1$*

13) a) i $x = 5$ *(1 mark)*
ii $x = 16$ *(1 mark)*
b) i $x < 5$ *(1 mark)*
ii $x \geq -3$ *(1 mark)*
Examiner's tip *In part b) ii $-x \leq 3$ you need to remember that multiplying by -1 "reverses" the inequality.*

14) a → E, b → A, c → C, d → D, e → B *(3 marks)*
3 marks all correct, 2 marks 3 or 4 correct, 1 mark 1 or 2 correct

15) d is correct – A, B, F, H are congruent *(1 mark)*
Examiner's tip *Congruent means exactly the same, irrespective of orientation.*

16) Line parallel to BC, *(1 mark)*
passing through A *(1 mark)*

17) d is correct, $a = 7$, $b = 1$,
allow 1 mark if answer is reversed *(2 marks)*

18) a) e.g. probably not a representative sample of shoppers
Not asking people who can shop during the week *(1 mark)*
b) Both questions are leading questions – customers may not be 100% honest when in the shop *(1 mark)*

19) A constant speed
B accelerates – going downhill
C car reaches top of climb
D car reaches bottom of slope
3 marks all correct, 2 marks 2 or 3 correct,
1 mark 1 correct *(3 marks)*
Examiner's tip *The graph is not the shape of the switchback ride.*

20) a) $\frac{15}{90} = \frac{1}{6}$ *(1 mark)*
b) $\frac{5}{6}$ *(1 mark)*
c) $\frac{1}{20}$ *(1 mark)*

21) a) $2 + x$ seen
$x + y$
$y + 8$
2 marks all correct,
1 mark 1 or 2 correct *(2 marks)*

b) $2x + y = 14$ *(2 marks)*
allow 1 mark for $2 + x + x + y = 16$ seen
$x + 2y = 16$ *(2 marks)*
allow 1 mark for $x + y + y + 8 = 24$ seen

c) $x = 4$, $y = 6$ *(3 marks)*
***Examiner's tip** In part c) show your working – you may get credit even if the answer is incorrect.*

Maths Set A Test Paper 2 Answers

1) 80 bag box *(2 marks)*
allow 1 mark for 1.8p and 1.9p seen
***Examiner's tip** Hint: find the cost of 1 tea bag for each box.*

2) a) 12.45(2389.......) *(1 mark)*
b) 40.24(08) *(1 mark)*
***Examiner's tip** Remember to put the denominator in brackets in both parts.*

3) e.g. 1.7 and 3.5 *(2 marks)*

4) a) 11 *(1 mark)*
b) 24 *(1 mark)*
c) 25 yellow and 30 red *(1 mark)*
***Examiner's tip** In part c) solve as follows:*
$Y \div R = 5 \div 6$, $R = Y + 5$
hence $Y \div (Y + 5) = 5 \div 6$

5) a) 22° *(1 mark)*
b) 125 or 126 *(2 marks)*
allow 1 mark for 31.4(1) seen
***Examiner's tip** The question says "about" so use $\pi = 3.14$*

6) 18.36(66.....) *(2 marks)*
1.634(.....) *(1 mark)*
allow 1 mark for each correct calculation in the range 18.3 and 1.7 to 18.5 and 1.5

7) a) 1000 g *(1 mark)*
b) 417 g *(1 mark)*

8) 0.54 m^3 *(3 marks)*
Allow 2 marks for cross-sectional area = 0.27 m^2, or 1 mark each for cross-sectional area of 1 step = $0.3 \times 0.15 = 0.045$ m^2 and volume of 1 step = $0.045 \times 2 = 0.09$ m^3.
Allow 1 mark for 6 identical steps so volume = $6 \times 0.09 = 0.54$ m^3.
Deduct 1 mark if units incorrect.
***Examiner's tip** Be consistent in the units used.*

9) a) 13.6(36.....)% *(1 mark)*
b) e.g. not really – this would give 499 ml *(1 mark)*
c) 439.5 ml *(1 mark)*

10) a) CB = 61 km *(2 marks)*
allow 1 mark for $35^2 + 50^2$
DA = 19.4 km *(2 marks)*
allow 1 mark for $40^2 - 35^2$
Distance = 170.4 km *(1 mark)*
b) time = 4.26h or 4h 16 min *(1 mark)*
***Examiner's tip** Convert the decimal part of the answer into minutes by multiplying by 60.*

11) a) 4.8 cm *(1 mark)*
b) 3.13 cm *(1 mark)*

12) 5.14, 2.14 *(3 marks)*
for 3 trials either side of correct answer allow 2 marks

13) a) $\frac{27}{60} = 45\%$ *(1 mark)*
b) $\frac{28}{70} = 40\%$ *(1 mark)*
c) $\frac{69}{130} = 53\%$ *(1 mark)*

14) a) i A is $6 + a$ *(1 mark)*
ii B is $6 + 2a$ *(1 mark)*
b) $12 + 3a = 36$ *(1 mark)*
c) $a = 8$ *(1 mark)*

15) a) 176 cm^2 *(1 mark)*
b) $A = 3 \times 15 \times (15 + 30)$
$= 45 \times 45 = 2025$ cm^2 *(1 mark)*
or $A = 3 \times 14 \times (14 + 28)$
$= 42 \times 42$
$= 1764$ cm^2
***Examiner's tip** In part b) use the dimensions correct to the nearest whole centimetre.*

16) a) i 32, 64, 128 *(1 mark)*
ii 2^n *(1 mark)*
b) i 31, 63, 127 *(1 mark)*
ii $2^n - 1$ *(1 mark)*

17) $P = 67.4$ million *(2 marks)*
allow 1 mark for 1.217 seen

18) a) 72 cm *(1 mark)*
b) i 144 cm *(1 mark)*
ii 36 cm *(1 mark)*
c) 648 cm^2 *(1 mark)*

19) a) 12.25 *(1 mark)*
b) $n^2 + n + \frac{1}{4}$ *(1 mark)*
c) $(61\frac{1}{2})^2$ *(1 mark)*

20) a) 120 *(1 mark)*
b) 140 *(1 mark)*
***Examiner's tip** In part a) take care – the question says "more than 4" – 80 answered 4 or fewer. In part b) the question says "fewer than 7" i.e. 6 or fewer.*

21) a) $8^2 + 12^2 = 208$,
$18^2 = 324$, so not possible
(Phillipa is correct) *(1 mark)*
b) angle = 30.96°, so not possible
(No, Irene is not correct) *(1 mark)*

Maths Set B Test Paper 1 Answers

1) a) –8 *(1 mark)*
b) –2 *(1 mark)*
***Examiner's tip** Remember that subtracting a negative number is the same as adding the positive.*

2) a) Trapezium *(1 mark)*
Isosceles or one pair of sides equal *(1 mark)*
b) Kite or arrowhead *(1 mark)*
Two pairs of adjacent sides equal *(1 mark)*
c) No line of symmetry or at least 2 lines of symmetry *(1 mark)*
***Examiner's tip** You may find it helpful to sketch the shapes.*

3) $4x + 7 = 25$ or $4x = 18$ *(1 mark)*
$x = 4.5$ *(1 mark)*

4) a) Alternate angles, AB parallel to DC *(1 mark)*
b) $w + y + 90 = 180$ *(1 mark)*
$w + z + 90 = 180$, so $y = z$ *(1 mark)*
***Examiner's tip** You can put an extra step in part b) by subtracting the 2 equations to give $y - z = 0$.*

5) $\dfrac{1+3+2}{12}$ or $\dfrac{6}{12}$ *(1 mark)*
$\dfrac{1}{2}$ *(1 mark)*
***Examiner's tip** There is no need for a larger denominator as 4 and 6 both divide into 12.*

6) a) B
D
C
A *(3 marks)*
3 marks all correct, 2 marks 2 or 3 correct, 1 mark 1 correct
b) *(1 mark)*

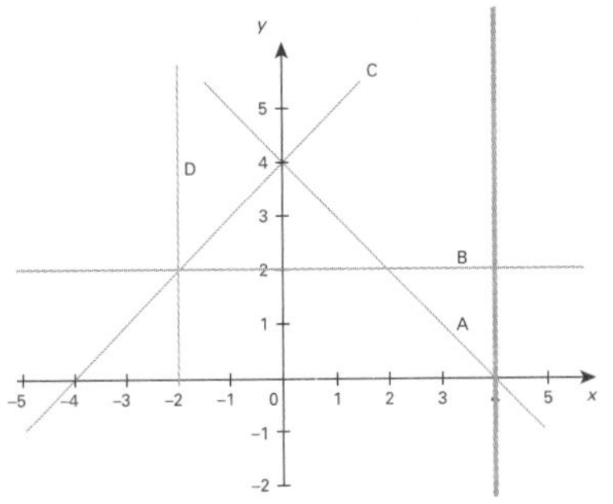

7) a) Integer × 2 is even *(1 mark)*
b) $2n + 1$ etc. *(1 mark)*
***Examiner's tip** Your explanation should be in general terms. Just giving examples will not earn marks.*

8) a) Negative *(1 mark)*
b) *(1 mark)*

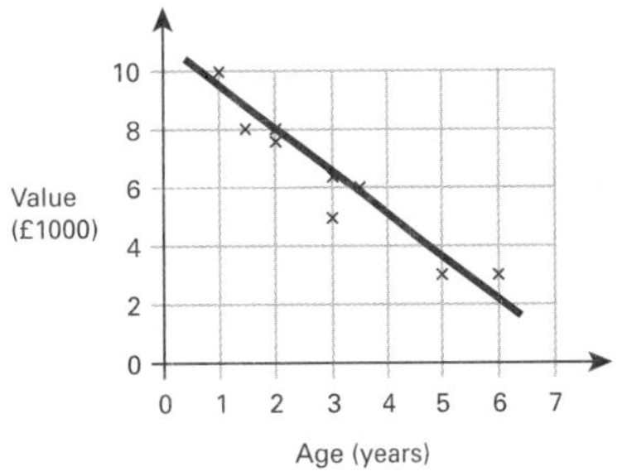

c) About £5000 *(1 mark)*
d) No – too far from other data *(1 mark)*
***Examiner's tip** In part b) you are only expected to draw the line of best fit by eye, as has been done here.*

9) $M = 10a + 20b$ or $\frac{M}{10} = a + 2b$
or $20b = M - 10a$ *(1 mark)*
$b = \frac{1}{20}(M - 10a)$ or $b = \frac{1}{2}(\frac{M}{10} - a)$ *(1 mark)*

10) a) Angle bisector drawn *(1 mark)*
Arcs clear and accurate *(1 mark)*

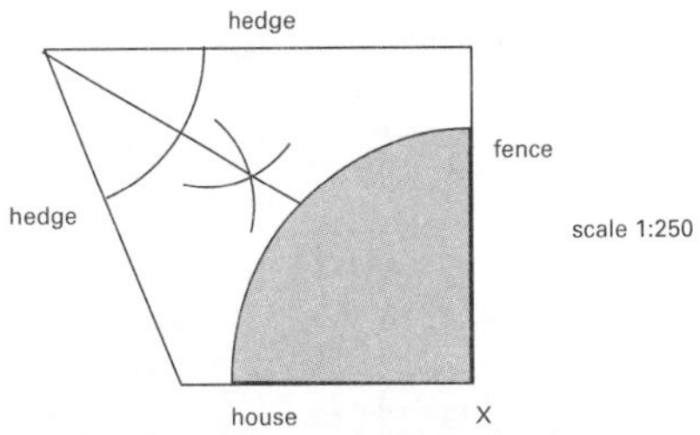

b) Circle radius 4 cm drawn, centre X *(1 mark)*
Correct region shaded *(1 mark)*
***Examiner's tip** Arcs must be accurately drawn with compasses.*

11) $\frac{3}{5}$ or $\frac{2}{3}$ used *(1 mark)*
$\frac{3}{5} \times \frac{2}{3}$ or $\frac{2}{5}$ *(1 mark)*
$\frac{3}{5}$ *(1 mark)*
***Examiner's tip** As $\frac{3}{5}$ appears in 2 places, it is important that you make clear how you found it.*

12) a) $\frac{1}{2}$ km in 20 minutes *(1 mark)*
1.5 km/hour *(1 mark)*
b) Straight line from (0810, 0) *(1 mark)*
to (0840, 2) *(1 mark)*

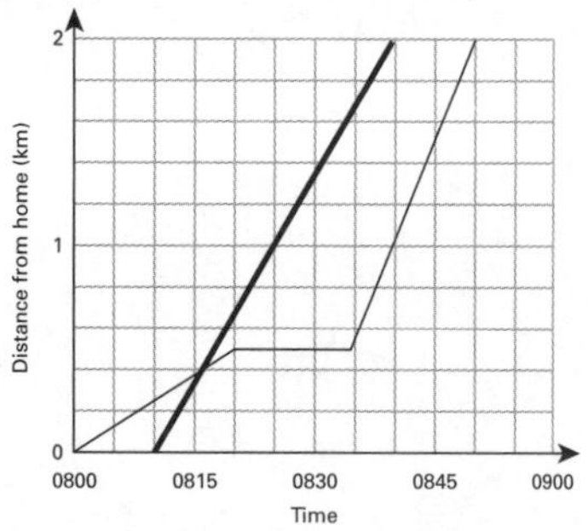

Examiner's tip *In another question, you might be asked to find where she caught up with him.*

13) Use of 36 *(1 mark)*
6 – 4, 5 – 3, 4 – 2, 3 – 1 (twice) *(1 mark)*
$\frac{8}{36}$ or $\frac{2}{9}$ *(1 mark)*
Examiner's tip *You may find it helpful to draw a possibility table, showing all 36 outcomes.*

14) a) $x(2x + 1) = \frac{1}{2}(x + 1)(x + 2)$ *(1 mark)*
$2x^2 + x = \frac{1}{2}x^2 + \frac{3}{2}x + 1$ *(1 mark)*
$\frac{3}{2}x^2 - \frac{1}{2}x - 1 = 0$ *(1 mark)*
Now × by 2
b) $(3x + 2)(x - 1) = 0$ *(1 mark)*
$x = 1$ or $-\frac{2}{3}$ *(1 mark)*
Rectangle 1 × 3, triangle 3 × 2 *(1 mark)*
(other solution negative)
Examiner's tip *This question is designed to see if you can manipulate algebraic expressions and equations. Unless you show this you will be awarded no marks, even if you correctly guess the final answer.*

15) a) 4.525×10^9 *(1 mark)*
b) No – data only 2 significant figures *(1 mark)*
Examiner's tip *When the numbers are subtracted, the smaller only affects the third and fourth figures, which are not known for the larger number.*

16) a) 2^4 *(1 mark)*
b) $\frac{b}{a}$ *(1 mark)*

17) a) Higher median (average) *(1 mark)*
Highest value (upper quartile) *(1 mark)*
b) Lower inter-quartile range (range) *(1 mark)*
Higher minimum value *(1 mark)*
c) X – better on average
or Y – less variation or equivalent *(1 mark)*
Examiner's tip *Either answer is possible in part c). All that is required is that your choice is justified by the chosen statistics.*

18) a) Angles of pentagon are 108° *(1 mark)*
In EBCD, angle EBC = $\frac{1}{2}$(360 – 108 – 108)
or Angle ABE = 36°, so angle EBC
= 108 – 36 *(1 mark)*
b) Angle AEB = 108 – 72 = 36°
(angles of triangle) *(1 mark)*
Angle DEC = angle AEB
(symmetry of pentagon) *(1 mark)*
Angle BEC = 108 – 36 – 36 = 36° *(1 mark)*
Examiner's tip *Show the steps of your argument clearly, with reasons where appropriate.*

Maths Set B Test Paper 2 Answers

1) $\frac{12}{85} \times 100$ *(1 mark)*
14.12, 14.1 or 14 *(1 mark)*

2) a) 588 or 587.(...) cm² *(2 marks)*
b) $\frac{1000}{2 \times \pi \times 7.5} - 7.5$ *(1 mark)*

13.7(...) cm *(1 mark)*
Examiner's tip *You must write the units in the answer spaces to score full marks. Make sure you write down your calculation in part b).*

3) a) Same *(1 mark)*
Both 24 cm³ *(1 mark)*
b) B – 76 cm² *(1 mark)*
A – 52 cm² *(1 mark)*
c) 6 × 2 correct *(1 mark)*
2 × 2 correct *(1 mark)*
Correctly assembled *(1 mark)*

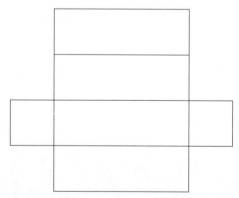

Examiner's tip *There are other ways of completing the net, but not all will fit on the page!*

4) Sector measured as 208 – 210° *(1 mark)*
$\times$ 5000 $\div$ 360 *(1 mark)*
2900 million *(1 mark)*
Examiner's tip *If you use a 180° protractor to measure the sector for Asia, you will need to subtract from 360.*

5) a) Ordinary:
$(2.66 + 2.50 + 1.30) \div 24 = 26.9$p per print *(1 mark)*
Digital: $6.99 \div 20 + 29.99 \div 500 =$ 40.95p per print *(1 mark)*
b) Digital now cheaper *(1 mark)*
Examiner's tip *If only half the photos are worth having, then every ordinary print effectively costs twice as much.*

6) a) 995 – 997 *(1 mark)*
b) $996 \times 94 + 998 \times 49 +$ etc or 174580 *(1 mark)*
$\div$ 175 *(1 mark)*
997.6 *(1 mark)*
Examiner's tip *Don't forget to use the midpoints in your calculation and to divide by the total frequency.*

7) Area of square $= 2 \times 3.5^2$
area of circle $= \pi \times 3.5^2$ *(1 mark)*
$\dfrac{\pi \times 3.5^2 - 2 \times 3.5^2}{\pi \times 3.5^2} \times 100$ *(1 mark)*
36.3% *(1 mark)*
Examiner's tip *Notice that the calculation simplifies to* $\dfrac{\pi - 2}{\pi} \times 100$. *The answer is independent of the size of the circle. Can you see why?*

8) $4x - 2y = 26$ or $2x + 4y = 8$ *(1 mark)*
$5x = 30$ or $5y = -5$ *(1 mark)*
$(6, -1)$ *(1 mark)*
Examiner's tip *Two ways of eliminating are shown here. You only need to use one, and then substitute to find the other coordinate.*

9) a) 15 *(1 mark)*
b) Use of 25 *(1 mark)*
20, 35 *(1 mark)*
Examiner's tip *Don't fall into the trap of thinking that the ratio will still be the same in 5 years' time!*

10) a) $3x < 1$, $x < \frac{1}{3}$ *(1 mark)*
b) $3x - 6 \leq 7x + 2$ or $-8 \leq 4x$ *(1 mark)*
$x \geq -2$ *(1 mark)*

Examiner's tip *Take care with the direction of the inequality signs. You could leave the answer in the form* $-2 \leq x$ *but the convention is to write it the other way round.*

11) a) $\sqrt{18.5^2 + 30^2}$ or 35.2(...) *(1 mark)*
$\times$ 3 *(1 mark)*
105.7(...) or 106 *(1 mark)*
b) 18.5×3 *(1 mark)*
$\div \sin 24°$ *(1 mark)*
136.5 or 136.4(...) *(1 mark)*

12) a) Multiplying by 1.2 gives the price including VAT (VAT is 20%) *(1 mark)*
b) $\dfrac{1}{1.2} \approx 0.833$ *(1 mark)*

Discount ≈ 17% *(1 mark)*

13) a) 1500 m^2 *(1 mark)*
b) Use of similar triangles *(1 mark)*
$PQ = 40 + \frac{x}{30} \times 20$ *(1 mark)*
c) Area $= \frac{x}{2}(40 + 40 + \frac{2x}{3})$ *(1 mark)*
$= x(40 + \frac{x}{3})$ *(1 mark)*
d) $x(40 + \frac{x}{3}) = 750$ or $x^2 + 120x - 2250 = 0$ *(1 mark)*
$16.5^2 + 120 \times 16.6 - 2250 = 2.25 \approx 0$ *(1 mark)*
Examiner's tip *You are not expected to be able to solve the equation. You are asked to show that a solution is approximately 16.5. This can be done by substitution.*

14) a) $\frac{1}{p}$, $\sqrt{p}$, p, p^2 *(1 mark)*
b) p^2, p, *(1 mark)*
$\sqrt{p}$, $\frac{1}{p}$ *(1 mark)*

15) a) 7.15×10^{-8} *(1 mark)*
b) $(7.15 \times 10^{-8})^2$ *(1 mark)*
5.11×10^{-15} *(1 mark)*

16) a) a is the hundreds digit, b is the tens digit *(1 mark)*
b) $99a + 9b$ *(1 mark)*
c) Difference has factor 3, $a + b + c$ has factor 3, so number has factor 3 *(1 mark)*
Examiner's tip *If 2 numbers have a common factor, then so does their difference.*

Maths Set C Test Paper 1 Answers

1) a) 25 *(1 mark)*
b) 3.9 *(1 mark)*
c) Use of 13th *(1 mark)*
3.7 *(1 mark)*
Examiner's tip *Don't forget the decimal point. It is shown in the key.*

2) a) $\frac{13}{15}$ *(1 mark)*
b) $\frac{1}{5}\times\frac{4}{5}$ or $\frac{12}{75}$ *(1 mark)*
$\frac{4}{25}$ *(1 mark)*
Examiner's tip *You need a common denominator of 15 in part a).*

3) a) $5x = -3$ *(1 mark)*
$x = -\frac{3}{5}$ *(1 mark)*
b) $10x - 5 = x + 4$ *(1 mark)*
$x = 1$ *(1 mark)*
Examiner's tip *Be sure to show the intermediate steps. Don't try to guess the answer.*

4) a) i $w = 61°$
Angles of triangle add up to 180° *(1 mark)*
ii $x = 47°$
Alternate angles, AB parallel to DC *(1 mark)*
iii $y = 133°$
Angles on straight line add up to 180° *(1 mark)*
iv $z = 47°$
Allied angles, AB parallel to DC *(1 mark)*
b) Parallelogram, angle BCE = angle AED, corresponding angles *(1 mark)*
Examiner's tip *Give your reasons clearly. Without them you will score no marks.*

5) $2 + 6p = at$ *(1 mark)*
$p = \frac{1}{6}(at - 2)$ *(1 mark)*

6) Use of area 10 cm^2 *(1 mark)*
Correct triangle, e.g. base 5 cm and height 4 cm *(1 mark)*
Examiner's tip *You must establish the area of the kite first (divide it into triangles). Any triangle of the right area will get the mark.*

7) a) Perpendicular in correct position *(1 mark)*
2 pairs of intersecting arcs, centred ends of the line *(1 mark)*
b) AP = PB *(1 mark)*
Examiner's tip *Set your compasses to a distance greater than half the line. Draw 4 arcs, 2 centred at each end of the line. Join the intersections of the arcs.*

8) 'Either' ticked and
if a and b are both odd, $a^2 + b^2$ is even *(1 mark)*
if a is 2 and b any other prime, $a^2 + b^2$ is odd *(1 mark)*
Examiner's tip *You must use a general argument. It is not enough to give examples.*

9) a) $\frac{76}{279}$ *(1 mark)*
b) $\frac{1}{76}$ *(1 mark)*
c) $\frac{1}{3}$ *(1 mark)*

10) $2\frac{1}{4}$ *(1 mark)*
$1\frac{1}{8}$ *(1 mark)*
$\frac{1}{4}$ *(1 mark)*
Examiner's tip *Given the context (and no calculator), fractions are appropriate. Give all answers in their lowest terms.*

11) a) $y = 2x$ *(1 mark)*
b) $y = 2x - 3$ *(1 mark)*
Examiner's tip *Parallel lines have the same gradient.*

12) a) 36 mph *(1 mark)*
b) 18 mph *(1 mark)*
c) 30 mph *(1 mark)*
Examiner's tip *The average speed for the whole journey is the total distance divided by the total time. Don't try to combine the 2 speeds.*

13) $360 \div 20$ *(1 mark)*
18 sides *(1 mark)*

14) a) $x > 2$ *(1 mark)*
b)

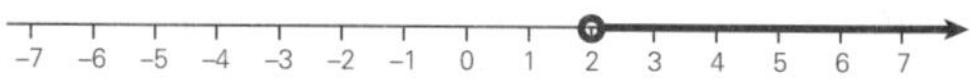

(1 mark)
Examiner's tip *The value 2 is not included, so the point has an open circle.*

15) a) 192 *(1 mark)*
b) 40 *(1 mark)*
c) 12 *(1 mark)*
Examiner's tip *To find the highest common factor, express 24 and 60 as products of primes.*

16) a) 22 years *(1 mark)*
accept 21 or 23
b) 4% *(1 mark)*
accept 3% or 5%
c) 19.9, 41.7, 66.0, 85.5, 97.2, 100 *(2 marks)*

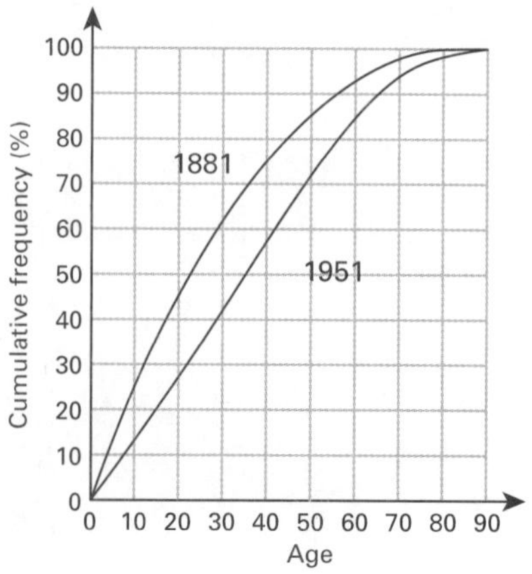

d) Any suitable answers, e.g. Average (median) age (35 years) much higher in 1951 *(1 mark)*
Greater proportion of older men in 1951 (10% over 65) *(1 mark)*
Higher proportion of boys in 1881 (37%, 20% under 15) *(1 mark)*
Examiner's tip *Remember to plot the points at the right of the interval. We do not know the actual size of the populations, so comments should be based upon proportions.*

17) a) $x^2 + 4x - 3x - 12$ *(1 mark)*
$x^2 + x - 12$ *(1 mark)*

b) $3(2x - 3) - 4(x - 1) = 30$ *(1 mark)*
$2x = 35$ *(1 mark)*
$x = 17\frac{1}{2}$ *(1 mark)*

18) QR = 6, RC = 9 *(1 mark)*
PQ = 6, AP = $6 \times \frac{6}{9} = 4$ *(1 mark)*
Area = $\frac{1}{2} \times 4 \times 6 = 12$ cm^2 *(1 mark)*
Examiner's tip *This is a true multistep question! The most important step is to recognise the similar triangles and use proportions.*

19) D, C *(1 mark)*
A *(1 mark)*
Examiner's tip *The quadratic graph is either B or D. For the straight lines, look for the negative gradient.*

Maths Set C Test Paper 2 Answers

1) a) 49×1.8 *(1 mark)*
\$88.20 *(1 mark)*
b) $\div 1.5$ *(1 mark)*
£0.67 *(1 mark)*
c) $(200 \div 1.5) \times 1.8$ *(1 mark)*
\$240 *(1 mark)*
Examiner's tip *Notice that some marks are given for showing method, even though this was not stated in the question.*

2) a) $x = \frac{10}{3}$ or $3\frac{1}{3}$ or $\frac{20}{6}$ *(1 mark)*
b) $\frac{3x}{2} = 6$ *(1 mark)*
$x = 4$ *(1 mark)*

3) a) 1 *(1 mark)*
b) 4 *(1 mark)*
c) 7 *(1 mark)*
Examiner's tip *You can work out the first value by noticing that it is 4 less but it is not so easy for the next expression. It is best to find the value of n first, then substitute.*

4) Use of 15° *(1 mark)*
Angles 210°, 30°, 75°, 45° *(1 mark)*
Accurately drawn *(1 mark)*
Labelled *(1 mark)*

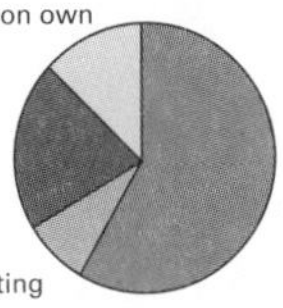

5) a) 57 or 56.7… *(1 mark)*
cm^2 *(1 mark)*
b) $160 \div \pi$ *(1 mark)*
51 or 50.9… mm *(1 mark)*
c) Use of *(1 mark)*

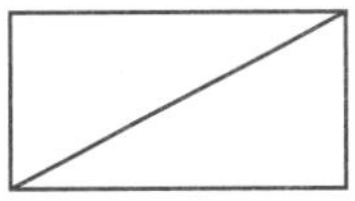

Use of 11.0 and $2 \times \pi \times 3.6$ or 22.6 *(1 mark)*
Use of Pythagoras $(22.6^2 + 11.0^2)$ *(1 mark)*
25.2 or 25.15… cm *(1 mark)*
Examiner's tip *Don't forget the units! In part c), it may help to think of the label around the tin being peeled off.*

6) a) i Mean = 56 *(1 mark)*
ii Range = 45 *(1 mark)*
b) 65×54 or 3510 *(1 mark)*
$- 60 \times 55$ or 3300 *(1 mark)*
$\div 5$ *(1 mark)*
42 years *(1 mark)*
Examiner's tip *In part b), it is necessary to work in total years and find the difference.*

7) a) 16.1… *(1 mark)*
b) $6.75 = \frac{V}{\pi \times 2.5^2} + \frac{2.5}{3}$ *(1 mark)*
116 cm^3 *(1 mark)*
Examiner's tip *You could rearrange the formula to make V the subject, but it is not necessary here.*

8) a) Exterior angle = $360 \div 8 = 45°$ *(1 mark)*
$180 - 45 = 135°$ *(1 mark)*
b) 45° *(1 mark)*
AFGH is an isosceles trapezium with other angles 135° *(1 mark)*
c) AE is a line of symmetry so angle AEF = $\frac{1}{2} \times 135 = 67\frac{1}{2}°$ *(1 mark)*
Angle AFE = $135 - 45 = 90°$ *(1 mark)*
$180 - 90 - 67\frac{1}{2} = 22\frac{1}{2}°$ *(1 mark)*
Examiner's tip *Make sure you give adequate reasons and calculations.*

9) a) 68×0.65 *(1 mark)*
b) $195 \div 0.65$ *(1 mark)*
£300 *(1 mark)*
Examiner's tip *The calculations in part a) were a broad hint that you need to divide in part b).*

10) a) Use of $x + y = 5$ *(1 mark)*
$x + y \leq 5$ *(1 mark)*
b)

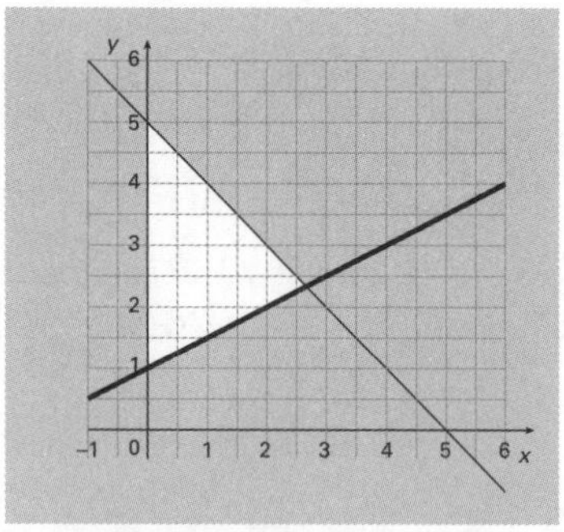

Line correct *(1 mark)*
Shading correct *(1 mark)*
c) $x = 2.7$ *(1 mark)*
Examiner's tip *Shade the region that does not satisfy the inequality.*

11) Use of $(x - y)(x + y)$ *(1 mark)*
$\frac{x - y}{x + y}$ *(1 mark)*

Examiner's tip *Take care to cancel* ***whole*** *factors.*

12) Use of this triangle *(1 mark)*

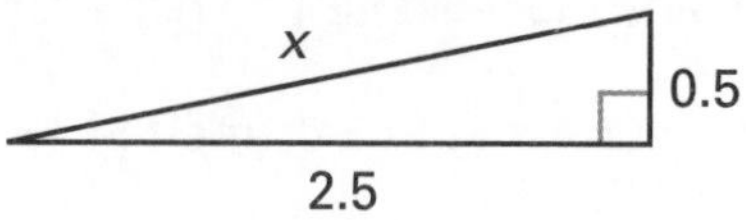

$\tan x = \frac{0.5}{2.5}$ *(1 mark)*

11.3° *(1 mark)*
Examiner's tip *It is important to identify the right-angled triangle to use.*

13) a) $\frac{1}{2}, \frac{1}{4}, \frac{1}{4}$ *(1 mark)*
b) $\frac{1}{2} \times \frac{1}{2}$ or $\frac{1}{4}$ *(1 mark)*
c) $\frac{1}{4} \times \frac{1}{2} + \frac{1}{4} \times \frac{1}{4}$ *(1 mark)*
$\frac{3}{16}$ *(1 mark)*

14) $(1.08 \times 10^9 \div 1.6) \times 5280$ *(1 mark)*
$\div 3600$ *(1 mark)*
$= 9.9 \times 10^8$ feet/second *(1 mark)*
Examiner's tip *Show the calculation you will make, as this earns marks even if you make a mistake on your calculator. Always check the answer, too!*

KS3 English

Practice Test Papers

Ages 11-14

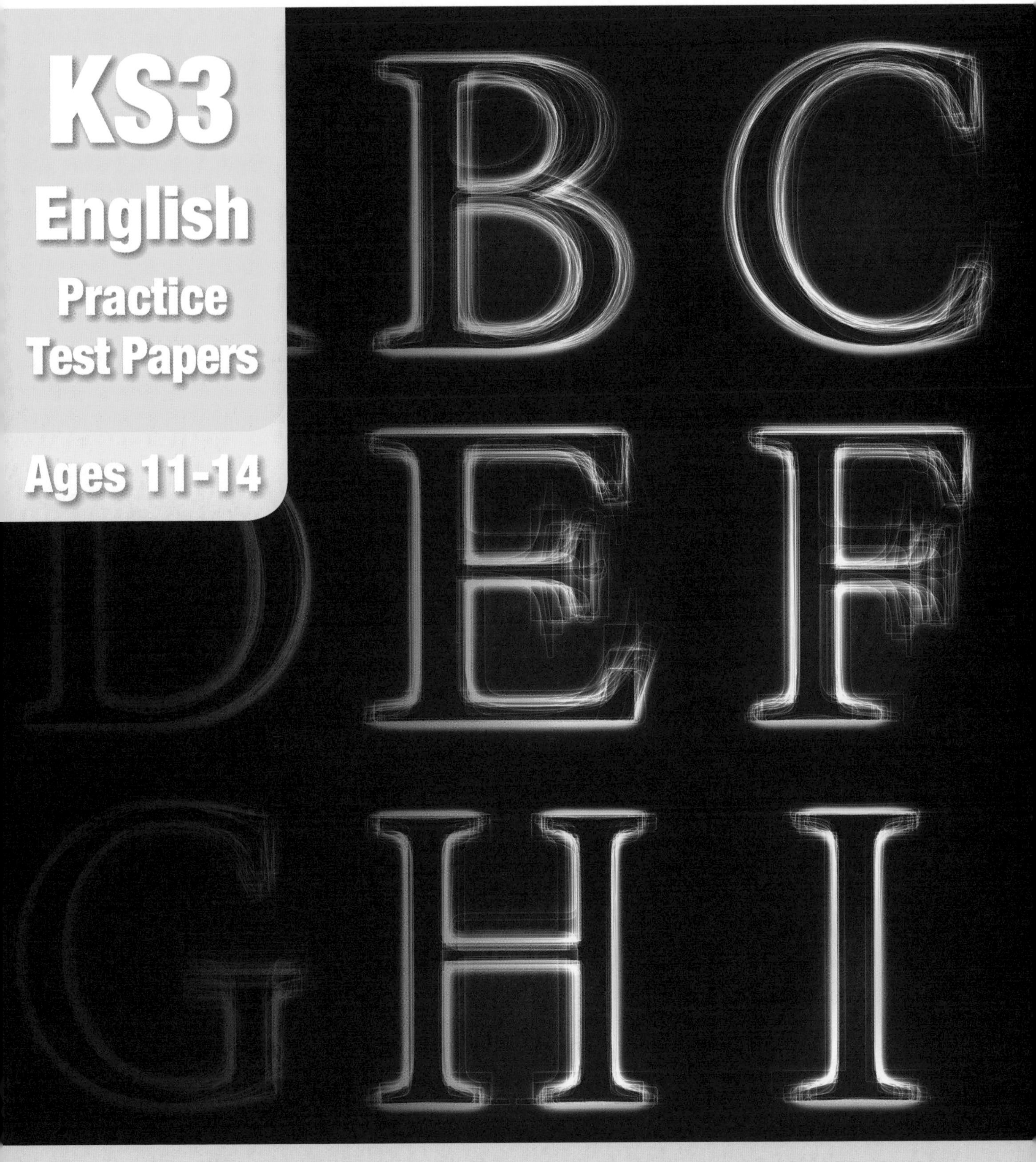

Nicolas Barber

Contents

Introduction

Instructions on using the Practice Test Papers

Understanding Assessment

At the end of Key Stage 3 (usually in Year 9 at the age of 14), teacher assessment is used to determine your level of attainment in subjects including English, Maths and Science. There are no national tests but assessments by your teacher will help them to determine your level of attainment (see page 9).

About these Practice Test Papers

This book contains three sets of practice test papers, which provide a means of parental or self-assessment that can be easily carried out at home. The papers will help you to evaluate an approximate level of attainment, highlight opportunities for further study and skills practice that will aid improvement, and record results to track progress. The instructions and guidelines in this Introduction provide guidance on how to use the papers for self-assessment.

The questions have been written by experienced teachers and are based on the programme of study for Key Stage 3.

Sets A, B and C each provide one complete assessment. Each set comprises of:

- 1 Reading Test Paper (1 hour 15 minutes), including Reading Material
- 1 Writing Test Paper (1 hour 15 minutes), including a Short and a Long Writing Task
- 2 Shakespeare Test Papers (45 minutes)*

* This book provides papers on *Much Ado About Nothing* and *Romeo and Juliet.* Only complete the Shakespeare Test Paper that is relevant to the play you are studying.

The tests can be taken at different times, but try to complete a set all within the same week. Take the tests at a time when you can work uninterrupted and do not feel too tired.

You should complete Sets A, B and C at intervals throughout Key Stage 3. Make sure you leave a reasonable amount of time between each assessment – it is unrealistic to expect to see an improvement in just a few weeks. You will feel much more motivated if you wait for a while, because your progress will be more obvious.

If you want to re-use the practice test papers, you can write in pencil and then rub out your answers. However, do not repeat the same test paper too soon, otherwise you will remember the questions and your results will not be an accurate reflection of your abilities.

Before you start:

- find a suitable place to complete the tests – somewhere quiet, where you won't be disturbed
- make sure you have a pen, pencil, ruler, rubber and a clock or watch to time yourself
- turn off your mobile phone
- read the instructions below and those on the front of the test paper carefully.

When completing the test papers:

- try to answer all of the questions and make sure you read them carefully
- write your answers for the Reading Test in the spaces provided on the test paper
- write your answers for the Writing Test and Shakespeare Test on lined paper
- keep an eye on the time – if you spend longer than the allocated time on the paper your results will not accurately reflect your abilities.

When you have finished:

- use the answers and marks provided in the pull-out Answers and Mark Scheme to mark the test paper
- read the top tips on how to improve your performance and remember the key points
- add up the total number of marks.

These tests are similar to tests you may have taken throughout Key Stages 2 and 3.

You should check how much time you have to complete each individual test. You should choose a period when you are not too tired and can work uninterrupted. You do not have to take the tests in one sitting. The questions have been written by experienced teachers, so important ideas are revisited.

Answers should be written on the test papers in the indicated spaces. At the end of the test, the paper can be marked by referring to the Answers and Mark Scheme. When you have taken the tests, they will be helpful to use to revise and prepare for actual assessments.

Tips for the Top

Make sure you have a suitable place to do the test and have a pen, pencil and rubber.

The number of marks is shown for each part of the question.

Remember to read the questions carefully.

Short Answer Questions

These questions test a range of different skills. You will do well on this test paper by thinking about a number of things:

1 Organise your time. People who do well on this paper make sure that they spend an appropriate amount of time on each question. There are 32 marks for this paper, and you have one hour to write your answers, so you should be spending just under 2 minutes on each mark. Stick to this. If you get stuck, move on and come back to the missed questions at the end, if you have time.

2 Know what the questions require. The questions are testing different reading skills. Some require short answers, others need examples and some require a mixture. Obviously, the number of marks available and the amount of space for the answer gives some idea of how much to write, but you should also know what the different instruction words in the questions mean. Here is a range of commonly used instruction words used in this paper and what they require from you:
"Give reasons" – explain – put things in your own words.
"What does ... suggest?" – give your own personal opinion based on the way the word is used in the text.
"Explain" – what it says! Use your own words.
"Identify" – give an example, or a quotation.
"What is the effect of …?" – give your own personal opinion based on the way the word is used in the text.
"Why is …?" – explain – put things in your own words.

3 When filling in charts and boxes, don't put more answers than you are allowed. You will simply be given zero!

4 On the questions worth 5 marks, make sure you have a quotation and a comment on every bullet point. To get the top marks on the 5-mark questions, pick out individual words from your quotations and use those individual words to show exactly where you have got your ideas from.

The Writing Tasks

In school, all through Key Stage 3, you will have learned about different styles of writing. The long and short writing tasks are testing to see if you know how to write in different styles. This means the following:

1 Revise what you have learned in school about how to write in different styles, e.g. How do you write to:
- imagine, explore, entertain?
- argue, persuade, advise?
- inform, explain, describe?
- analyse, review, comment?

If you revise what you have done on each of these writing types, then it will help you to get more marks for "Communication and effect" which carries the most marks on both the long and short tasks.

2 Plan your answer! If you want to get good marks for paragraphing and organisation, then it is essential to do a short plan first. It doesn't matter how you plan – you could brainstorm, mind map – do whatever suits your learning style. At the very least, decide what will happen in the beginning, middle and end of your writing. If you have time, decide what you are going to put in each paragraph.

3 Leave a short amount of time to proof-read what you have written. On the short task, make sure you check spelling, because you gain marks for "Spelling" on that task.

4 You don't have to worry about writing vast amounts, especially on the short answer task. The marker is looking for quality, not quantity.

The Shakespeare Papers

Before you do a paper:

- make sure that you understand what is happening in your scenes first
- make sure that you know what the important quotations are in your scenes – what they are, what they mean and how you might explain them
- know how your scenes relate to the rest of the play.

In a Shakespeare – or other Literature – exam you should do the following:

1 Read the question carefully.

2 Write on the question paper or provided text, if there is one – underline the key words in the question, or in the text. Use these to identify what you have to include in your answer. A highlighter pen would be handy!

3 Use the words you have underlined in the question to help identify the quotations you are going to use from the extracts.

4 Plan your answer – make sure you cover all parts of the question required.

5 Use a quotation for every point you make. Pick words out of the quotations where possible, because you will show more exactly where you have got your ideas from, which is essential to achieve Level 6 and Level 7.

6 To show your personal opinion on the language of the play, pick out words and use sentences like "the word ... suggests to me ... because ..." and "the words ... imply that ... because ...".

Frame your comments using sentence frames like these and you will be showing personal opinion and developing your ideas in depth, which should mean that you are commenting at least at Level 5 or above, depending on how thoroughly and sensibly you phrase your comments.

Using your Marks to Assess Levels

Record your test marks in the progress grid below:

	Set A Week beginning: _/_/_	Set B Week beginning: _/_/_	Set C Week beginning: _/_/_
Reading Test			
Shakespeare Test			
Reading Total			
Reading Level			
Writing Test – Short Task			
Writing Test – Long Task			
Writing Total			
Writing Level			

When you have completed all three tests in a set:

- add the marks for the Reading Test and Shakespeare Test together to give a total mark out of 50 for Reading
- add the marks for the Writing Test Short Task and Long Task together to give a total mark out of 50 for Writing.

The table below will give you an indication of your Reading, Writing and Overall levels based on your marks:

Level	Reading mark range	Writing mark range	Overall
No level	0–7	0–4	0–10
3	8–10	5–10	11–15
4	11–16	11–12	16–30
5	17–26	13–22	31–50
6	27–33	23–31	51–65
7	34–50	32–50	66–100

Remember that the level obtained in these tests may be different from the level that your teacher reports you are working at. This is because they can only test a limited range of skills and knowledge. Your teacher will have a better idea of your overall performance. However, these tests will help you to identify areas of weakness that you can improve upon with a bit of hard work and extra study, which will help you to get a better mark on your next assessment test and progress at school.

Improving your Results and Making Progress

Go back through your test papers and make a note of all the questions that you got wrong. This will help you to identify skills that require further practice.

If you want to improve your understanding and make progress, you need to be proactive! Use Study Guides and Workbooks for home study – they include lots of practice questions, which test your knowledge, reinforce what you have learned and help to develop essential skills.

With a little bit of time and effort, when you take the next set of tests in the pack you will achieve a higher mark. Remember to record the date alongside your marks in the grid above. This will allow you to track your progress over time and will help to build your confidence and a sense of achievement.

What do Levels Mean?

Attainment levels are used to measure your progress through Key Stages 1, 2 and 3. They are concerned with your knowledge, skills and understanding of a subject.

There are eight levels and they each have a description, which sets out the skills, knowledge and understanding that you are expected to demonstrate at that level. The descriptions for Levels 1 to 8 get increasingly difficult.

Although there are eight levels, at Key Stage 3 you are generally expected to work between Levels 3 and 7, where Level 7 represents excellent knowledge, skills and understanding.

The table below shows the expected National Curriculum levels for 14 year olds.

Level	Aged 14
Level 1	
Level 2 Level 2c Level 2b Level 2a	
Level 3	Below average
Level 4	Below average
Level 5	At level expected
Level 6	At level expected
Level 7	Excellent
Level 8	Exceptional

As you can see, it is expected that a majority of 14 year olds will achieve Level 5 or 6 by the end of Year 9. If you achieve Level 7, it is a real success. A 14 year old who achieves Level 8 is working at an exceptionally high level. For comparison, a student who gains a GCSE grade C has achieved Level 7.

Your teacher will carry out regular assessments to ensure that you are working at an appropriate level and progressing at the expected rate. The test papers in this book support this process. Provided you follow the instructions and address any potential problems that the tests highlight, they will help to ensure you are always working to the best of your abilities.

Set
A

KEY STAGE 3
Levels 4–7

Reading Test Paper

English

Food!

Reading Test Paper

Food!

Instructions:

- find a quiet place where you can sit down and complete the test paper undisturbed
- make sure you have all the necessary equipment to complete the test paper
- read the questions carefully
- answer all the questions
- go through and check your answers when you have finished the test paper

Time:

This test paper is **1 hour 15 minutes** long.

You have **15 minutes** to read the Reading Material. During this time you are not allowed to refer to the Reading Paper to look at the questions.

You have **1 hour** to write the answers.

Write the answers in this paper, then check how you have done using pages 105–107 of the Answers and Mark Scheme.

Page	19	21	23	Max. Mark	**Actual Mark**
Score	....	....	....	32	....

First name ....

Last name ....

Food!

Contents

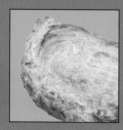

'Real' Cornish Pasties

1 The European Commission has cracked down on companies based outside Cornwall producing and selling 'Cornish' pasties. It comes after years of campaigning by the CPA (Cornish Pasty Association).

2 The name 'Cornish pasty' has now been given a PGI (protected geographical indication) status by the EC. But some producers outside Cornwall objected to the move 'cos it might have a bad effect on their sales.

3 The PGI status means that, to be called a 'Cornish pasty' the pasty has to be prepared in Cornwall. If it isn't, it can't go by the name 'Cornish pasty'!

4 A real Cornish pasty must include beef, potato, swede (also called turnip) and onion, and a pinch of salt and pepper, whilst the filling should have a thick, chunky texture.

5 Cornish pasties should be folded into a semi-circle and sealed on one side. When baked, the pastry should look tasty and golden.

6 There's no hard and fast rule on what kind of pastry should be used but a short crust pastry is often used.

7 'Cornish pasties aren't just food – they're a way of life here in Cornwall,' says top chef Meredith Gordon.

8 Cornish pasties are also known as 'oggies', 'oggins', 'teddies' and 'tiddies'.

Made in Cornwall?

9 The Cornish pasty originated in the United Kingdom, but there's some debate over whether it originally came from Cornwall or Devon.

10 The Cornish pasty is considered the national dish of Cornwall and in 2008 87 million Cornish pasties were sold by members of the CPA.

Oliver Twist

Oliver Twist is a young boy who is living in a kind of Victorian orphanage. The boys there are very badly treated and underfed. On this day, the boys decide that they want to be fed better …

1 Oliver Twist and his companions suffered the tortures of slow starvation for three months: at last they got so voracious and wild with hunger, that one boy, who was tall for his age, and hadn't been used to that sort of thing (for his father had kept a small cookshop), hinted darkly to his companions, that unless he had another basin of gruel, he was afraid he might some night happen to eat the boy who slept next him, who happened to be a weakly youth of tender age. He had a wild, hungry eye; and they implicitly believed him. A council was held; lots were cast who should walk up to the master after supper that evening, and ask for more; and it fell to Oliver Twist.

2 The evening arrived; the boys took their places. The master, in his cook's uniform, stationed himself at the copper; his pauper assistants ranged themselves behind him; the gruel was served out; and a long grace was said over the short commons. The gruel disappeared; the boys whispered to each other, and winked at Oliver; while his next neighbours nudged him. Child as he was, he was desperate with hunger, and reckless with misery. He rose from the table; and advancing to the master, basin and spoon in hand, said, somewhat alarmed at his own temerity:

3 "Please, sir, I want some more."

4 The master was a fat, healthy man; but he turned very pale. He gazed in stupefied astonishment on the small rebel for some seconds, and then clung for support to the copper. The assistants were paralysed with wonder; the boys with fear.

5 "What!" said the master at length, in a faint voice.

"Please, sir," replied Oliver, "I want some more."

6 The master aimed a blow at Oliver's head with the ladle; pinioned him in his arms; and shrieked aloud for the beadle.

7 The board were sitting in solemn conclave, when Mr. Bumble rushed into the room in great excitement, and addressing the gentleman in the high chair, said,

8 "Mr. Limbkins, I beg your pardon, sir! Oliver Twist has asked for more!"

9 There was a general start. Horror was depicted on every countenance.

10 "For more!" said Mr. Limbkins. "Compose yourself, Bumble, and answer me distinctly. Do I understand that he asked for more, after he had eaten the supper allotted by the dietary?"

11 "He did, sir," replied Bumble.

12 "That boy will be hung," said the gentleman in the white waistcoat. "I know that boy will be hung."

From *Oliver Twist* by Charles Dickens

Why is water good for you?

The importance of drinking plenty of water and advice for adults on how much they should drink on a daily basis.

1 Water is vital for ensuring that our bodies function correctly. This is because water is responsible for transporting nutrients around the body and most of the chemical reactions within our cells take place in water.

2 As your body works it produces waste products. Some of these waste products are toxic and the body gets rid of them through the kidneys in urine, which mainly consists of water.

3 We also lose water by evaporation when we breathe and sweat. As the temperature rises and we do more activity, the amount of water lost by the body increases. To stay healthy, we must replace the fluids that we lose.

4 In moderate climates, such as the UK, we should drink at least 6 to 8 cups or glasses of water (or other fluid) to prevent dehydration. In hotter climates, your body will need more fluids to avoid becoming dehydrated.

5 Drinks that contain caffeine (such as tea, coffee and cola) can act as diuretics, which means they can make your body lose greater volumes of water than normal. As a result, these drinks can result in an increased need for water or other fluids that don't have a diuretic effect.

6 Drinks containing sugar, such as fruit juice and fizzy drinks, should also be drunk in moderation, because they can contribute to tooth decay. But, one glass of fruit juice can count towards the five portions of fruit and vegetables that we should eat each day.

Questions 1–4 are about the "'Real' Cornish Pasties" article on page 13 of the Reading Material.

1 From the first three paragraphs, give two examples of what the European Commission has done.

(2 marks) Q1

i ______________________________

ii ______________________________

2 a) In paragraph one, what does the choice of words in the following phrase suggest?
"The European Commission has cracked down on companies based outside Cornwall producing and selling 'Cornish' pasties." *(1 mark)* Q2a

"crack down" suggests ______________________________

____

b) What do the words *"'cos"*, *"isn't"* and *"tasty"* suggest about the writer's audience?

(1 mark) Q2b

____

____

3 a) The article is split into paragraphs with different topics. Complete this table by writing the correct paragraph number in the box next to the paragraph's topic. *(2 marks)* Q3a

Topic	Paragraph Number
Rules about pasty ingredients	
What PGI stands for	
A reaction from a top chef	
An introduction to the article	

b) Explain one reason why the text has paragraphs with personal comments as well as paragraphs about historical background. *(1 mark)* Q3b

____

____

____

4 How does the article try to appeal to young people?
You should comment on the effect of:

- the language used
- the length of paragraphs
- the content of the article.

(5 marks)

Q4

subtotal

Questions 5–9 are about the extract from "Oliver Twist" on pages 14–15 of the Reading Material.

5 a) From the first part of the first sentence, *"Oliver Twist and his companions suffered the tortures of slow starvation for three months"*, write down one word which suggests that the boys are suffering. *(1 mark)* Q5a

b) What is the effect of this word? *(1 mark)* Q5b

6 In the second sentence, it says *"He had a wild, hungry eye"*. What does the phrase "hungry eye" suggest about the boy's character? *(1 mark)* Q6

7 a) From the whole text, identify one feature of Oliver Twist's character. *(1 mark)* Q7a

b) From the whole text, identify one feature of the master's character. *(1 mark)* Q7b

8 a) The extract from the story begins with long paragraphs and ends with short paragraphs. Explain one reason why this is. *(1 mark)*

Q8a

____

____

____

____

____

____

b) Explain how the line '*"Please, sir," replied Oliver, "I want some more"*' makes you feel sorry for Oliver. *(1 mark)*

Q8b

____

____

____

____

____

____

____

9 What do you learn about the writer's viewpoint and purpose from the passage? Show whether the following statements are TRUE or FALSE by writing T for TRUE or F for FALSE in each of the boxes. *(2 marks)*

Q9

The writer wants us to feel sorry for Oliver. ☐

The writer is trying to criticise the way that boys like Oliver were treated by authority. ☐

The writer is trying to give a factual historical account. ☐

The writer is trying to entertain the reader. ☐

subtotal

Questions 10–13 are about the article "Why is Water Good for You?" on pages 16–17 of the Reading Material.

10 Explain two ways that the first paragraph gives us information. Support each explanation with a quotation. *(2 marks)* Q10

i ______________________________

____

____

ii ______________________________

____

____

11 How does the writer, in paragraphs three and four, try to convince the reader that drinking water is important? Choose two different words or phrases and explain how they create this effect on the reader. *(2 marks)* Q11

Word/Phrase	Effect on the reader	How it creates this effect on the reader
	makes the reader think that drinking water is important	because it suggests
	makes the reader think that drinking water is important	because it suggests

12 a) In paragraph five, what is described as the main effect of caffeine? *(1 mark)* Q12a

____

____

____

b) Why are brackets used at the start of paragraph five in the phrase "*Drinks that contain caffeine (such as tea, coffee and cola)*"? *(1 mark)* Q12b

____

____

____

13 In this article, how are language, grammar and content used to influence the reader? You should comment in your answer on the effect of the following.

- The use of scientific words and phrases.
- Sentence lengths.
- The use of facts.

(5 marks) Q13

END OF TEST

subtotal

Set
A

KEY STAGE 3
Levels 4–7

Writing Test Paper

English

Food!

Writing Test Paper

Food!

Instructions:

- find a quiet place where you can sit down and complete the test paper undisturbed
- make sure you have all the necessary equipment to complete the test paper
- read the questions carefully
- answer the questions on lined paper
- go through and check your answers when you have finished writing

Time:

This test paper is **1 hour 15 minutes** long.

You should spend **30 minutes** on the short writing task, including planning time.

You should spend **45 minutes** on the long writing task, including planning time.

Write the answers on lined paper, then check how you have done using pages 114–118 of the Answers and Mark Scheme.

Short Writing Task

Strand	Max. Mark	**Actual Mark**
Sentence structure, punctuation and text organisation	6	
Composition and effect	10	
Spelling	4	

Long Writing Task

Strand	Max. Mark	**Actual Mark**
Sentence structure and punctuation	8	
Text structure and organisation	8	
Composition and effect	14	

First name ....

Last name ....

Writing Paper - Short Writing Task

Spend about 30 minutes on this section.

You write reviews for a school magazine – this week you have been asked to write a review of one of last week's school dinners.

Here is last week's menu:

Day	Main Course	Dessert
Monday	Fish and Chips	Ice-Cream
Tuesday	Cabbage Pie & Mashed Potatoes	Grapefruit Surprise
Wednesday	Broccoli & Cucumber Salad	Rhubarb Crumble
Thursday	Pizza	Melon Juice
Friday	Chicken Curry	Chocolate Sticky Pudding

In your review, the school magazine editor wants you to:

- analyse what was in the meal
- comment on what you thought about it.

Write your review on one of the school dinners above.

(20 marks, including 4 for spelling)

Writing Paper – Long Writing Task

Spend about 15 minutes planning your answer and 30 minutes writing.

Your local area has been named the least healthy in the whole country. You are a local newspaper journalist and you have been given the job of writing an article telling people about this and persuading them to adopt a more healthy lifestyle. Here are some of the facts that you have been given:

75% of the people in your area do not take regular exercise.

85% of the people in your area eat junk food, on average, four times a week.

60% of the people in your area visit the doctor once a month.

The average life expectancy for men and women is five years below the national average.

Your editor wants you to write an article to:

- advise people about the situation in your area
- persuade them to change their ways.

Write the article.

(30 marks)

END OF TEST

Shakespeare Test Paper

Much Ado About Nothing

Instructions:

- find a quiet place where you can sit down and complete the test paper undisturbed
- make sure you have all the necessary equipment to complete the test paper
- read the question carefully
- answer the question on lined paper
- go through and check your answer when you have finished writing

Time:

This test paper is **45 minutes** long.

Check how you have done using pages 119–120 of the Answers and Mark Scheme.

	Max. Mark	**Actual Mark**
Score	18	....

First name ....

Last name ....

Much Ado About Nothing

You should spend about 45 minutes on this section.

Much Ado About Nothing

In these scenes, the audience see Benedick and Beatrice's relationship.

What do we learn about Benedick and Beatrice in these two scenes?

Support your ideas by referring to both of the extracts which are printed on the following pages.

(18 marks)

Use the printed scenes to answer the question set on page 29.

Act 4 Scene 1

BENEDICK	Come, bid me do anything for thee.
BEATRICE	Kill Claudio.
BENEDICK	Ha! Not for the wide world.
BEATRICE	You kill me to deny it. Farewell.
BENEDICK	Tarry, sweet Beatrice.
BEATRICE	I am gone though I am here. There is no love in you. Nay, I pray you, let me go.
BENEDICK	Beatrice –
BEATRICE	In faith, I will go.
BENEDICK	We'll be friends first.
BEATRICE	You dare easier be friends with me than fight with mine enemy.
BENEDICK	Is Claudio thine enemy?
BEATRICE	Is he not approved in the height a villain that hath slandered, scorned, dishonoured my kinswoman? O that I were a man! What, bear her in hand until they come to take hands, and then, with public accusation, uncovered slander, unmitigated rancour – O God, that I were a man! I would eat his heart in the market-place.
BENEDICK	Hear me, Beatrice –
BEATRICE	Talk with a man out at a window! A proper saying!
BENEDICK	Nay, but Beatrice –
BEATRICE	Sweet Hero! She is wronged, she is slandered, she is undone.
BENEDICK	Beat –

BEATRICE Princes and counties! Surely, a princely testimony, a goodly count, Count Comfect – a sweet gallant, surely! o that I were a man for his sake, or that I had any friend would be a man for my sake! But manhood is melted into curtsies, valour into compliment; and men are only turned into tongue, and trim ones too. He is now as valiant as Hercules that only tells a lie and swears it. I cannot be a man with wishing: therefore I will die a woman with grieving.

BENEDICK Tarry, good Beatrice. By this hand, I love thee.

BEATRICE Use it for my love some other way than swearing by it.

BENEDICK Think you in your soul the Count Claudio hath wronged Hero?

BEATRICE Yea, as sure as I have a thought or a soul.

BENEDICK Enough: I am engaged. I will challenge him. I will kiss your hand, and so I leave you. By this hand, Claudio shall render me a dear account. As you hear of me, so think of me. Go, comfort your cousin: I must say she is dead; and so, farewell.

Exeunt

Act 5 Scene 4

BENEDICK — Soft and fair, Friar. Which is Beatrice?

BEATRICE — *(Unmasking)* I answer to that name. What is your will?

BENEDICK — Do not you love me?

BEATRICE — Why no – no more than reason.

BENEDICK — Why, then your uncle and the Prince and Claudio
Have been deceived. They swore you did.

BEATRICE — Do not you love me?

BENEDICK — Troth, no – no more than reason.

BEATRICE — Why, then my cousin, Margaret and Ursula
Are much deceived: for they did swear you did.

BENEDICK — They swore that you were almost sick for me.

BEATRICE — They swore that you were well-nigh dead for me.

BENEDICK — 'Tis no such matter. Then you do not love me?

BEATRICE — No, truly, but in friendly recompense.

LEONATO — Come, cousin, I am sure you love the gentleman.

CLAUDIO — And I'll be sworn upon't that he loves her;
For here's a paper written in his hand,
A halting sonnet of his own pure brain,
Fashioned to Beatrice.

HERO — And here's another,
Writ in my cousin's hand, stolen from her pocket,
Containing her affection unto Benedick.

BENEDICK — A miracle! Here's our own hands against our hearts.
Come, I will have thee: but, by this light, I take thee
for pity.

BEATRICE I would not deny you; but, by this good day, I yield upon great persuasion – and partly to save your life, for I was told you were in a consumption.

BENEDICK Peace! I will stop your mouth. *(Kissing her)*

END OF TEST

Set A

KEY STAGE 3
Levels 4–7

Shakespeare Test Paper

English

Romeo and Juliet

Shakespeare Test Paper

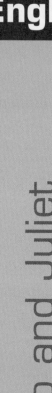

Romeo and Juliet

Instructions:

- find a quiet place where you can sit down and complete the test paper undisturbed
- make sure you have all the necessary equipment to complete the test paper
- read the question carefully
- answer the question on lined paper
- go through and check your answer when you have finished writing

Time:

This test paper is **45 minutes** long.

Check how you have done using pages 123–124 of the Answers and Mark Scheme.

	Max. Mark	**Actual Mark**
Score	18	....

First name ....

Last name ....

Romeo and Juliet

You should spend about 45 minutes on this section.

Romeo and Juliet

In these scenes, the audience see Romeo in different situations.

What do we learn about Romeo in these two scenes?

Support your ideas by referring to both of the extracts which are printed on the following pages.

(18 marks)

Use the printed scenes to answer the question set on page 36.

Act 1 Scene 1

ROMEO Ay me, sad hours seem long.
Was that my father that went hence so fast?

BENVOLIO It was. What sadness lengthens Romeo's hours?

ROMEO Not having that which, having, makes them short.

BENVOLIO In love?

ROMEO Out –

BENVOLIO Of love?

ROMEO Out of her favour where I am in love.

BENVOLIO Alas, that Love, so gentle in his view,
Should be so tyrannous and rough in proof!

ROMEO Alas, that Love, whose view is muffled still,
Should without eyes see pathways to his will!
Where shall we dine? O me! What fray was here?
Yet tell me not, for I have heard it all.
Here's much to do with hate, but more with love.
Why then, O brawling love, O loving hate,
O anything of nothing first create!
O heavy lightness, serious vanity,
Misshapen chaos of well-seeming forms!
Feather of lead, bright smoke, cold fire, sick health,
Still-waking sleep, that is not what it is!
This love feel I, that feel no love in this.
Dost thou not laugh?

BENVOLIO No, coz, I rather weep.

ROMEO Good heart, at what?

BENVOLIO At *thy* good heart's oppression.

ROMEO Why, such is love's transgression.
Griefs of mine own lie heavy in my breast,
Which thou wilt propagate to have it pressed
With more of thine. This love that thou hast shown
Doth add more grief to too much of mine own.

Love is a smoke made with the fume of sighs:
Being purged, a fire sparkling in lovers' eyes;
Being vexed, a sea nourished with loving tears.
What is it else? A madness most discreet,
A choking gall, and a preserving sweet.
Farewell, my coz.

BENVOLIO

Soft, I will go along –
And if you leave me so, you do me wrong.

ROMEO

Tut, I have lost myself. I am not here.
This is not Romeo: he's some other where.

BENVOLIO

Tell me in sadness, who is that you love?

ROMEO

What, shall I groan and tell thee?

BENVOLIO

Groan? Why no –
But sadly tell me who.

ROMEO

Bid a sick man in sadness make his will –
A word ill urged to one that is so ill.
In sadness, cousin, I do love a woman.

BENVOLIO

I aimed so near when I supposed you loved.

ROMEO

A right good mark-man! And she's fair I love.

BENVOLIO

A right fair mark, fair coz, is soonest hit.

ROMEO

Well, in that hit you miss. She'll not be hit
With Cupid's arrow. She hath Dian's wit,
And in strong proof of chastity well-armed,
From Love's weak childish bow she lives uncharmed.
She will not stay the siege of loving terms,
Nor bide th' encounter of assailing eyes,
Nor ope her lap to saint-seducing gold.
O, she is rich in beauty – only poor
That when she dies, with beauty dies her store.

BENVOLIO

Then she hath sworn that she will still live chaste?

ROMEO

She hath, and in that sparing makes huge waste,
For beauty, starved with her severity,
Cuts beauty off from all posterity.
She is too fair, too wise, wisely too fair,
To merit bliss by making me despair.
She hath forsworn to love, and in that vow
Do I live dead, that live to tell it now.

BENVOLIO Be ruled by me: forget to think of her.

ROMEO O, teach me how I should forget to think!

BENVOLIO By giving liberty unto thine eyes:
Examine other beauties.

ROMEO 'Tis the way
To call hers – exquisite – in question more.
These happy masks that kiss fair ladies' brows,
Being black, puts us in mind they hide the fair.
He that is strucken blind cannot forget
The precious treasure of his eyesight lost.
Show me a mistress that is passing fair:
What doth her beauty serve, but as a note
Where I may read who passed that passing fair?
Farewell. Thou canst not teach me to forget.

BENVOLIO I'll pay that doctrine, or else die in debt.

Exeunt.

Act 2 Scene 2

The garden, beside the Capulet house.
ROMEO comes forward (reacting to MERCUTIO's joking).

ROMEO He jests at scars that never felt a wound.

Enter JULIET, coming to her window-balcony above.
ROMEO, below, sees the light at the window, then realises it is JULIET.

– But soft! What light through yonder window breaks?
It is the east, and Juliet is the sun.
Arise, fair sun, and kill the envious moon,
Who is already sick and pale with grief
That thou her maid art far more fair than she.
Be not her maid, since she is envious:
Her vestal livery is but sick and green,
And none but fools do wear it. Cast it off.
– It is my lady! – O, it is my love!
O that she knew she were!
She speaks – yet she says nothing. What of that?
Her eye discourses. I will answer it.
– I am too bold. 'Tis not to me she speaks.
Two of the fairest stars in all the heaven,
Having some business, do entreat her eyes
To twinkle in their spheres till they return.

What if her eyes were there, they in her head?
The brightness of her cheek would shame those stars
As daylight doth a lamp. Her eyes in heaven
Would through the airy region stream so bright
That birds would sing and think it were not night!
See how she leans her cheek upon her hand.
O that I were a glove upon that hand,
That I might touch that cheek!

JULIET Ay me!

ROMEO *(Aside)* She speaks.
O speak again, bright angel! – For thou art
As glorious to this night, being o'er my head,
As is a wingèd messenger of heaven
Unto the white-upturnèd wondering eyes
Of mortals that fall back to gaze on him
When he bestrides the lazy-pacing clouds,
And sails upon the bosom of the air.

JULIET
O Romeo, Romeo! Wherefore art thou Romeo?
Deny thy father and refuse thy name –
Or if thou wilt not, be but sworn my love
And I'll no longer be a Capulet.

ROMEO
(Aside) Shall I hear more, or shall I speak at this?

JULIET
'Tis but thy name that is my enemy.
Thou art myself, though not a Montague.
What's 'Montague'? It is nor hand, nor foot,
Nor arm, nor face, nor any other part
Belonging to a man. O, be some other name!
What's in a name? That which we call a rose
By any other word would smell as sweet.
So Romeo would, were he not Romeo called,
Retain that dear perfection which he owes
Without that title. Romeo, doff thy name –
And for that name, which is no part of thee,
Take all myself.

ROMEO
I take thee at thy word.
Call me but love, and I'll be new-baptized.
Henceforth, I never will be Romeo.

END OF TEST

Reading Test Paper

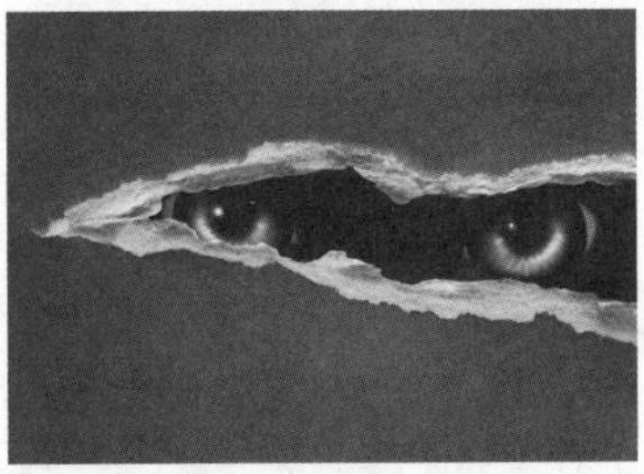

Monsters

Set B

KEY STAGE 3
Levels 4–7

Reading Test Paper

English

Monsters

Instructions:

- find a quiet place where you can sit down and complete the test paper undisturbed
- make sure you have all the necessary equipment to complete the test paper
- read the questions carefully
- answer all the questions
- go through and check your answers when you have finished the test paper

Time:

This test paper is **1 hour 15 minutes** long.

You have **15 minutes** to read the Reading Material. During this time you are not allowed to refer to the Reading Paper to look at the questions.

You have **1 hour** to write the answers.

Write the answers in this paper, then check how you have done using pages 108–110 of the Answers and Mark Scheme.

Page	50	52	54	Max. Mark	**Actual Mark**
Score	....	....	....	32	....

First name ....

Last name ....

Set B Reading Material

Monsters

Contents

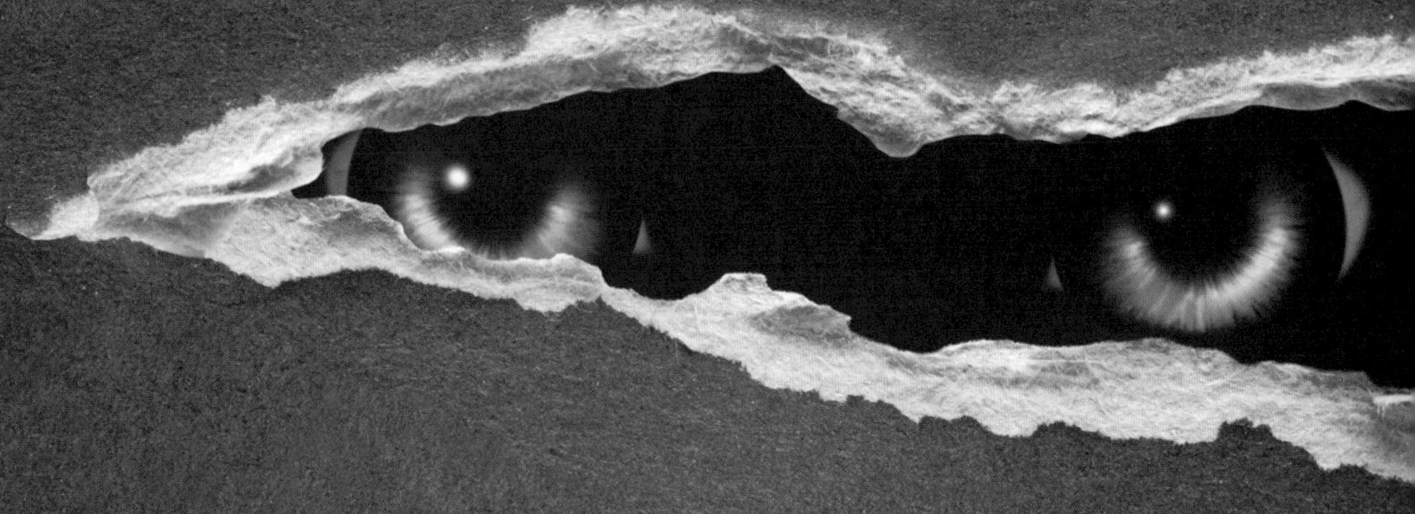

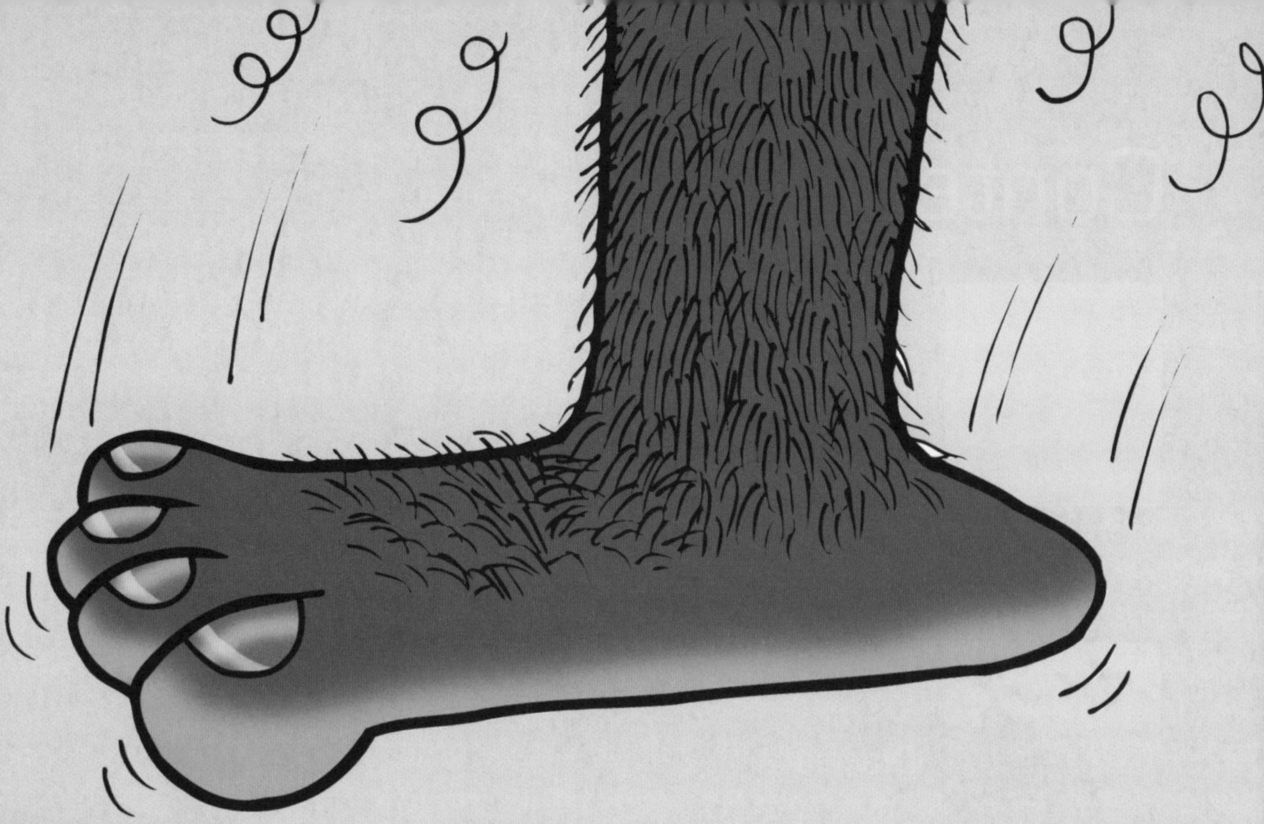

Bigfoot of North America

1 If the Himalayas of Asia has its Yeti, the Pacific Northwest of America has its Bigfoot: a hairy, ape-like, biped that stands seven to nine feet tall and weighs between 600 and 900 pounds.

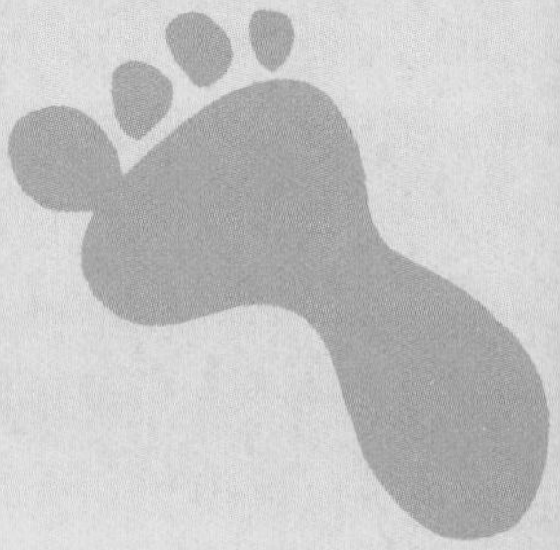

2 Bigfoot, or as it's often called in Canada, the *Sasquatch*, is mentioned in several native American legends. In fact, the term "Sasquatch" is Indian for "hairy giant". The first sighting of a Sasquatch footprint by a white man apparently came in 1811 near what is now the town of Jasper, Alberta, Canada. A trader named David Thompson found some strange footprints, fourteen inches long and eight inches wide, with four toes, in the snow.

3 In 1884 the newspaper, *Daily Colonist*, of Victoria, British Columbia, told of the capture of a "Sasquatch". The creature was spotted by a train crew along the Fraser River. The crew stopped the train, gave chase, and captured the animal after following it up a rocky hill. The creature was given the name "Jacko" and was "... something of the gorilla type, standing four feet seven inches in height and weighing 127 pounds. He has long, black, strong hair and resembles a human being, with one exception –

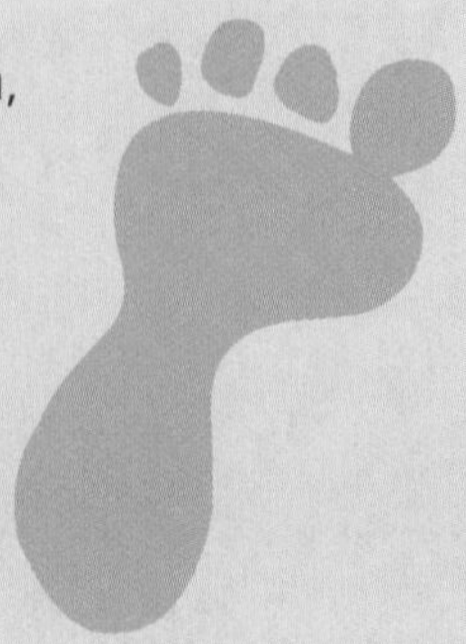

his entire body, excepting his hands (or paws) and feet, are covered with glossy hair about one inch long … he possesses extraordinary strength, as he will take hold of a stick and break it by wrenching it or twisting it, which no man could break in the same way."

4 The description of Jacko is so much like that of a chimpanzee, and so unlike later Bigfoot reports, that some have suggested the animal actually was a chimpanzee. If brought back by a sailor from Africa, the animal might have escaped or been turned loose. There is also the strong possibility that the entire story was a hoax. Newspapers of that era often printed hoax stories to amuse their readers (perhaps not unlike some tabloids sold today).

5 Rumours about the Sasquatch continued through the end of the century. Then, in 1910, the murder of two miners, found with their heads cut off, was attributed to the creatures, though there was little supporting evidence that the killing wasn't human in origin. In any case, the place of the murders, Nahanni Valley, in Canada, was changed to Headless Valley, because of the incident.

6 Interest in Bigfoot began to pick up in the United States in 1958 when a bulldozer operator named Jerry Crew found enormous footprints around where he was working in Humboldt County, California. Crew made a cast of the footprint. A local newspaper ran the story of Crew and his footprint with a photo. The story was picked up by other papers and ran throughout the country. It was the picture of Crew holding the "Bigfoot" that made the name stick.

7 In 1967 Roger Patterson and Bob Gimlin, Bigfoot buffs, announced they'd captured Bigfoot with a movie camera. They filmed a few seconds of an ape-like creature, apparently female, moving across a clearing near Bluff Creek in northern California. While the film is not perfectly clear, there is no mistaking the creature in the film for a common animal. The movie shows either a real Bigfoot, or a man in a clever costume. Nobody has ever proved the film fake, though some viewers were suspicious about the unnatural stride the creature had. One scientist who viewed the film, John Napier, of the Smithsonian Institution, admitted, "I couldn't see the zipper, and I still can't."

8 Scientists have a right to be suspicious of Bigfoot evidence. Two known hoax films exist. A controversial carcass, the "Minnesota Iceman", was thought to be a hoax, too. In addition, hoax footprints have been made from fake wooden feet and altered boots. One company even produced a set of oversized plastic strap-on feet that you could use to fool your friends and family.

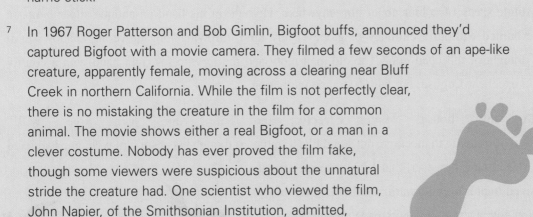

Dracula

1 **I stood in silence where I was, for I did not know what to do. Of bell or knocker there was no sign.** Through these frowning walls and dark window openings it was not likely that my voice could penetrate. The time I waited seemed endless, and I felt doubts and fears crowding upon me. What sort of place had I come to, and among what kind of people? What sort of grim adventure was it on which I had embarked? Was this a customary incident in the life of a solicitor's clerk sent out to explain the purchase of a London estate to a foreigner? Solicitor's clerk! Mina would not like that. Solicitor, for just before leaving London I got word that my examination was successful, and I am now a full-blown solicitor! I began to rub my eyes and pinch myself to see if I were awake. It all seemed like a horrible nightmare to me, and I expected that I should suddenly awake, and find myself at home, with the dawn struggling in through the windows, as I had now and again felt in the morning after a day of overwork. But my flesh answered the pinching test, and my eyes were not to be deceived. I was indeed awake and among the Carpathians. All I could do now was to be patient, and to wait the coming of morning.

2 Just as I had come to this conclusion I heard a heavy step approaching behind the great door, and saw through the chinks the gleam of a coming light. Then there was the sound of rattling chains and the clanking of massive bolts drawn back. A key was turned with the loud grating noise of long disuse, and the great door swung back.

3 Within, stood a tall old man, clean shaven save for a long white moustache, and clad in black from head to foot, without a single speck of colour about him anywhere. He held in his hand an antique silver lamp, in which the flame burned without a chimney or globe of any kind, throwing long quivering shadows as it flickered in the draught of the open door. The old man motioned me in with his right hand with a courtly gesture, saying in excellent English, but with a strange intonation.

"Welcome to my house! Enter freely and of your own free will!"

4 He made no motion of stepping to meet me, but stood like a statue, as though his gesture of welcome had fixed him into stone. The instant, however, that I had stepped over the threshold, he moved impulsively forward, and holding out his hand grasped mine with a strength which made me wince, an effect which was not lessened by the fact that it seemed cold as ice, more like the hand of a dead than a living man.

From Chapter 2 of *Dracula* by Bram Stoker

The Loch Ness Monster

1 The Loch Ness Monster is supposedly living in Scotland's Loch (Lake) Ness. "Nessie", as she is called, is the best known cryptozoological creature in the world.

2 Carvings of this unidentified animal, made by the ancient inhabitants of the Scottish Highlands some 1,500 years ago, are the earliest evidence that Loch Ness harbours a strange aquatic creature.

3 The earliest recorded sighting of the Loch Ness Monster was in the biography of St. Columba by Adamnan in the year 565 AD. The monster apparently attacked and killed a man who was swimming in the River Ness.

4 The monster didn't make headlines again until August 27, 1930 when 3 fishermen reported seeing a disturbance in the water. The men watched as a creature 20 feet long approached their boat throwing water in the air. As it passed them, its wake caused their boat to rock violently.

5 The men were convinced that the disturbance was caused by a living creature. Following the story, the newspaper received several letters from people claiming also to have seen a strange creature in the Loch.

6 In 1962, The Loch Ness Investigation Bureau was formed to act as a research organization and clearing house for information about the creature. In the beginning they only conducted research for a few weeks in the year, but by 1964 they established a more permanent presence around the Loch. Eventually the Bureau established camera stations with both still and cinema cameras with telephoto lenses. They had vans which served as mobile camera stations, and underwater listening devices. Searches were conducted using hot-air balloons and infrared night-time cameras, sonar scanners and submarines.

7 A great deal of information was discovered about the Loch, but they have yet to produce any concrete evidence of a monster.

8 Loch Ness is located in the north of Scotland and is one of a series of interlinked lochs which run along the Great Glen. The Great Glen is a distinctive incision which runs across the country and represents a large geological fault zone. The interlinking was completed in the 19th century following the completion of the Caledonian Canal.

9 The Great Glen is more than 700 ft (213 m) deep and ice free. It is fed by the Oich and other streams and drained by the Ness to the Moray Firth. It forms part of the Caledonian Canal. By volume, Loch Ness is the largest freshwater lake in Great Britain.

10 Since December 1933, when newspapers published accounts of a "monster", 40 to 50 ft (12–15 m) long, said to have been seen in the Loch, there have been alleged sightings.

11 As a result of the publicity, Loch Ness has become a major tourist attraction.

12 Several scientific studies have been conducted, including thorough sonar surveys of the Loch, and these have not revealed any presence of such a "monster".

13 Many people believe that the size and great depth of the Loch, together with potential underwater caves, gives the monster many places to hide.

14 Most of the Nessie witnesses describe something with two humps, a tail, and a snake-like head. A V-shape was often mentioned, as well as a gaping red mouth and horns or antennae on the top of the creature's head. Nessie's movements have been studied, and the films and photos analysed to determine what Nessie might be, if she exists.

15 There are numerous theories as to Nessie's identity, including a snake-like primitive whale known as a zeuglodon, a type of long-necked aquatic seal, giant eels, walruses, floating mats of plants, giant molluscs, otters, a "paraphysical" entity, mirages, and diving birds, but many lake monster researchers seem to favour the plesiosaur theory. The case has occasionally been supported by indistinct photographic evidence – though – in 1994 – a famous 1934 photograph was revealed to be a hoax.

Reproduced with thanks to Crystalinks (http://www.crystalinks.com)

Questions 1–4 are about the "Bigfoot of North America" article on pages 44–45 of the Reading Material.

1 From paragraphs one and two, give two features of Bigfoot. *(2 marks)* Q1

i ______________________________

ii ______________________________

2 a) In paragraph two, what does the word "apparently" suggest in this sentence – "*The first sighting of a Sasquatch by a white man apparently came in 1811*"? *(1 mark)* Q2a

The word "apparently" suggests ______________________________

____

b) In paragraph two, why does the writer refer to "*strange footprints*"? *(1 mark)* Q2b

____

____

____

3 a) Here are the topics of the first four paragraphs. Match up the topic with the correct paragraph number. *(2 marks)* Q3a

Topic	**Paragraph Number**
A description of a captured Sasquatch	
An introduction to what Bigfoot is	
An explanation of what the captured Sasquatch might have been	
The first sightings of a Sasquatch	

b) Explain why the text has quotations about personal experiences as well as dates and facts. *(1 mark)* Q3b

____

____

____

4 How does the writer make you feel that Bigfoot is probably a fake? You should comment on the effect of:

- the historical examples chosen
- the writer's comments on those examples
- the language used by the writer. *(5 marks)*

Q4

subtotal

Questions 5–9 are about the extract from "Dracula" on page 46 of the Reading Material.

5 a) From the first sentence, write down the phrase that shows the writer is confused. *(1 mark)* Q5a

______

______

______

b) How does this phrase help to keep the reader's interest? *(1 mark)* Q5b

______

______

______

6 In the first paragraph, the writer describes "*these frowning walls and dark window openings*". What does the word "frowning" suggest about the walls? *(1 mark)* Q6

______

______

______

7 a) From paragraph three, identify one thing about the old man that suggests he is well-mannered. *(1 mark)* Q7a

______

______

______

b) From paragraph four, identify one thing about the old man that suggests he is unusual or strange. *(1 mark)* Q7b

______

______

______

8 a) Paragraphs one and two and paragraphs three and four are about different characters and are written in different styles.

Explain one difference in the way that they are written. *(1 mark)* Q8a

____

____

____

____

____

____

b) Explain how the fact that we don't know the old man's name at this point, or who he is, makes the story interesting. *(1 mark)* Q8b

____

____

____

____

____

____

9 What do you learn about the writer's viewpoint and purpose from the passage? Show whether the following statements are TRUE or FALSE by writing T for TRUE or F for FALSE in each of the boxes. *(2 marks)* Q9

The writer wants us to feel that the narrator is confident. ☐

The writer's aim is to entertain and interest the reader. ☐

The writer wants us to like the old man. ☐

The aim of the writer is to build up tension in the reader. ☐

subtotal

Questions 10–13 are about the Loch Ness Monster article on pages 47–48 of the Reading Material.

10 In the first two paragraphs, the writer gets the reader interested straight away by creating a feeling of mystery.

Find two examples of where the writer does this and explain how each one makes the article mysterious. *(2 marks)* Q10

i ____

____

ii ____

____

11 In paragraph five (from *"The men ..."* to *"..in the Loch."*) the writer tries to make the reader feel that there might be some truth in the monster stories. Choose two different words or phrases and explain how they create this effect on the reader. *(2 marks)* Q11

Word/Phrase	**Effect on the reader**	**How it creates this effect on the reader**
	makes the reader think that there might be some truth in the monster stories	because it suggests
	makes the reader think that there might be some truth in the monster stories	because it suggests

12 a) In paragraph twelve, it says *"Several scientific studies have been conducted, including thorough sonar surveys of the Loch, and these have not revealed any presence of such a "monster"*. Q12a

Why does the writer use the word "thorough" in this sentence? *(1 mark)*

____

____

b) Why is the word "monster" in inverted commas? *(1 mark)* Q12b

____

____

13 In this article, how does the writer use language and content to create a serious account about the monster?

You should comment on how the choice of content and language:

- makes the article sound scientific
- makes the article sound well researched
- includes a sense of mystery. *(5 marks)*

Q13

END OF TEST

subtota

Writing Test Paper

Monsters

Instructions:

- find a quiet place where you can sit down and complete the test paper undisturbed
- make sure you have all the necessary equipment to complete the test paper
- read the questions carefully
- answer the questions on lined paper
- go through and check your answers when you have finished writing

Time:

This test paper is **1 hour 15 minutes** long.

You should spend **30 minutes** on the short writing task, including planning time.

You should spend **45 minutes** on the long writing task, including planning time.

Write the answers on lined paper, then check how you have done using pages 114–118 of the Answers and Mark Scheme.

Short Writing Task

Strand	Max. Mark	**Actual Mark**
Sentence structure, punctuation and text organisation	6	
Composition and effect	10	
Spelling	4	

Long Writing Task

Strand	Max. Mark	**Actual Mark**
Sentence structure and punctuation	8	
Text structure and organisation	8	
Composition and effect	14	

First name ....

Last name ....

Set **B**

KEY STAGE 3
Levels 4–7

Writing Test Paper

English

Monsters

Writing Paper – Short Writing Task

Spend about 30 minutes on this section.

You write ghost stories. You are about to start writing your next novel. The publisher wants you to write a convincing opening for your next story before they give you the money to go ahead and write it in full. The publisher wants you to write just the opening two or three paragraphs to show how you are going to get the reader's attention.

The publisher wants you to:

- Set the scene
- Create the mood
- End on a cliffhanger.

Write your opening, based on the ideas given above.

(20 marks, including 4 for spelling)

Writing Paper – Long Writing Task

Spend about 15 minutes planning your answer and 30 minutes writing.

Over the years, many people have reported sightings of ghosts and other supernatural events, but no one has been able to prove whether ghosts or other supernatural things actually exist or not.

Here are some reasons why people *don't* believe in ghosts and the supernatural.

- There is no scientific evidence to prove they exist.
- Often, they are witnessed by people alone, who could be making things up.
- Many of them have been proven to be fakes.

Here are some reasons why people *do* believe in ghosts and the supernatural.

- If only one of the thousands of cases is true, then they exist.
- There are many things that science cannot explain.
- People who have experienced them have been honest and trustworthy.

A Sunday magazine wants you to write an article arguing the case for and against ghosts existing, before you come to your own opinion. You can use the ideas above and any of your own ideas or examples, if you wish.

Write the article.

(30 marks)

END OF TEST

Set
B

KEY STAGE 3
Levels 4–7

Shakespeare
Test Paper

English

Much Ado About Nothing

Shakespeare Test Paper

Much Ado About Nothing

Instructions:

- find a quiet place where you can sit down and complete the test paper undisturbed
- make sure you have all the necessary equipment to complete the test paper
- read the question carefully
- answer the question on lined paper
- go through and check your answer when you have finished writing

Time:

This test paper is **45 minutes** long.

Check how you have done using pages 119 and 121 of the Answers and Mark Scheme.

	Max. Mark	**Actual Mark**
Score	18	....

First name ....

Last name ....

Much Ado About Nothing

You should spend about 45 minutes on this section.

Much Ado About Nothing

In these two scenes we learn a lot about the way that love shows itself.

What do the audience learn about love from these two scenes?

Support your ideas by referring to both of the extracts which are printed on the following pages.

(18 marks)

Use the printed scenes to answer the question set on page 60.

Act 4 Scene 1

All exit except BENEDICK and BEATRICE.

BENEDICK Lady Beatrice, have you wept all this while?

BEATRICE Yea, and I will weep a while longer.

BENEDICK I will not desire that.

BEATRICE You have no reason: I do it freely.

BENEDICK Surely I do believe your fair cousin is wronged.

BEATRICE Ah, how much might the man deserve of me that would right her!

BENEDICK Is there any way to show such friendship?

BEATRICE A very even way, but no such friend.

BENEDICK May a man do it?

BEATRICE It is a man's office, but not yours.

BENEDICK I do love nothing in the world so well as you. Is not that strange?

BEATRICE As strange as the thing I know not. It were as possible for me to say I loved nothing so well as you. But believe me not, and yet I lie not: I confess nothing, nor I deny nothing. I am sorry for my cousin.

BENEDICK By my sword, Beatrice, thou lovest me.

BEATRICE Do not swear and eat it.

BENEDICK I will swear by it that you love me; and I will make him eat it that says I love not you.

BEATRICE Will you not eat your word?

BENEDICK With no sauce that can be devised to it. I protest I love thee.

BEATRICE	Why, then, God forgive me!
BENEDICK	What offence, sweet Beatrice?
BEATRICE	You have stayed me in a happy hour. I was about to protest I loved *you*.
BENEDICK	And do it with all thy heart.
BEATRICE	I love you with so much of my heart that none is left to protest.
BENEDICK	Come, bid me do anything for thee.
BEATRICE	Kill Claudio.
BENEDICK	Ha! Not for the wide world.

Act 5 Scene 4

DON PEDRO — How dost thou, Benedick the married man?

BENEDICK — I'll tell thee what, Prince; a college of wit-crackers cannot flout me out of my humour. Dost thou think I care for a satire or an epigram? No: if a man will be beaten with brains, a' shall wear nothing handsome about him. In brief, since I do purpose to marry, I will think nothing to any purpose that the world can say against it; and therefore never flout at me for what I have said against it; for man is a giddy thing, and this is my conclusion. For thy part, Claudio, I did think to have beaten thee, but in that thou art like to be my kinsman, live unbruised, and love my cousin.

CLAUDIO — I had well hoped thou wouldst have denied Beatrice, that I might have cudgelled thee out of thy single life, to make thee a double-dealer; which, out of question, thou wilt be, if my cousin do not look exceedingly narrowly to thee.

BENEDICK — Come, come, we are friends. Let's have a dance ere we are married, that we may lighten our own hearts and our wives' heels.

LEONATO — We'll have dancing afterward.

BENEDICK — First, of my word! Therefore play, music. Prince, thou art sad; get thee a wife, get thee a wife! There is no staff more reverend than one tipped with horn.

Enter a Messenger

Messenger — My lord, your brother John is ta'en in flight,
And brought with armed men back to Messina.

BENEDICK — Think not on him till to-morrow:
I'll devise thee brave punishments for him.
Strike up, pipers.

(Dance)

Exeunt

END OF TEST

Shakespeare Test Paper

Romeo and Juliet

Instructions:

- find a quiet place where you can sit down and complete the test paper undisturbed
- make sure you have all the necessary equipment to complete the test paper
- read the question carefully
- answer the question on lined paper
- go through and check your answer when you have finished writing

Time:

This test paper is **45 minutes** long.

Check how you have done using pages 123 and 125 of the Answers and Mark Scheme.

	Max. Mark	**Actual Mark**
Score	18	....

First name ....

Last name ....

Set **B**

KEY STAGE 3
Levels 4–7

Shakespeare
Test Paper

English

Romeo and Juliet

Romeo and Juliet

You should spend about 45 minutes on this section.

Romeo and Juliet

In these scenes, Romeo thinks that, and behaves like, he is in love.

What do we learn about lovers' behaviour in these scenes?

Support your ideas by referring to both of the extracts which are printed on the following pages.

(18 marks)

Use the printed scenes to answer the question set on page 67.

Act 1 Scene 1

LADY MONTAGUE

O where is Romeo? Saw you him today?
Right glad I am he was not at this fray.

BENVOLIO

Madam, an hour before the worshipped sun
Peered forth the golden window of the east,
A troubled mind drove me to walk abroad –
Where, underneath the grove of sycamore
That westward rooteth from this city side,
So early walking did I see your son.
Towards him I made, but he was ware of me,
And stole into the covert of the wood.
I, measuring his affections by my own,
Which then most sought where most might not be found,
Being one too many by my weary self,
Pursued my humour not pursuing his,
And gladly shunned who gladly fled from me.

MONTAGUE

Many a morning hath he there been seen,
With tears augmenting the fresh morning's dew,
Adding to clouds more clouds with his deep sighs.
But all so soon as the all-cheering sun
Should in the farthest east begin to draw
The shady curtains from Aurora's bed,
Away from light steals home my heavy son,
And private in his chamber pens himself,
Shuts up his windows, locks fair daylight out,
And makes himself an artificial night.
Black and portentous must this humour prove,
Unless good counsel may the cause remove.

BENVOLIO

My noble uncle, do you know the cause?

MONTAGUE

I neither know it, nor can learn of him.

BENVOLIO

Have you importuned him by any means?

MONTAGUE

Both by myself and many other friends:
But he, his own affections' counsellor,
Is to himself – I will not say how true –
But to himself so secret and so close,
So far from sounding and discovery
As is the bud bit with an envious worm
Ere he can spread his sweet leaves to the air,
Or dedicate his beauty to the sun.
Could we but learn from whence his sorrows grow,
We would as willingly give cure as know.

Enter ROMEO.

BENVOLIO
See where he comes. So please you, step aside.
I'll know his grievance or be much denied.

MONTAGUE
I would thou wert so happy by thy stay
To hear true shrift. Come, madam, let's away.

Exit MONTAGUE, with LADY MONTAGUE.

BENVOLIO
Good morrow, cousin.

ROMEO
Is the day so young?

BENVOLIO
But new struck nine.

ROMEO
Ay me, sad hours seem long.
Was that my father that went hence so fast?

BENVOLIO
It was. What sadness lengthens Romeo's hours?

ROMEO
Not having that which, having, makes them short.

BENVOLIO
In love?

ROMEO
Out –

BENVOLIO
Of love?

ROMEO
Out of her favour where I am in love.

BENVOLIO
Alas, that Love, so gentle in his view,
Should be so tyrannous and rough in proof!

ROMEO
Alas, that Love, whose view is muffled still,
Should without eyes see pathways to his will!
Where shall we dine? O me! What fray was here?
Yet tell me not, for I have heard it all.
Here's much to do with hate, but more with love.
Why then, O brawling love, O loving hate,
O anything of nothing first create!
O heavy lightness, serious vanity,
Misshapen chaos of well-seeming forms!
Feather of lead, bright smoke, cold fire, sick health,
Still-waking sleep, that is not what it is!
This love feel I, that feel no love in this.
Dost thou not laugh?

BENVOLIO
No, coz, I rather weep.

JULIET
What man art thou, that thus bescreened in night
So stumblest on my counsel?

ROMEO
By a name
I know not how to tell thee who I am.
My name, dear saint, is hateful to myself
Because it is an enemy to thee.
Had I it written, I would tear the word.

JULIET
My ears have yet not drunk a hundred words
Of thy tongue's uttering, yet I know the sound.
Art thou Romeo, and a Montague?

ROMEO
Neither, fair maid, if either thee dislike.

JULIET
How cam'st thou hither, tell me, and wherefore?
The orchard walls are high and hard to climb –
And the place death, considering who thou art,
If any of my kinsmen find thee here.

ROMEO
With love's light wings did I o'erperch these walls,
For stony limits cannot hold love out –
And what love can do, that dares love attempt.
Therefore thy kinsmen are no stop to me.

JULIET
If they do see thee, they will murder thee.

ROMEO
Alack, there lies more peril in thine eye
Than twenty of their swords. Look thou but sweet
And I am proof against their enmity.

JULIET
I would not for the world they saw thee here.

ROMEO
I have night's cloak to hide me from their eyes.
And but thou love me, *let* them find me here.
My life were better ended by their hate
Than death proroguèd, wanting of thy love.

JULIET
By whose direction found'st thou out this place?

ROMEO
By love, that first did prompt me to inquire.
He lent me counsel, and I lent him eyes.
I am no pilot, yet wert thou as far
As that vast shore washed with the farthest sea,
I should adventure for such merchandise.

JULIET
Thou knowest the mask of night is on my face,
Else would a maiden blush bepaint my cheek
For that which thou hast heard me speak tonight.
Fain would I dwell on form – fain, fain deny
What I have spoke. – But farewell compliment!

Dost thou love me? I know thou wilt say 'Ay' –
And I will take thy word. Yet if thou swear'st
Thou mayst prove false. At lovers' perjuries
They say Jove laughs. O gentle Romeo,
If thou dost love, pronounce it faithfully.
Or if thou think I am too quickly won,
I'll frown, and be perverse, and say thee nay,
So thou wilt woo – but else, not for the world.
In truth, fair Montague, I am too fond,
And therefore thou mayst think my 'haviour light.
But trust me, gentleman, I'll prove more true
Than those that have more cunning to be strange.
I should have been more strange, I must confess,
But that thou overheard'st, ere I was ware,
My true-love passion. Therefore pardon me,
And not impute this yielding to light love,
Which the dark night hath so discoverèd.

ROMEO

Lady, by yonder blessèd moon I vow,
That tips with silver all these fruit-tree tops –

JULIET

O swear not by the moon, th' inconstant moon,
That monthly changes in her circled orb,
Lest that thy love prove likewise variable.

ROMEO

What shall I swear by?

JULIET

Do not swear at all. –
Or if thou wilt, swear by thy gracious self,
Which is the god of my idolatry,
And I'll believe thee.

ROMEO

If my heart's dear love –

JULIET

Well, do not swear. Although I joy in thee,
I have no joy of this contract tonight.
It is too rash, too unadvised, too sudden –
Too like the lightning, which doth cease to be
Ere one can say 'It lightens'. Sweet, good night.
This bud of love, by summer's ripening breath,
May prove a beauteous flower when next we meet.
Good night, good night! As sweet repose and rest
Come to thy heart as that within my breast.

ROMEO

O wilt thou leave me so unsatisfied?

JULIET

What satisfaction canst thou have tonight?

ROMEO

Th' exchange of thy love's faithful vow for mine.

END OF TEST

Set
C

KEY STAGE 3
Levels 4–7

Reading Test Paper

English

Down South

Reading Test Paper

Down South

Instructions:

- find a quiet place where you can sit down and complete the test paper undisturbed
- make sure you have all the necessary equipment to complete the test paper
- read the questions carefully
- answer all the questions
- go through and check your answers when you have finished the test paper

Time:

This test paper is **1 hour 15 minutes** long.

You have **15 minutes** to read the Reading Material. During this time you are not allowed to refer to the Reading Paper to look at the questions.

You have **1 hour** to write the answers.

Write the answers in this paper, then check how you have done using pages 111–113 of the Answers and Mark Scheme.

Page	81	83	85	Max. Mark	**Actual Mark**
Score	....	....	....	32	....

First name ....

Last name ....

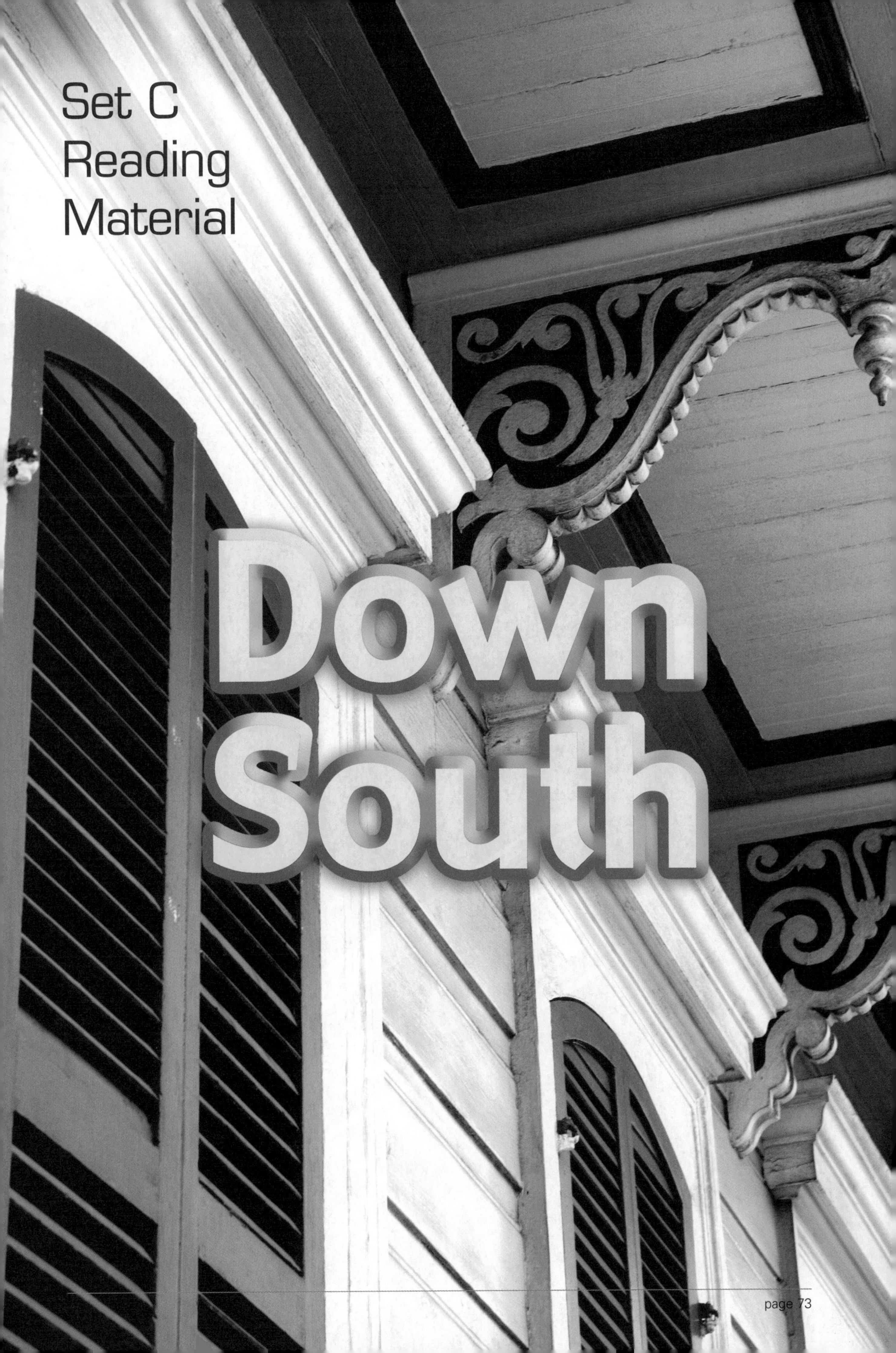

Set C Reading Material

Down South

Contents

Jean Lafitte

1 Jean Lafitte or Laffite (*ca*1780 – *ca*1826?), was a pirate in the Gulf of Mexico in the early 19th century. He established his own "kingdom" of Barataria in the swamps and bayous near New Orleans after the Louisiana Purchase of 1803. He claimed to command more than 1000 men and provided them as troops for the Battle of New Orleans (1815). Afterwards he engaged in the slave trade after it had been banned.

2 Lafitte was a colourful character, said to have been born in France. He engaged in smuggling and privateering, with his "Kingdom of Barataria" (in what is now Louisiana) recognising the sovereignty of no other nation.

3 A controversial manuscript, known as the "Journal" of Jean Laffite, relates how, after his announced death in the 1820s, he lived in several states in the United States, raised a family and wrote this journal. At his request the publication of the journal was delayed for 100 years. In the 1950s the journal was translated from the French language and published. The original manuscript was purchased by Texas Governor Price Daniel and is on display at the Sam Houston Regional Library and Archives in Liberty, Texas.

4 Lafitte claimed never to have plundered an American vessel, and though he engaged in the contraband slave trade, he is accounted as a great romantic figure in Cajun Louisiana. His legend was perpetuated in Cecil B. DeMille's classic, *The Buccaneer* and even by a poem of Byron:

He left a corsair's name to other times,
Linked one virtue to a thousand crimes.

5 After the War of 1812, Lafitte or Laffite was active in the Neutral strip of coast between Spanish Texas and American Louisiana, left unoccupied and lawless until 1821.

6 His later years are obscure; a man many said was Lafitte died in Yucatan.

7 A U.S. National Park is named after him, in six physically separate sites in southeastern Louisiana, interpreting the local Acadian culture. The Barataria Preserve (in Jefferson Parish, Louisiana) interprets the natural and cultural history of the uplands, swamps, and marshlands of the region. Six miles southeast of New Orleans is the Chalmette Battlefield and National Cemetery, actual site of the 1815 battle and the final resting place for soldiers from the Civil War, Spanish – American War, World Wars I and II, and Vietnam.

8 **Jean Lafitte** is the name of a Cajun fishing village and tourist spot sited on Bayou Barataria.

With thanks to www.fact-index.com/j/je/jean_lafitte.html

Arriving in

1 They coasted into the delta, breathed its odour of mud and wood smoke under sunset clouds, gold curls combed out of the west, or the powdered stamens of a broad-throated flower. In the dusk they could see flickering lights in the side channels, sometimes hear a gruesome roar – the alligators, said a deckhand; no, a cow bogged in mud, said the woman with the nephews. The immigrants crowded the rail as the quivering ship moved into the Mississippi River, within the pincer of land. Silvano stood next to his father. A red moon crawled out of the east. On the shore the boy heard a horse snort. Hours before New Orleans the odour of the city reached them – a fetid stink of cesspools and the smell of burning sugar.

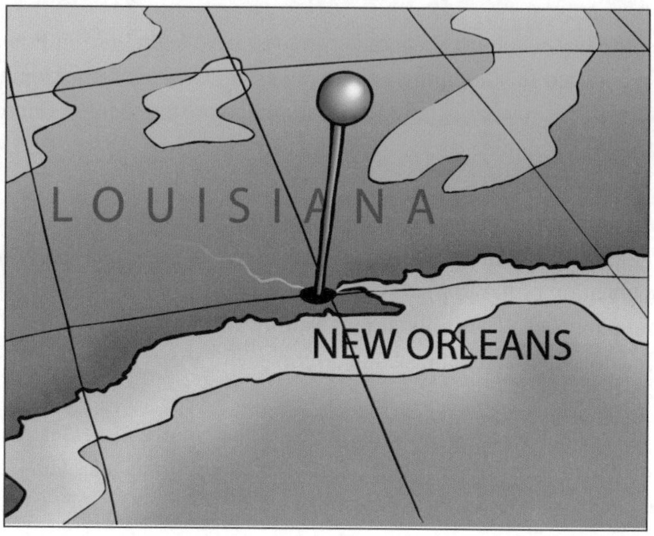

A demon in the backhouse

2 Nothing went as the accordion maker anticipated. The young man from the train was not at the dock. They waited hours for him while the other passengers disappeared into the teeming streets.

3 "True friends are as rare as white flies," said the accordion maker bitterly. Silvano gaped at the black men and especially the women, whose heads were wrapped in turbans as though they concealed emeralds and rubies and chains of gold beneath the winded cloth. They puzzled their way along the noisy, thronged streets with the young man's map and found Decatur Street, but there was no number 16 there, only charred timbers among rampant fireweed, a gap in the row of frowsty tenements. The accordion maker forced his courage, spoke to an approaching man who looked Sicilian; at least his hair appeared Sicilian.

4 "Excuse me, I seek a boardinghouse, number sixteen, but it seems there is no building here – " The man did not answer, spat to his right as he passed. Silvano saw the punishment for not knowing American. The man must be American – one who despised Sicilians ...

New Orleans

WELCOME TO NEW ORLEANS

Back Forward Stop Refresh Home AutoFill Print Mail

Address: www.lonelyplanet.com › go

Live Home Page | Apple | Apple Support | Apple Store | .Mac | Mac OS X | Microsoft MacTopia »

Favorites | History | Search | Scrapbook | Page Holder

New Orleans

INTRODUCTION
ORIENTATION
WHEN TO GO
EVENTS
ATTRACTIONS
OFF THE BEATEN TRACK
HISTORY
GETTING THERE & AWAY
GETTING AROUND
LONELY PLANET GUIDES
FURTHER READING
MAPS

1 New Orleans seduces with Caribbean colour and waves of sultry southern heat. Enshrouding us in dreams and ancient melodies, its sweet-tasting cocktails are laced with voodoo potions. The unofficial state motto, *laissez les bons temps rouler* ("let the good times roll"), pretty much says it all.

2 Called by some "The City That Care Forgot," New Orleans has a well-earned reputation for excess and debauchery. It's a cultural gumbo of African, Indian, Cajun and Creole influences. Whether you're looking for history, drama and intrigue or just a damn good bop in the street, New Orleans is it.

Area: 468 sq km
Population: 1.2 million
Country: USA
Time Zone: GMT/UTC -6 (Central Time)
Telephone Area Code: 504

BACK TO TOP

3 At the big toe of boot-shaped Louisiana, New Orleans nestles between Lake Pontchartrain, a huge but shallow body of saltwater that forms the northern edge of town, and a meniscus-shaped bend of the Mississippi River, about 145 river kilometres (90 miles) above where it empties into the Gulf of Mexico. The original and most visited portions of the city parallel the northern riverbank. Directions upriver or downriver are relative to the water flow, which bends maddeningly to all points of the compass. The Mississippi and Lake Pontchartrain also provide "riverside" or "lakeside" orientation.

4 New Orleans comprises a checkerboard of neighborhoods of different wealth and ethnicity – it's often only a few steps from ghetto to endowed estates. At the easternmost point of the city's crescent-shaped core is the heart of the original city, the French Quarter. To the southwest, the Uptown area encompasses the Garden District, universities and palatial mansions along the St Charles Ave Streetcar Line, which leads to the Riverbend area at the other end of the crescent.

5 Older *faubourgs* (suburbs) border the crowded French Quarter – to the east, the Faubourg Marigny appeals to a bohemian, mostly gay crowd, while the more down-at-heels Faubourg Tremé to the north is a black neighborhood known for its music. Downriver from Faubourg Marigny is the Bywater, a burgeoning artist hangout in an otherwise marginal district.

6 New Orleans International Airport (MSY) is 18 km (11 miles) west of the city center in Kenner, while both trains and buses share New Orleans Union Passenger Terminal ("Union Station") on Loyola Ave in the Central Business District (CBD), between the French Quarter and the Uptown area.

7 West of New Orleans you'll find the Cajun wetlands, an area of French patois-speaking rural people who still depend on the natural resources of the swamps. The Cajuns' Spanish counterparts, the Isleños, live in the coastal fishing villages south of New Orleans. Upstream along the Mississippi River, antebellum sugar plantations attract visitors who marvel at elegant plantation homes. An occasional slave cabin remains as a reminder of how the wealth was gained.

BACK TO TOP

Questions 1–4 are about the "Jean Lafitte" extract on page 75 of the Reading Material.

1 From paragraph one, give two different things that Jean Lafitte was well known for. *(2 marks)* Q1

i ______________________________

ii ______________________________

2 In paragraphs two and four, what does the choice of words in the following phrases suggest about Jean Lafitte?

a) *"Lafitte was a colourful character"* *(1 mark)* Q2a

suggests ______________________________

____

b) *"he is accounted as a great romantic figure in Cajun Louisiana"* *(1 mark)* Q2b

suggests ______________________________

____

3 a) The article is split into a number of paragraphs. Each paragraph has a topic. Fill in the table with the missing paragraph numbers. *(2 marks)* Q3a

Topic	Paragraph Number
The end of Jean Lafitte's life	
Two places that exist today, connected to Jean Lafitte	
A summary of Jean Lafitte's main achievements	
The history of a diary about Jean Lafitte	
A place named after Jean Lafitte	
Reasons why Jean Lafitte became famous	

b) Give one reason why the text contains so many facts and very few opinions. *(1 mark)* Q3b

____

____

4 How does the writer try to give the reader a fair view of the story of Jean Lafitte? You should comment on the effect of:

- the language used to describe Jean Lafitte and his life
- the use of facts and dates
- the content of the writing *(5 marks)*

Q4

subtotal

Questions 5–9 are about the "Arriving in New Orleans" extract on pages 76–77 of the Reading Material.

5 a) From the sentence at the start of paragraph one, write down one word which suggests that the boat is moving slowly but effortlessly. *(1 mark)* Q5a

____

b) What does the word "*gruesome*" suggest in paragraph one? *(1 mark)* Q5b

____

____

____

____

6 In paragraph one, the writer says "*The immigrants crowded the rail as the quivering ship moved into the Mississippi River ...*" What does the phrase "*crowded the rail*" suggest about the people? *(1 mark)* Q6

____

____

____

____

____

7 From the whole text, identify two bad things about New Orleans. *(2 marks)* Q7

i ____

____

____

ii ____

____

____

8 a) This story is divided by a sub-heading: "*A demon in the backhouse*". Which event has the writer chosen to leave out and not describe, where the sub-heading is? *(1 mark)*

Q8a

____

____

b) Explain how the first paragraph prepares us for the fact that the accordion maker's arrival in New Orleans was not going to be easy? *(1 mark)*

Q8b

____

____

____

____

____

____

____

9 What do you learn about the writer's viewpoint and purpose from the passage? Show whether the following statements are TRUE or FALSE by writing T for TRUE or F for FALSE in each of the boxes. *(2 marks)*

Q9

The writer wants us to be aware that New Orleans is a smelly place. ☐

The writer wants the reader to feel like the accordion maker. ☐

The aim of the writer is to scare the reader. ☐

The aim of the writer is to put people off visiting New Orleans. ☐

subtotal

Questions 10–13 are about the "New Orleans" web-page on pages 78–79 of the Reading Material.

10 The web-page begins "*New Orleans seduces with Caribbean colour and waves of sultry southern heat.*"

Explain two ways that this sentence makes the reader want to read more. Support each answer with a quotation from the sentence. *(2 marks)* Q10

i ______________________________

____

ii ______________________________

____

11 Paragraph one, from "*Enshrouding us ...*" to the end of paragraph two, "*New Orleans is it,*" makes us feel that New Orleans is an exciting place but with a darker side. Choose two different words or phrases and explain how they create this effect on the reader. *(2 marks)* Q11

Word/Phrase	Effect on the reader	How it creates this effect on the reader
	makes the reader think that New Orleans is exciting	because it suggests
	makes the reader think that New Orleans has a darker side	because it suggests

12 In the fourth paragraph, it says "*New Orleans comprises a checkerboard of neighbourhoods of different wealth and ethnicity*".

a) Why is New Orleans compared to a checkerboard? *(1 mark)* Q12a

____

____

b) In paragraph five, the word "suburbs" is in brackets. Why? *(1 mark)* Q12b

____

____

13 How is language used in the whole text to make New Orleans sound like an exciting place to visit?

You should comment on how the choice of words and phrases:

- makes New Orleans sound lively
- makes New Orleans sound mysterious
- makes New Orleans sound historical and cultured. *(5 marks)*

Q13

END OF TEST

subtotal

Set
C

KEY STAGE 3
Levels 4–7

Writing Test Paper

English

Down South

Writing Test Paper

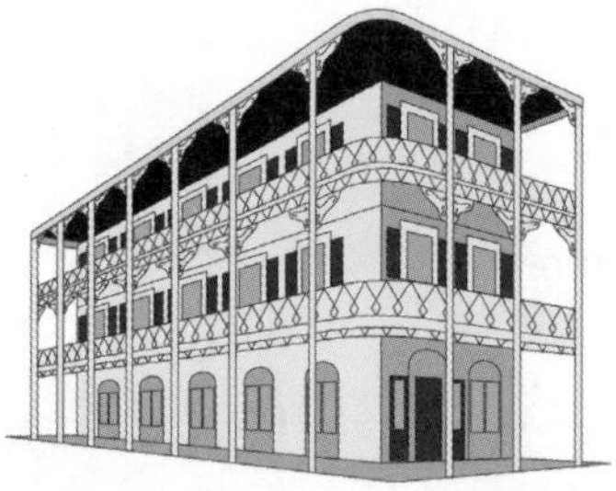

Down South

Instructions:

- find a quiet place where you can sit down and complete the test paper undisturbed
- make sure you have all the necessary equipment to complete the test paper
- read the questions carefully
- answer the questions on lined paper
- go through and check your answers when you have finished writing

Time:

This test paper is **1 hour 15 minutes** long.

You should spend **30 minutes** on the short writing task, including planning time.

You should spend **45 minutes** on the long writing task, including planning time.

Write the answers on lined paper, then check how you have done using pages 114–118 of the Answers and Mark Scheme.

Short Writing Task

Strand	Max. Mark	**Actual Mark**
Sentence structure, punctuation and text organisation	6	
Composition and effect	10	
Spelling	4	

Long Writing Task

Strand	Max. Mark	**Actual Mark**
Sentence structure and punctuation	8	
Text structure and organisation	8	
Composition and effect	14	

First name ____________________

Last name ____________________

Writing Paper – Short Writing Task

Spend about 30 minutes on this section.

You have just returned from a holiday which turned out to be a nightmare. The following things went wrong.

Your flights were delayed by 30 hours and you had to sleep in the airport lounge.
When you arrived, your rooms had been double-booked and were taken.
All your family got food-poisoning from the hotel's own food.

Write a letter to your local newspaper about what happened.

Analyse what went wrong and comment on the company you used.

You do not need to put any addresses – just start your letter with "Dear Sir or Madam".

Write the letter.

(20 marks, including 4 for spelling)

Writing Paper – Long Writing Task

Spend about 15 minutes planning your answer and 30 minutes writing.

Your local council have allocated a large part of their budget to attracting more tourists to your area. You are the council's publicity officer and it is your job to write the text for the brochure. You need to persuade tourists to visit your area.

In your brochure, you need to do these things.

- Tell people what your area has to offer them.
- Describe your area honestly, but make it sound as good as possible without telling lies!
- Sell your area to those people it might appeal to. Old or young? Single or married?

The council **DO NOT** need you to **design** the brochure – they **just** want you to write the text for it.

Write the text for the brochure.

(30 marks)

END OF TEST

Shakespeare Test Paper

Much Ado About Nothing

Instructions:

- find a quiet place where you can sit down and complete the test paper undisturbed
- make sure you have all the necessary equipment to complete the test paper
- read the question carefully
- answer the question on lined paper
- go through and check your answer when you have finished writing

Time:

This test paper is **45 minutes** long.

Check how you have done using pages 119 and 122 of the Answers and Mark Scheme.

	Max. Mark	**Actual Mark**
Score	18	....

First name ....

Last name ....

Much Ado About Nothing

You should spend about 45 minutes on this section.

Much Ado About Nothing

In these two scenes we learn about the relationships of key characters in the play.

What do we learn about relationships in these scenes?

Support your ideas by referring to both of the extracts which are printed on the following pages.

(18 marks)

Use the printed scenes to answer the question set on page 91.

Act 4 Scene 1

BENEDICK	Come, bid me do anything for thee.
BEATRICE	Kill Claudio.
BENEDICK	Ha! Not for the wide world.
BEATRICE	You kill me to deny it. Farewell.
BENEDICK	Tarry, sweet Beatrice.
BEATRICE	I am gone though I am here. There is no love in you. Nay, I pray you, let me go.
BENEDICK	Beatrice –
BEATRICE	In faith, I will go.
BENEDICK	We'll be friends first.
BEATRICE	You dare easier be friends with me than fight with mine enemy.
BENEDICK	Is Claudio thine enemy?
BEATRICE	Is he not approved in the height a villain that hath slandered, scorned, dishonoured my kinswoman? O that I were a man! What, bear her in hand until they come to take hands, and then, with public accusation, uncovered slander, unmitigated rancour – O God, that I were a man! I would eat his heart in the market-place.
BENEDICK	Hear me, Beatrice –
BEATRICE	Talk with a man out at a window! A proper saying!
BENEDICK	Nay, but Beatrice –
BEATRICE	Sweet Hero! She is wronged, she is slandered, she is undone.
BENEDICK	Beat –

BEATRICE Princes and counties! Surely, a princely testimony, a goodly count, Count Comfect – a sweet gallant, surely! O that I were a man for his sake, or that I had any friend would be a man for my sake! But manhood is melted into curtsies, valour into compliment; and men are only turned into tongue, and trim ones too. He is now as valiant as Hercules that only tells a lie and swears it. I cannot be a man with wishing: therefore I will die a woman with grieving.

BENEDICK Tarry, good Beatrice. By this hand, I love thee.

BEATRICE Use it for my love some other way than swearing by it.

BENEDICK Think you in your soul the Count Claudio hath wronged Hero?

BEATRICE Yea, as sure as I have a thought or a soul.

BENEDICK Enough: I am engaged. I will challenge him. I will kiss your hand, and so I leave you. By this hand, Claudio shall render me a dear account. As you hear of me, so think of me. Go, comfort your cousin: I must say she is dead; and so, farewell.

Exeunt.

Act 5 Scene 4

BENEDICK Soft and fair, Friar. Which is Beatrice?

BEATRICE *(Unmasking)* I answer to that name. What is your will?

BENEDICK Do not you love me?

BEATRICE Why no – no more than reason.

BENEDICK Why, then your uncle and the Prince and Claudio
Have been deceived. They swore you did.

BEATRICE Do not you love me?

BENEDICK Troth, no – no more than reason.

BEATRICE Why, then my cousin Margaret and Ursula
Are much deceived: for they did swear you did.

BENEDICK They swore that you were almost sick for me.

BEATRICE They swore that you were well-nigh dead for me.

BENEDICK 'Tis no such matter. Then you do not love me?

BEATRICE No, truly, but in friendly recompense.

LEONATO Come, cousin, I am sure you love the gentleman.

CLAUDIO And I'll be sworn upon't that he loves her;
For here's a paper written in his hand,
A halting sonnet of his own pure brain,
Fashioned to Beatrice.

HERO And here's another,
Writ in my cousin's hand, stolen from her pocket,
Containing her affection unto Benedick.

BENEDICK A miracle! Here's our own hands against our hearts.
Come, I will have thee: but, by this light, I take thee
for pity.

BEATRICE — I would not deny you; but, by this good day, I yield upon great persuasion – and partly to save your life, for I was told you were in a consumption.

BENEDICK — Peace! I will stop your mouth. *(Kissing her)*

END OF TEST

Set C

KEY STAGE 3
Levels 4–7

Shakespeare
Test Paper

English

Romeo and Juliet

Shakespeare Test Paper

Romeo and Juliet

Instructions:

- find a quiet place where you can sit down and complete the test paper undisturbed
- make sure you have all the necessary equipment to complete the test paper
- read the question carefully
- answer the question on lined paper
- go through and check your answer when you have finished writing

Time:

This test paper is **45 minutes** long.

Check how you have done using pages 123 and 126 of the Answers and Mark Scheme.

	Max. Mark	**Actual Mark**
Score	18	....

First name ....

Last name ....

Romeo and Juliet

You should spend about 45 minutes on this section.

Romeo and Juliet

In these scenes, other characters give their opinions on Romeo.

What do we learn about attitudes towards Romeo in these scenes?

Support your ideas by referring to both of the extracts which are printed on the following pages.

(18 marks)

Use the printed scenes to answer the question set on page 98.

Act 1 Scene 1

LADY MONTAGUE
O where is Romeo? Saw you him today?
Right glad I am he was not at this fray.

BENVOLIO
Madam, an hour before the worshipped sun
Peered forth the golden window of the east,
A troubled mind drove me to walk abroad –
Where, underneath the grove of sycamore
That westward rooteth from this city side,
So early walking did I see your son.
Towards him I made, but he was ware of me,
And stole into the covert of the wood.
I, measuring his affections by my own,
Which then most sought where most might not be found,
Being one too many by my weary self,
Pursued my humour not pursuing his,
And gladly shunned who gladly fled from me.

MONTAGUE
Many a morning hath he there been seen,
With tears augmenting the fresh morning's dew,
Adding to clouds more clouds with his deep sighs.
But all so soon as the all-cheering sun
Should in the farthest east begin to draw
The shady curtains from Aurora's bed,
Away from light steals home my heavy son,
And private in his chamber pens himself,
Shuts up his windows, locks fair daylight out,
And makes himself an artificial night.
Black and portentous must this humour prove,
Unless good counsel may the cause remove.

BENVOLIO
My noble uncle, do you know the cause?

MONTAGUE
I neither know it, nor can learn of him.

BENVOLIO
Have you importuned him by any means?

MONTAGUE
Both by myself and many other friends:
But he, his own affections' counsellor,
Is to himself – I will not say how true –
But to himself so secret and so close,
So far from sounding and discovery
As is the bud bit with an envious worm
Ere he can spread his sweet leaves to the air,
Or dedicate his beauty to the sun.
Could we but learn from whence his sorrows grow,
We would as willingly give cure as know.

Enter ROMEO.

BENVOLIO

See where he comes. So please you, step aside.
I'll know his grievance or be much denied.

MONTAGUE

I would thou wert so happy by thy stay
To hear true shrift. Come, madam, let's away.

Exit MONTAGUE, with LADY MONTAGUE.

BENVOLIO

Good morrow, cousin.

ROMEO

Is the day so young?

BENVOLIO

But new struck nine.

ROMEO

Ay me, sad hours seem long.
Was that my father that went hence so fast?

BENVOLIO

It was. What sadness lengthens Romeo's hours?

ROMEO

Not having that which, having, makes them short.

BENVOLIO

In love?

ROMEO

Out –

BENVOLIO

Of love?

ROMEO

Out of her favour where I am in love.

BENVOLIO

Alas, that Love, so gentle in his view,
Should be so tyrannous and rough in proof!

Act 2 Scene 2

JULIET

What man art thou, that thus bescreened in night
So stumblest on my counsel?

ROMEO

By a name
I know not how to tell thee who I am.
My name, dear saint, is hateful to myself
Because it is an enemy to thee.
Had I it written, I would tear the word.

JULIET

My ears have yet not drunk a hundred words
Of thy tongue's uttering, yet I know the sound.
Art thou Romeo, and a Montague?

ROMEO

Neither, fair maid, if either thee dislike.

JULIET
How cam'st thou hither, tell me, and wherefore?
The orchard walls are high and hard to climb –
And the place death, considering who thou art,
If any of my kinsmen find thee here.

ROMEO
With love's light wings did I o'erperch these walls,
For stony limits cannot hold love out –
And what love can do, that dares love attempt.
Therefore thy kinsmen are no stop to me.

JULIET
If they do see thee, they will murder thee.

ROMEO
Alack, there lies more peril in thine eye
Than twenty of their swords. Look thou but sweet
And I am proof against their enmity.

JULIET
I would not for the world they saw thee here.

ROMEO
I have night's cloak to hide me from their eyes.
And but thou love me, *let* them find me here.
My life were better ended by their hate
Than death prorogued, wanting of thy love.

JULIET
By whose direction found'st thou out this place?

ROMEO
By love, that first did prompt me to inquire.
He lent me counsel, and I lent him eyes.
I am no pilot, yet wert thou as far
As that vast shore washed with the farthest sea,
I should adventure for such merchandise.

JULIET
Thou knowest the mask of night is on my face,
Else would a maiden blush bepaint my cheek
For that which thou hast heard me speak tonight.
Fain would I dwell on form – fain, fain deny
What I have spoke. – But farewell compliment!
Dost thou love me? I know thou wilt say 'Ay' –
And I will take thy word. Yet if thou swear'st
Thou mayst prove false. At lovers' perjuries
They say Jove laughs. O gentle Romeo,
If thou dost love, pronounce it faithfully.
Or if thou think I am too quickly won,
I'll frown, and be perverse, and say thee nay,
So thou wilt woo – but else, not for the world.
In truth, fair Montague, I am too fond,
And therefore thou mayst think my 'haviour light.
But trust me, gentleman, I'll prove more true
Than those that have more cunning to be strange.
I should have been more strange, I must confess,
But that thou overheard'st, ere I was ware,
My true-love passion. Therefore pardon me,
And not impute this yielding to light love,
Which the dark night hath so discoverèd.

ROMEO
Lady, by yonder blessèd moon I vow,
That tips with silver all these fruit-tree tops –

JULIET
O swear not by the moon, th' inconstant moon,
That monthly changes in her circled orb,
Lest that thy love prove likewise variable.

ROMEO
What shall I swear by?

JULIET
Do not swear at all. –
Or if thou wilt, swear by thy gracious self,
Which is the god of my idolatry,
And I'll believe thee.

ROMEO
If my heart's dear love –

JULIET
Well, do not swear. Although I joy in thee,
I have no joy of this contract tonight.
It is too rash, too unadvised, too sudden –
Too like the lightning, which doth cease to be
Ere one can say 'It lightens'. Sweet, good night.
This bud of love, by summer's ripening breath,
May prove a beauteous flower when next we meet.
Good night, good night! As sweet repose and rest
Come to thy heart as that within my breast.

ROMEO
O wilt thou leave me so unsatisfied?

JULIET
What satisfaction canst thou have tonight?

ROMEO
Th' exchange of thy love's faithful vow for mine.

JULIET
I gave thee mine before thou didst request it –
And yet I would it were to give again.

ROMEO
Would'st thou withdraw it? For what purpose, love?

JULIET
But to be frank and give it thee again:
And yet I wish but for the thing I have.
My bounty is as boundless as the sea,
My love as deep. The more I give to thee,
The more I have, for both are infinite.

END OF TEST

Notes

Notes

Answers and Mark Scheme

Set A Answers – "Food!" Reading Test Paper

'Real' Cornish Pasties

1 It has cracked down on companies based outside Cornwall producing and selling 'Cornish' pasties.
It has given the name 'Cornish pasty' a PGI status.
(1 mark for each different response, up to a maximum of 2 marks)

2 a) It suggests that they wanted to take firm action. *(1 mark)*

b) They suggest that the audience is one which accepts informal language, i.e. children/young people. *(1 mark)*

3 a)

Topic	Paragraph Number
Rules about pasty ingredients	4
What PGI stands for	2
A reaction from a top chef	7
An introduction to the article	1

1 correct paragraph *(0 marks)*
2 or 3 correct paragraphs *(1 mark)*
4 correct paragraphs *(2 marks)*

b) It has these different kinds of paragraphs because:
the writer is trying to entertain as well as inform
it shows a variety of ways of convincing the reader of the truth of the story
(1 mark for either explanation)

4 Simple points made about the article, with limited awareness of how the writer tries to appeal to young people. *(1 mark)*

Two examples of how the article is trying to appeal to young people, with some comment on how the text has this effect. Some awareness of effect is evident. Two of the three bullet points are addressed briefly. *(2 marks)*

Shows some understanding of how facts and dates are used to make the article appeal to young people and an awareness of how the language and content affect the reader. Some references to the text are included to support ideas. The third bullet point is only briefly addressed. *(3 marks)*

Some exploration of how the text tries to affect the reader through all three bullet points. A consistent attempt to comment on all three bullet points. References are used appropriately to support all ideas. *(4 marks)*

A focused response which explores in detail, with close precise reference to the text, picking out individual words and phrases, how the article affects the reader. All three bullet points are addressed and a high level of awareness is shown by an understanding of different techniques that the writer has used. *(5 marks)*

Oliver Twist

5 a) "suffered" or "tortures" (NOT "slow starvation" – the question says one word) *(1 mark)*

b) "suffered" – makes the reader think that they were in pain/had to put up with discomfort
"tortures" – makes the reader think that their pain was terrible/really bad/inflicted by someone else/on purpose

(1 mark for each valid response, linked to the answer to 5a)

6 It suggests that he is greedy. *(1 mark)*

7 a) Features of Oliver Twist's character from this extract:

- He is brave (he accepts the challenge to ask for more/he accepts his beating)
- He is persistent (he asks for more twice)
- He doesn't care about his fate because he's so hungry
- He is surprised by his own bravery

(1 mark for identifying any of the above)

b) Features of the master's character:

- He is not used to being questioned or contradicted
- He is easily angered
- He is violent in nature *(1 mark for identifying any of the above)*

8 a) It begins with long paragraphs and ends with shorter ones because:

- The writer switches from narrative description to dialogue
- The writer builds up the tension by describing the background first

(1 mark for either explanation)

b) It makes you feel sorry for Oliver because:

- It is the second time he has had to ask
- He is being well-mannered and reasonable and you would not expect anyone to refuse him

(1 mark for either explanation)

9

The writer wants us to feel sorry for Oliver.	TRUE
The writer is trying to criticise the way that boys like Oliver were treated by authority.	TRUE
The writer is trying to give a factual historical account.	FALSE
The writer is trying to entertain the reader.	TRUE

1 correct	*(0 marks)*
2 – 3 correct	*(1 mark)*
4 correct	*(2 marks)*

Why is water good for you?

10 i It includes facts, e.g. "Water is vital for ensuring that our bodies function correctly"
(1 mark – both reason and quotation needed)

ii It gives reasons, e.g. " ... because water is responsible for transporting nutrients around the body"/"because ... most of the chemical reactions within our cells take place in water"
(1 mark – reason and either valid quotation needed, but quotation must include the word "because" up to a maximum of 2 marks)

11

Word/Phrase	Effect on the reader	How it creates this effect on the reader
We also lose water by evaporation	makes the reader think that drinking water is important	because it suggests that we need to replace this water
To stay healthy	makes the reader think that drinking water is important	because it suggests that you will be ill if you don't drink it
We should drink at least 6 to 8 cups or glasses	makes the reader think that drinking water is important	because it suggests that there is a great need for it

(1 mark for a quotation accompanied by an appropriate explanation, up to a maximum of 2 marks)

12 a) It acts as a diuretic.
You lose more water than normal.
It makes you need more water than normal. *(1 mark for any of these responses)*

b) Brackets are used to provide examples of drinks that include caffeine. *(1 mark)*

13 Simple points made about language or content, with limited awareness of how the writer tries to influence the reader. *(1 mark)*

Two examples of how the language or content is making the article sound serious, with some comment on how the words influence the reader. Some awareness of effect is evident. Two of the three bullet points are addressed briefly. *(2 marks)*

Shows some understanding of how the language and content make the article influence the reader. Some references to the text are included to support ideas. The third bullet point is only briefly addressed. *(3 marks)*

Some exploration of how the language and content in the text try to influence the reader through all three bullet points. A consistent attempt to comment on all three bullet points. References are used appropriately to support all ideas. *(4 marks)*

A focused response which explores in detail, with close precise reference to the text, picking out individual words and phrases, how the article affects the reader. All three bullet points are addressed and a high level of awareness is shown by an understanding of different techniques that the writer has used. *(5 marks)*

Set B Answers – "Monsters" Reading Test Paper

Bigfoot of North America

1
- hairy
- ape-like
- biped
- 7 – 9 feet tall
- 600 – 900 pounds
- 14" by 8" footprint size
- 4 toes *(1 mark for any of the above, up to a maximum of 2 marks)*

2 a) It suggests that:
- It might not be true
- There might have been earlier sightings that we don't know of

(1 mark for either of these responses)

b) It suggests that:
- They're unusual
- They're not of a human or recognisable creature *(1 mark for either of these responses)*

3 a)

Topic	Paragraph Number
A description of a captured Sasquatch	3
An introduction to what Bigfoot is	1
An explanation of what the captured Sasquatch might have been	4
The first sightings of a Sasquatch	2

1 correct paragraph *(0 marks)*
2 or 3 correct paragraphs *(1 mark)*
4 correct paragraphs *(2 marks)*

b) To make the passage more convincing
To show that the Bigfoot has been sighted by a variety of people
(1 mark for either of these responses)

4 Simple points made about how Bigfoot is a fake, with limited awareness of how the writer makes the reader feel this. *(1 mark)*

Two examples of how the article makes Bigfoot out to be a fake, with some comment on how the text has this effect. Some awareness of effect is evident. Two of the three bullet points are addressed briefly. *(2 marks)*

Shows some understanding of how historical examples are used to make the account believable and an awareness of how the descriptions of Bigfoot affect the reader. Some references to the text are included to support ideas. The third bullet point is only briefly addressed. *(3 marks)*

Some exploration of how the text tries to affect the reader through all three bullet points. A consistent attempt to comment on all three bullet points. References are used appropriately to support all ideas. *(4 marks)*

A focused response which explores in detail, with close precise reference to the text, picking out individual words and phrases, how the article affects the reader. All three bullet points are addressed and a high level of awareness is shown by an understanding of different techniques that the writer has used. *(5 marks)*

Dracula

5 a) "for I did not know what to do" *(1 mark)*

b) Because s/he has to read on to find out what the narrator does. *(1 mark)*

6 It suggests that:

- They disapprove of the narrator
- They don't like him *(1 mark for either appropriate response)*

7 a) "The old man motioned me in ... with a courtly gesture" *(1 mark)*

b) Either of these quotations, or a summary of them, is acceptable:

- The man is unusually strong/"grasped mine with a strength which made me wince"
- The man does not seem alive or human/"more like the hand of a dead than a living man"

(1 mark for an acceptable answer)

8 a) One mark for a difference that refers to both pairs of paragraphs – commenting on either paragraphs one and two or three and four alone gets no marks. The bit in brackets is not needed to get the mark – it is just to help you understand the answer.

Valid comments about paragraphs one and two:

- The writer uses lots of personal thoughts (to show us what he is thinking)
- The writer uses a lot of self-questioning (to show he is confused)

Valid comments about paragraphs three and four:

- The writer describes the old man from the narrator's viewpoint (so that we see him through his eyes)
- The writer describes the old man from the outside (so that we don't know what he's thinking, to make him more mysterious) *(1 mark)*

b) It makes the story interesting because it:

- Creates a sense of mystery
- Makes us want to read on to find out who he is *(1 mark for either valid comment)*

9 The writer wants us to feel that the narrator is confident. *FALSE*
The writer's aim is to entertain and interest the reader. *TRUE*
The writer wants us to like the old man. *FALSE*
The writer's aim is to build up tension in the reader. *TRUE*

1 correct *(0 marks)*
2 – 3 correct *(1 mark)*
4 correct *(2 marks)*

The Loch Ness Monster

10 "The Loch Ness Monster is <u>supposedly</u> living in Scotland's Loch Ness"
"this <u>unidentified</u> animal"
"a <u>strange</u> aquatic creature"

(1 mark for identifying two of the above, up to a maximum of 2 marks for explanations of why these examples create a feeling of mystery – see the question)

11

Word/Phrase	Effect on the reader	How it creates this effect on the reader
convinced	makes the reader think that there might be some truth in the monster stories	because it suggests that the men had no doubts/believed what they saw
received several letters	makes the reader think that there might be some truth in the monster stories	because it suggests that the account made other people confess their experiences/come out with stories
claiming also to have seen	makes the reader think that there might be some truth in the monster stories	because it suggests that the account was backed up by other witnesses/other people had seen it

(1 mark for a quotation accompanied by an appropriate explanation, up to a maximum of 2 marks)

12 a) The writer uses the word "thorough" because:
- It suggests that the scientists had done their job properly
- It suggests that the entire loch has been surveyed *(1 mark for either response)*

b) It is in inverted commas because the writer is casting doubt on whether the monster deserves to be called a monster/whether it really is a monster. *(1 mark for either response)*

13 Simple points made about language or content, with limited awareness of how the writer tries to make it sound serious. *(1 mark)*

Two examples of how the language or content makes the article sound serious, with some comment on how the words affect the reader. Some awareness of effect is evident. Two of the three bullet points are addressed briefly. *(2 marks)*

Shows some understanding of how the language and content make the article sound serious. Some references to the text are included to support ideas. The third bullet point is only briefly addressed. *(3 marks)*

Some exploration of how the language and content in the text try to affect the reader through all three bullet points. A consistent attempt to comment on all three bullet points. References are used appropriately to support all ideas. *(4 marks)*

A focused response which explores in detail, with close precise reference to the text, picking out individual words and phrases, how the article affects the reader. All three bullet points are addressed and a high level of awareness is shown by an understanding of different techniques that the writer has used. *(5 marks)*

Set C Answers – "Down South" Reading Test Paper

Jean Lafitte

1 He established his own kingdom of Barataria.
He claimed to command more than 1000 men/provided them as troops for the Battle of New Orleans.
He engaged in the slave trade after it was banned. *(1 mark for each up to a maximum of 2)*

2 a) He had a varied life/it contained a mixture of exciting/good/bad incidents.
(1 mark for an answer containing either of these explanations)

b) His life has been exaggerated/his life is legendary
(1 mark for an answer containing either of these explanations)

3 a)

Topic	Paragraph Number
The end of Jean Lafitte's life	6
Two places that exist today, connected to Jean Lafitte	7
A summary of Jean Lafitte's main achievements	1
The history of a diary about Jean Lafitte	3
A place named after Jean Lafitte	8
Reasons why Jean Lafitte became famous	4

1 correct paragraph *(0 marks)*
2 or 3 correct paragraphs *(1 mark)*
4 correct paragraphs *(2 marks)*

b) Because it's writing to inform/it's from a reference book/encyclopaedia.
(1 mark for an answer containing either of these explanations)

4 Simple points made about Jean Lafitte, with limited awareness of how the article tries to give the reader a fair view. *(1 mark)*

Two examples of how the article gives the reader a fair view, with some comment on how the text has this effect. Some awareness of effect is evident. Two of the three bullet points are addressed briefly. *(2 marks)*

Shows some understanding of how facts and dates are used to make the account believable and an awareness of how the descriptions of Jean Lafitte and his life affect the reader. Some references to the text are included to support ideas. The third bullet point is only briefly addressed. *(3 marks)*

Some exploration of how the text tries to affect the reader through all three bullet points.
A consistent attempt to comment on all three bullet points. References are used appropriately to support all ideas. *(4 marks)*

A focused response which explores in detail, with close precise reference to the text, picking out individual words and phrases, how the article affects the reader. All three bullet points are addressed and a high level of awareness is shown by an understanding of different techniques that the writer has used. *(5 marks)*

Arriving In New Orleans

5 a) coasted *(1 mark)*

b) That the roar is either:
- hideous
- frightening
- suggesting that something is being killed or badly hurt

(1 mark for any of these acceptable responses)

6 They were eager to see their destination. *(1 mark)*

7 It is smelly/"odour of mud"/"fetid stink of cesspools"/"smell of burning sugar".
It is crowded/"teeming streets"/"noisy, thronged streets".
It is derelict/"only charred timbers among rampant fireweed".
The people are unfriendly/"The man did not answer, spat to his right".
(1 mark for any two of the above up to a maximum of 2 marks. Quotations or explanations are acceptable for a mark)

8 a) Getting off the boat. *(1 mark)*

b) There is an emphasis on bad things, e.g. the cow bogged in the mud, the smell.
There are hints of fear – the "quivering ship", the "gruesome roar", the "red moon crawled".
(1 mark for including one of the above reasons in the answer. No mark for an explanation not backed up with an example or quotation)

New Orleans

9

The writer wants us to be aware that New Orleans is a smelly place	TRUE
The writer wants the reader to feel like the accordion maker	TRUE
The aim of the writer is to scare the reader	FALSE
The aim of the writer is to put people off visiting New Orleans	FALSE

1 correct	*(0 marks)*
2 – 3 correct	*(1 mark)*
4 correct	*(2 marks)*

10 "seduces" – makes it sound like the place is chatting you up/enticing you/drawing you in like a lover.
"sultry southern heat" – makes it sound sexy or steamy/alliteration "sultry southern" used to create a hot, steamy effect.
"Caribbean colour" – it makes it seem lively and exotic/alliteration "Caribbean colour" used to create a lively effect.
(1 mark for each explanation supported by a quotation from this list of acceptable responses up to a maximum of 2 marks)

11

Word/Phrase	Effect on the reader	How it creates this effect on the reader
Enshrouding us in dreams	makes the reader think that New Orleans is exciting	because it suggests that it is a place of mystery/fantasy
sweet-tasting cocktails	makes the reader think that New Orleans is exciting	because it suggests that you can enjoy drinks that are better tasting than in other places
laissez les bons temps rouler	makes the reader think that New Orleans is exciting	because it suggests that it is a party town where people are just out to enjoy themselves
laced with voodoo potions	makes the reader think that New Orleans has a darker side	because it suggests that evil and black magic might affect you there without your knowledge
a well-earned reputation for excess and debauchery	makes the reader think that New Orleans has a darker side	because it suggests that people get out of control
The City That Care Forgot	makes the reader think that New Orleans has a darker side	because it suggests that the place is run down and abused

(1 mark for a quotation accompanied by an appropriate explanation, up to a maximum of 2 marks)

12 a) Because a checkerboard has a mix of black and white squares, just as New Orleans has a mix of contrasting neighbourhoods. *(1 mark)*

b) Because it's an explanation of the French word that comes before it. *(1 mark)*

13 Simple points made about language, with limited awareness of how the article tries to make it sound an exciting place. *(1 mark)*

Two examples of how the language makes the article exciting, with some comment on how the words affect the reader. Some awareness of effect is evident. Two of the three bullet points are addressed briefly. *(2 marks)*

Shows some understanding of how the language makes New Orleans sound lively and mysterious. Some references to the text are included to support ideas. The third bullet point is only briefly addressed. *(3 marks)*

Some exploration of how the language in the text tries to affect the reader through all three bullet points. A consistent attempt to comment on all three bullet points. References are used appropriately to support all ideas. *(4 marks)*

A focused response which explores in detail, with close precise reference to the text, picking out individual words and phrases, how the article affects the reader. All three bullet points are addressed and a high level of awareness is shown by an understanding of different techniques that the writer has used. *(5 marks)*

Writing Test Papers

The bands for writing give descriptions of the main features to look out for in your writing. Different bands have different amounts of marks in them.

For bands with three different marks, check the following:

- If your writing fits everything in that band, but shows no evidence of the bands above or below, give yourself the middle mark.
- If your writing fits everything in that band, but shows one piece of evidence of lower bands, give yourself the lower mark in the band.
- If your writing fits everything in that band, but shows one piece of evidence of higher bands, give yourself the higher mark in the band.

For bands with two marks, you need to do two of the things in the band to get the lower mark and everything in the band to get the higher mark.

For bands with one mark, you need to do everything in that band to get that mark.

It is important to look at the different marks you are getting in order to build up an accurate picture of the strengths and weaknesses of your writing – for example, you might get high marks on composition and effect, but your spelling may be letting you down. If you know this, then you should focus on these areas in order to improve your writing.

Long Writing Task Papers – Mark Scheme

Section A: Sentence structure and punctuation

Band A1
Sentences and phrases are mostly linked with joining words like "and", "but" and "when".
Sentences are simple and may contain lots of repeated words and phrases.
Full stops, capital letters and exclamation marks are used to punctuate sentences, mostly accurately. *(0 marks)*

Band A2
Sentences are varied, and more complex joining words like "who" and "which" are used.
Words like "if" and "because" are used to help give reasons and for emphasising ideas.
Commas are used quite accurately within sentences. *(1 or 2 marks)*

Band A3
Simple and more complex sentences are used – long sentences and short sentences are used successfully.
Suggestions are given, by using words like "can" or "would".
A variety of punctuation is used with accuracy.
Different types of sentences, e.g. commands, questions or exclamations, are used in order to create more interesting effects. *(3 or 4 marks)*

Band A4
The writer begins sentences more skillfully, with words like "usually", "hopefully" etc. or by being impersonal, e.g. "Some people believe that ...".
A range of punctuation is used and this is sometimes done for deliberate effect, e.g. brackets are used to put in asides and thoughts. *(5 or 6 marks)*

Band A5
Sentences are varied, depending on the effect that the writer wishes to create.
Simple sentences might be used, but to create effects, e.g. shock or surprise.
Punctuation is used skillfully in order to make the reader speed up and slow down and to make the meaning of the writing perfectly clear. *(7 marks)*

Band A6
A wide range of sentence types is used with skill, accuracy and thought to control the writing.
There might be some non-standard sentences, but used for deliberate effect.
There is a very wide range of different types of punctuation used, in order to create a number of different effects. *(8 marks)*

Section B: Text structure and organisation

This section focuses on how overall meaning and effect is put across through the way that the writing is organised and planned.

Band B1
Ideas are mainly linked because they happen to be on the same topic.
Points might be put in a list, but not necessarily in any sort of order of importance.
Paragraphs might be used to show some of the obvious different topics in the writing. *(0 marks)*

Band B2
Paragraphs usually start with the main topic in the first sentence.
Paragraphs contain examples.
The writing has some brief opening and closing comments, but they will be fairly brief and undeveloped. *(1 or 2 marks)*

Band B3
Paragraphs are written in a logical order.
The introduction and conclusion are clear.
Paragraphs of different lengths are used, e.g. short paragraphs might take the form of a persuasive question. *(3 or 4 marks)*

Band B4
Detailed content is well handled within and between paragraphs.
Some phrases like "On the other hand" or "In addition to this" etc. are used to link the paragraphs.
The introduction and conclusion are developed and help to make it more persuasive.
(5 or 6 marks)

Band B5
Paragraphs are varied in length to suit the different ideas being discussed.
Paragraphs are linked with a variety of words and phrases.
Paragraphs are ordered in such a way that the writer might have used them to highlight contrasts, or to be ironic. *(7 marks)*

Band B6
The whole piece of writing is organised, shaped and controlled to achieve a range of effects, or to get the reader thinking in a certain way.
Within paragraphs, the writer has used a wide range of links that are precisely and carefully chosen.
(8 marks)

Section C: Composition and effect

This section focuses on the overall impact of the writing and the effect it has on the reader.

Band C1
The writing shows some awareness of the reader.
There is some relevant content. *(0 marks)*

Band C2
The writing is generally lively and attempts to interest the reader.
The content of the writing shows that the writer recognises its purpose.
Some reasons are given for the ideas and opinions, but perhaps not that many. *(1, 2 or 3 marks)*

Band C3
The writing is detailed and gives clear reasons for the opinions and viewpoints expressed.
The writing engages the reader's interest.
The writing gives a range of relevant ideas and the writer's viewpoint is clear. *(4, 5 or 6 marks)*

Band C4
The piece is well written because it uses a range of techniques such as repetition, humour and a consideration of the reader's needs in order to persuade.
The writer's view is consistent. *(7, 8 or 9 marks)*

Band C5
The tone and content of the writing are appropriate and well judged.
The writing deliberately interacts with the reader.
Content is relevant throughout and is used to support the ideas. *(10, 11 or 12 marks)*

Band C6
The writing has been done skillfully and the writer is totally in control of the writing type.
The viewpoint of the writer has been maintained throughout.
There is a strong individual style, created by a range of methods. *(13 or 14 marks)*

Short Writing Task Papers – Mark Scheme

Section D: Sentence structure, punctuation and paragraph organisation

This section focuses on how you choose to organise your writing and how this contributes to its overall effect.

Band D1
Sentences are fairly simple.
Sentences are linked by simple joining words like "and" or "then".
Full stops and capital letters are used with accuracy.
Paragraphs are used to separate the more obvious different topics given in the task. *(0 marks)*

Band D2
Sentences are varied and use linking words like "who" or "which".
The writing is written in the same tense throughout.
Words like "he", "she", "it", "they" and other pronouns are generally used correctly.
Paragraphs are mainly put into a logical order, as is the detail within them. *(1 or 2 marks)*

Band D3
A variety of longer sentences is used. This includes those sentences that have been built up from joining simpler ones together to make longer ones and sentences where the word order has been successfully re-arranged for effect.
Words like "completely", "partly" and others which help to make meaning more precise, are used.
Words like "he", "she", "it", "they" and other pronouns are used correctly.
Tenses are used correctly.
Paragraphs are used for appropriate reasons and are put into a logical order.
The detail in them is put into a logical order. *(3 or 4 marks)*

Band D4
Sentences are written in a variety of ways to achieve interesting effects that suit the purpose of the writing.
A range of punctuation is used – sometimes to create effects.
Paragraphs are of different lengths and the information in them is organised cleverly to suit what is being written about. *(5 marks)*

Band D5
There is a wide range of sentence structures that use a sophisticated range of verbs and tenses.
Within paragraphs, the writer has used a wide range of links that are precisely and carefully chosen.
There is a very wide range of punctuation used, in order to make meaning clear and create a range of effects. *(6 marks)*

Section E: Composition and effect

This section is to do with the overall impact of your writing and how well it fits the audience you are writing for.

Band E1
The writing shows some awareness of the reader.
Simple techniques, like repetition, are used.
Content is relevant to the question, but might well be unevenly used. *(0 marks)*

Band E2
The writing tries to interest the reader.
Some techniques, e.g. use of adjectives, are used to help writing, but they might not be very imaginative. *(1, 2 or 3 marks)*

Band E3
The writer interests the reader.
The writer is clearly aware of what type of writing he/she is doing and for whom.
The tone of the writing is consistent throughout. *(4, 5 or 6 marks)*

Band E4
The writing is well written and convincing throughout.
The writer really engages the reader's interest.
There is a very good range of well-chosen details.
The viewpoint of the writer is consistent throughout. *(7, 8 or 9 marks)*

Band E5
The writing has been done skillfully and the writer is totally in control of the writing type.
The viewpoint of the writer has been maintained throughout.
There is a strong individual style, created by a range of methods. *(10 marks)*

Section F: Spelling

This section focuses on accuracy in spelling. Choose the section that best fits the writing.

Band F1
Simple words and those with more than one or two syllables are generally accurate. *(1 mark)*

Band F2
More complicated words that fit to regular patterns and rules are generally accurate. *(2 marks)*

Band F3
Most spelling, including irregular words, is accurate. *(3 marks)*

Band F4
Virtually all spelling, including complex words that don't fit to regular rules or patterns, is correct. *(4 marks)*

Shakespeare Test Papers – Mark Scheme

Much Ado About Nothing mark scheme

The mark bands apply to all three Much Ado About Nothing questions.

Find the band that best fits your answer and for every bullet point in that band that you achieve, give yourself one mark within that band, e.g. if you think you are in Band 4 and you have done two of the bullet points, then you should give yourself 11.

Band 1
A few simple facts and opinions about these extracts.
There may be some misunderstandings.
Parts of the extracts are retold or copied and answers may be only partly relevant. *(1, 2 or 3 marks)*

Band 2
Contains a little explanation, showing some awareness of the needs of the question.
Comments are relevant but are mostly about the plot.
Some broad references to how the characters speak or act. *(4, 5 or 6 marks)*

Band 3
Some general understanding of the question, although some points might not be developed.
Some comments on the language that the characters use or the effect of the plot on the audience.
Some points backed up with reference to the text. *(7, 8 or 9 marks)*

Band 4
Some discussion of how the extracts relate to the question, even though all the ideas might not be of equal quality.
Awareness of the characters' use of language and its effects.
Most points backed up with references to the text. *(10, 11 or 12 marks)*

Band 5
Clear focus on how the extracts relate to the question.
Good consistent comments on the characters' language and its effect on the audience.
Well-chosen quotations linked together to present an overall argument. *(13, 14 or 15 marks)*

Band 6
Every quotation is analysed in depth with relation to the question and there is an evaluation.
Every quotation is commented on in terms of the language that the characters use, or the difference between what they don't know and the audience does.
Individual words are picked out of quotations and linked into the overall argument. *(16, 17 or 18 marks)*

Useful quotations for Much Ado About Nothing Set A

Act 4 Scene 1

Come, bid me do anything for thee.

This shows the degree to which Benedick has changed since the start of the play, in that he is no longer a stubborn bachelor.

We'll be friends first.

The fact that Benedick says this to Beatrice, shows that he doesn't want his newly admitted relationship with her spoiled.

Is he not approved in the height a villain that hath
slandered, scorned, dishonoured my kinswoman?

Here we see the strength of feeling that has arisen in Beatrice and her passionate nature.

o that I were a man for his sake

The repetition of this sentiment by Beatrice in the scene shows how she feels trapped by society in not being able to take revenge for Hero.

Act 5 Scene 4

BEATRICE
Do not you love me?
BENEDICK
Troth, no – no more than reason.

Here, the witty exchange shows the good-natured banter that is at the core of Benedick and Beatrice's relationship.

A miracle! Here's our own hands against our hearts.
Come, I will have thee: but, by this light, I take thee
for pity.

Benedick shows that he cannot resist teasing Beatrice.

I yield
upon great persuasion – and partly to save your life,
for I was told you were in a consumption.

Beatrice shows her wit and sarcasm, mirroring that of Benedick, showing how they are well matched.

Useful quotations for Much Ado About Nothing Set B

Act 4 Scene 1

BEATRICE
Yea, and I will weep a while longer.
BENEDICK
I will not desire that.

In these lines, we see how concern is an important ingredient in showing love.

It were as possible
for me to say I loved nothing so well as you. But believe
me not, and yet I lie not: I confess nothing, nor I deny
nothing. I am sorry for my cousin.

Beatrice shows the audience that words alone don't show evidence of love.

I will swear by it that you love me; and I will make him
eat it that says I love not you.

Benedick is talking of his sword here and it shows how people often want or need to show their love through deeds and promises.

Act 5 Scene 4

I'll tell thee what, Prince; a college of
wit-crackers cannot flout me out of my humour.

Benedick's attitude shows that there is nothing so good as being in love.

for man is a giddy thing, and this is my
conclusion.

Benedick realises how the effect of being in love is to throw a person emotionally and intellectually out of balance.

Think not on him till to-morrow:

Benedick's comment shows that being in love leads to an absence of care.

Useful quotations for Much Ado About Nothing Set C

Act 4 Scene 1
You dare easier be friends with me than fight with mine enemy.
Beatrice shows how relationships involve emotional blackmail and conflicting demands.

Enough: I am engaged. I will challenge him. I will kiss your hand, and so I leave you.
Benedick's words show how sacrifices need to be made in relationships.

Act 5 Scene 4
Do not you love me?
Beatrice's words show how people are sometimes insecure in relationships and need reassurance.

Why, then my cousin Margaret and Ursula
Are much deceived: for they did swear you did.
Beatrice's words show how people's relationships are viewed differently by the people in them.

I would not deny you; but, by this good day, I yield upon great persuasion - and partly to save your life, for I was told you were in a consumption.
Beatrice's sarcastic humour shows how relationships take different forms – not all people would engage in banter like this.

Peace! I will stop your mouth.
Benedick shows how someone has to take the lead in a relationship.

Romeo and Juliet mark scheme

The mark bands apply to all three Romeo and Juliet questions.

Find the band that best fits your answer and for every bullet point in that band that you achieve, give yourself one mark within that band. e.g. if you think you are in Band 4 and you have done two of the bullet points, then you should give yourself 11.

Band 1
A few simple facts and opinions about these extracts.
There may be some misunderstandings.
Parts of the extracts are retold or copied and answers may be only partly relevant. *(1, 2 or 3 marks)*

Band 2
Contains a little explanation, showing some awareness of the needs of the question.
Comments are relevant but are mostly about the plot.
Some broad references to how the characters speak. *(4, 5 or 6 marks)*

Band 3
Some general understanding of the question, although some points might not be developed.
Some comments on the language that the characters use.
Some points backed up with reference to the text. *(7, 8 or 9 marks)*

Band 4
Some discussion of how the extracts relate to the question, even though all the ideas might not be of equal quality.
Awareness of the characters' use of language and its effects.
Most points backed up with references to the text. *(10, 11 or 12 marks)*

Band 5
Clear focus on how the extracts relate to the question.
Good consistent comments on the characters' language and its effect on the audience.
Well-chosen quotations linked together to present an overall argument. *(13, 14 or 15 marks)*

Band 6
Every quotation is analysed in depth with relation to the question and there is an evaluation.
Every quotation is commented on in terms of the language that the characters use.
Individual words are picked out of quotations and linked into the overall argument. *(16, 17 or 18 marks)*

Useful quotations for Romeo and Juliet Set A

Act 1 Scene 1

Out of her favour where I am in love.
Romeo is depressed about his love for Rosaline being unrequited.

O brawling love, O loving hate,
O anything of nothing first create!
O heavy lightness, serious vanity,
Misshapen chaos of well-seeming forms!
The use of oxymorons shows how Romeo is confused.

Love is a smoke made with the fume of sighs:
Romeo is acting out what he thinks a lover should do, but he has, as yet, no experience himself.

In sadness, cousin, I do love a woman.
Romeo shows he still has a sense of humour, when with people he likes, like his cousin, Benvolio.

She will not stay the siege of loving terms,
Nor bide th' encounter of assailing eyes,
Romeo is frustrated that Rosaline does not love him in return.

Farewell. Thou canst not teach me to forget.
Romeo is stubborn.

Act 2 Scene 2

Her eye discourses. I will answer it.
– I am too bold.
Romeo is anxious not to mess things up with Juliet.

O that I were a glove upon that hand,
That I might touch that cheek!
Romeo displays the typically obsessive and exaggerated behaviour of a lover.

O speak again, bright angel! – For thou art
As glorious to this night, being o'er my head,
As is a wingèd messenger of heaven
Romeo uses the clichéd language of love because he knows no better.

Call me but love, and I'll be new-baptized.
Henceforth, I never will be Romeo.
Romeo makes strong promises, showing his innocence and strength of feeling.

Useful quotations for Romeo and Juliet Set B

Act 1 Scene 1
So early walking did I see your son.
Towards him I made, but he was ware of me,
And stole into the covert of the wood.
This shows the secretive behaviour of lovers.

Many a morning hath he there been seen,
With tears augmenting the fresh morning's dew,
Romeo is acting like a typical courtly lover of the time by showing his emotions to "prove" he is in love.

And makes himself an artificial night.
Black and portentous must this humour prove,
Romeo's behaviour is stereotypical of a depressed lover.

Could we but learn from whence his sorrows grow,
We would as willingly give cure as know.
This shows how others get concerned when someone is supposedly in love.

ROMEO
Dost thou not laugh?
BENVOLIO
No, coz, I rather weep.
This shows how lovers get things out of proportion and lose their sense of emotional balance.

Act 2 Scene 2
What man art thou, that thus bescreened in night
So stumblest on my counsel?
This shows how a lover's behaviour can seem shocking and unsettling.

JULIET
Art thou Romeo, and a Montague?
ROMEO
Neither, fair maid, if either thee dislike.
This shows how lovers make extreme promises that they can't necessarily keep.

For stony limits cannot hold love out –
This shows how love gives a person strength.

Alack, there lies more peril in thine eye
Than twenty of their swords.
This shows how love makes a person reckless.

Useful quotations for Romeo and Juliet Set C

Act 1 Scene 1

O where is Romeo? Saw you him today?
Right glad I am he was not at this fray.

This shows how Romeo's mother is concerned for his physical well-being.

Could we but learn from whence his sorrows grow,
We would as willingly give cure as know.

This shows that Romeo's parents are concerned about his emotional well-being.

BENVOLIO
It was. What sadness lengthens Romeo's hours?
ROMEO
Not having that which, having, makes them short.
BENVOLIO
In love?
ROMEO
Out –
BENVOLIO
Of love?
ROMEO
Out of her favour where I am in love.

These short, sensitive questions show Benvolio's concern for his cousin.

Act 2 Scene 2

What man art thou, that thus bescreened in night
So stumblest on my counsel?

This shows how Juliet is, at first, shocked by Romeo's behaviour – until she realises who it is.

I would not for the world they saw thee here.

This shows how quickly Juliet reveals the strength of her feelings for Romeo.

But farewell compliment!
Dost thou love me? I know thou wilt say 'Ay' –
And I will take thy word. Yet if thou swear'st
Thou mayst prove false. At lovers' perjuries
They say Jove laughs.

Juliet shows here that she thinks that she is rushing into a relationship with Romeo, but can't stop herself.

O swear not by the moon, th' inconstant moon,
That monthly changes in her circled orb,
Lest that thy love prove likewise variable.

Juliet is worried that Romeo will prove to be fickle in his feelings.

My bounty is as boundless as the sea,
My love as deep. The more I give to thee,
The more I have, for both are infinite.

Juliet shows how quickly she has completely fallen for Romeo.

Notes

Notes

KS3 Science

Practice Test Papers

Ages 11-14

Jackie Clegg, Bob McD
and Tim Green

Contents

Introduction

Instructions on using the Practice Test Papers

Understanding Assessment

At the end of Key Stage 3 (usually in Year 9 at the age of 14), teacher assessment is used to determine your level of attainment in subjects including English, Maths and Science. There are no national tests but assessments by your teacher will help them to determine your level of attainment (see page 7).

About these Practice Test Papers

This book contains three sets of practice test papers, which provide a means of parental or self-assessment that can be easily carried out at home. The papers will help you to evaluate an approximate level of attainment, highlight opportunities for further study and skills practice that will aid improvement, and record results to track progress. The instructions and guidelines in this Introduction provide guidance on how to use the papers for self-assessment.

The questions have been written by experienced teachers and are based on the programme of study for Key Stage 3. Important ideas may be revisited in order to ensure understanding and provide an opportunity for improvement.

Sets A, B and C each provide one complete assessment, consisting of two 60-minute tests. The two tests can be taken at different times, but try to complete them both within the same week. Take the tests at a time when you can work uninterrupted and do not feel tired.

You should complete Sets A, B and C towards the end of Key Stage 3. Make sure you leave a reasonable amount of time between each assessment – it is unrealistic to expect to see an improvement in just a few weeks. You will feel much more motivated if you wait for a while, because your progress will be more obvious.

If you want to re-use the practice test papers, you can write in pencil and then rub out your answers. However, do not repeat the same test paper too soon, otherwise you will remember the questions and your results will not be an accurate reflection of your abilities.

Before you start:

- find a suitable place to complete the tests – somewhere quiet, where you won't be disturbed
- make sure you have a pen, pencil, ruler, rubber and a clock or watch to time yourself
- turn off your mobile phone
- read the instructions on the front of the test paper carefully.

When completing the test papers:

- try to answer all of the questions and make sure you read them carefully
- write your answers in the spaces where you see the pencil icon 
- keep an eye on the time – if you spend longer than an hour on the paper, your results will not accurately reflect your abilities.

When you have finished:

- use the answers and marks provided in the pull-out Answers and Mark Scheme to mark the test paper
- read the top tips on how to improve your performance and remember the key points
- add up the total number of marks.

Tips for the Top

Make sure you have a suitable place to do the test and have a pen, pencil, rubber and ruler.

Try all of the questions and write your answers where you see the pencil:

The number of marks is shown for each part of the question.

Remember to read the questions carefully.

Make your answers clearly legible. If you make a mistake, put a cross through it and write the correct answer clearly next to it. Use an eraser as little as possible.

Don't panic! These practice papers are meant to provide you with a guide to your progress and the level you are working at. They are not the be-all and end-all. If you cannot do a question, just go on to the next question and come back to it later if you have time.

Using your Marks to Assess Levels

Record your test marks in the progress grid below:

	Week Beginning (Date)	Test Paper 1	Test Paper 2	Total	Level
Set A					
Set B					
Set C					

When you have completed Test Paper 1 and Test Paper 2 for each set, add the two marks out of 75 together to give a total mark out of 150.

The table below will give you an indication of your level based on your marks:

Level 4 and below	Level 5	Level 6	Level 7
0–39	40–74	75–104	105–150

Remember that the level obtained in these tests may be different from the level that your teacher reports you are working at. This is because they can only test a limited range of skills and knowledge. Your teacher will have a better idea of your overall performance.

However, these tests will help you to identify areas of weakness that you can improve upon with a bit of hard work and extra study. This will help you to get a better mark on your next assessment test and progress at school.

Improving your Results and Making Progress

Go back through your test papers and make a note of all the questions that you got wrong. This will help you to identify topics that require further study.

If you want to improve your understanding and make progress, you need to be proactive! Use Study Guides and Workbooks for home study – they include lots of practice questions, which test your knowledge and reinforce what you have learned.

With a little bit of time and effort, when you take the next set of tests in the book you will achieve a higher mark. Remember to record the date alongside your marks in the grid above. This will allow you to track your progress over time and will help to build your confidence and a sense of achievement.

What do Levels Mean?

Attainment levels are used to measure your progress through Key Stages 1, 2 and 3. They are concerned with your knowledge, skills and understanding of a subject.

There are eight levels and they each have a description, which sets out the skills, knowledge and understanding that you are expected to demonstrate at that level. The descriptions for Levels 1 to 8 get increasingly difficult.

Although there are eight levels, at Key Stage 3 you are generally expected to work between Levels 3 and 7, where Level 7 represents excellent knowledge, skills and understanding.

The table below shows the expected National Curriculum levels for 14 year olds.

Level	Aged 14
Level 1	
Level 2 Level 2c Level 2b Level 2a	
Level 3	Below average
Level 4	Below average
Level 5	At level expected
Level 6	At level expected
Level 7	Excellent
Level 8	Exceptional

As you can see, it is expected that a majority of 14 year olds will achieve Level 5 or 6 by the end of Year 9. If you achieve Level 7, it is a real success. A 14 year old who achieves Level 8 is working at an exceptionally high level. For comparison, a student who gains a GCSE grade C has achieved Level 7.

Your teacher will carry out regular assessments to ensure that you are working at an appropriate level and progressing at the expected rate. The test papers in this book support this process. Provided you follow the instructions and address any potential problems that the tests highlight, they will help to ensure you are always working to the best of your abilities.

Set
A

KEY STAGE 3
Levels 5–7

Test Paper 1

Science

Test Paper 1

Test Paper 1

Instructions:

- find a quiet place where you can sit down and complete the test paper undisturbed
- make sure you have all the necessary equipment to complete the test paper
- read the questions carefully
- answer all the questions in this paper
- write your answers where you see this symbol
- show all your working as marks may be awarded for this
- go through and check your answers when you have finished the test paper
- check how you have done using pages 105–106 of the Answers and Mark Scheme

Time:

This test paper is **1 hour** long.

Page	9	11	13	15	17	19	21	23	Max. Mark	**Actual Mark**
Score	....	....	....	....	....	....	....	....	75	....

First name Marina

Last name Argirova

1 Jason is using a periscope to see who is behind him.

a) **On the diagram** below, draw a line to show how light passes through the periscope.

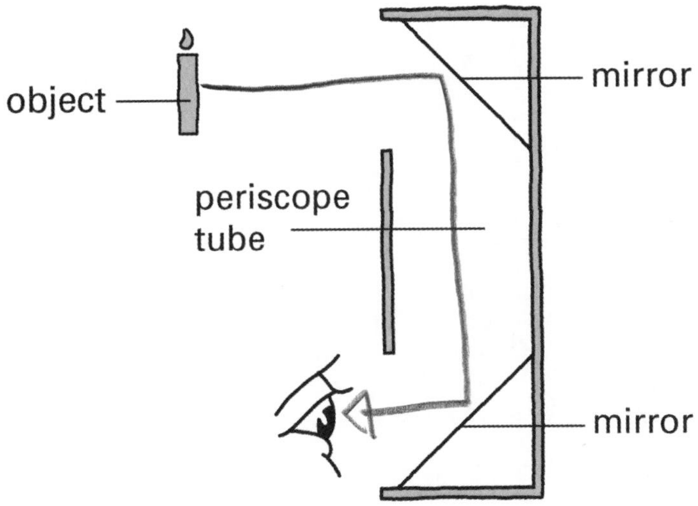

(3 marks) Q1a

b) Jason can see Ben, but he cannot see Shaun.

Suggest why.

Because the mirror isn't pointing towards Shaun.

(1 mark) Q1b

subtotal

c) The light ray reaches the mirror then bounces off again.

What is the name given to this movement of light?

Tick the correct box.

radiation ☐

reflection ☑

refraction ☐

(1 mark) ☐ Q1c

(Total 5 marks)

2 The female body has a menstrual cycle.

a) **At what age will a female usually start her menstrual cycle?**

Tick the correct box.

between 1 and 4 years ☐

between 10 and 16 years ☑

between 35 and 40 years ☐

between 60 and 65 years ☐

(1 mark) ☐ Q2a

The diagram shows the menstrual cycle.

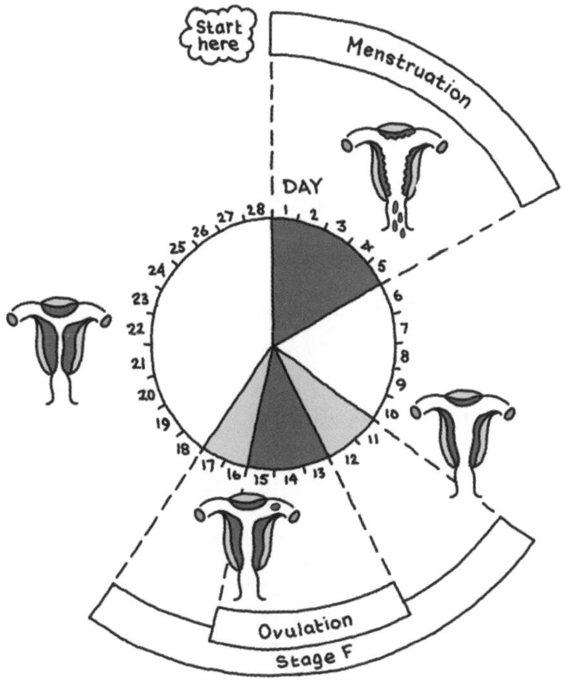

Use the information in the diagram to help you answer these questions.

b) i **For how many days does menstruation take place?**

5 days *(1 mark)* Q2bi

ii **What is meant by menstruation?**

Tick the correct box.

- [ ] An egg is released.
- [x] Blood from the uterus wall is lost.
- [ ] Fertilisation takes place.
- [ ] The lining of the uterus starts to grow again.

(1 mark) Q2bii

c) i **Between which days does ovulation take place?**

12 and 16. *(1 mark)* Q2ci

 subtotal

ii What is meant by ovulation?

Tick the correct box.

- An egg is released. ☑
- Blood from the uterus wall is lost. ☐
- Fertilisation takes place. ☐
- The lining of the uterus starts to grow again. ☐

(1 mark) Q2cii

d) i Explain why fertilisation may take place at stage F.

An egg is released from the ovary. and starts travelling down the fellopian tube

(2 marks) Q2di

ii Describe what happens to the sperm if fertilisation does not take place.

It dies and passes out of the female body.

(1 mark) Q2dii

iii How does a female know if she is pregnant?

No menstruation, gains weight.

(1 mark) Q2diii

iv How long does the female carry the baby (called the gestation period) before the baby is born?

9 months

(1 mark) Q2div

(Total 10 marks)

3 Four boys have a race over 100 metres.

Jimmy is younger, so he is given a 10 metre start. They all start at the same time.

The table gives their times for the race.

Boy	Time in seconds
John	15.0
Jimmy	18.0
Jamil	14.6
Jay	17.5

a) **Write down the order in which they cross the finishing line. Start with the boy who finishes first.**

Jamil John Jay Jimmy. *(1 mark)* Q3a

b) **Calculate Jimmy's average speed in the race. Include the unit in your answer.**

Speed = Speed / time

Speed = 90 / 18.

Speed = 5 m/s *(3 marks)* Q3b

(Total 4 marks)

4 The diagram shows two magnets repelling each other.

a) **Label the poles on the right-hand magnet.** *(1 mark)* Q4a

b) **Draw an arrow to show the magnetic force acting on the right-hand magnet.** *(1 mark)* Q4b

subtotal

c) Write down the name of a metal that can be used to make a magnet.

Nickel (1 mark)

Q4c

d) Circle the object that contains a magnet.

hairdryer **microscope** **torch** (1 mark)

Q4d

(Total 4 marks)

5 Sarah and Paul shine a ray of light through a prism.

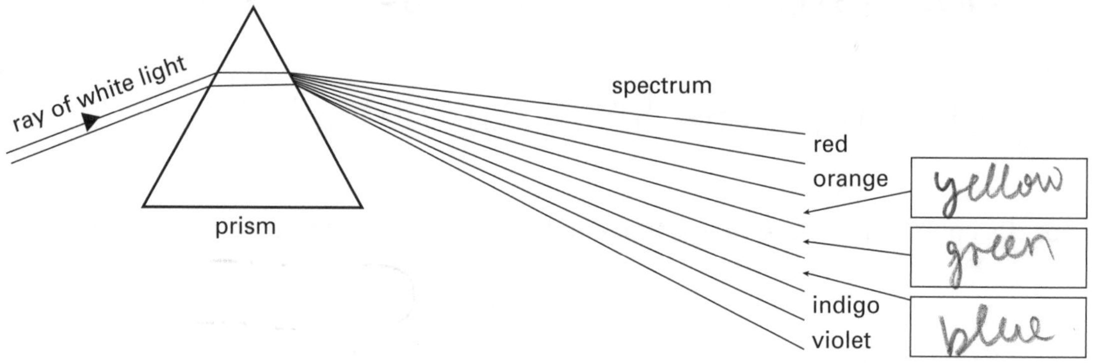

a) The white light produces a spectrum as it passes through the prism. What is this process called?

Dispersion (1 mark)

Q5a

b) On the diagram, write in the boxes to finish labelling the spectrum. (1 mark)

Q5b

c) Explain why the prism produces a spectrum when white light passes through it.

different colours travel at different speeds so are "refracted" by different amounts. (3 marks)

Q5c

(Total 5 marks)

6 The table gives information about three fuels that can be used to heat houses.

Fuel	State at room temperature	Substances produced on combustion		
		carbon dioxide	**water**	**sulphur dioxide**
coal	solid	✔	✔	✔
natural gas	gas	✔	✔	
wood	solid	✔	✔	

a) **Which fuel in the table is most difficult to store? Explain your answer.**

Gas because it needs to be kept in a sealed underpressure container.

(2 marks) Q6a

b) **Which gas in the air is needed for these fuels to burn?**

Circle the correct answer.

carbon dioxide **hydrogen** **nitrogen** **oxygen** *(1 mark)* Q6b

c) Burning large amounts of fossil fuels can cause major environmental problems.

Explain how burning fossil fuels contributes to global warming.

Carbon dioxide is a greenhouse gas which takes in heat in the atmosphere.

(2 marks) Q6c

subtotal

d) Coal and natural gas supplies will eventually run out.

i Why should this not be a problem with wood?

Wood can be re-goown (1 mark) Q6di

ii When could there be a problem with wood?

When its use exceeds replanting (1 mark) Q6dii

(Total 7 marks)

7 Four metals, P, Q, R and S, are used in a series of reactions to find the order in the reactivity series.

The table summarises the results.

Solution	Add P	Add Q	Add R	Add S
nitrate of P	✘	✘	✘	✔
nitrate of Q	✔	✘	✔	✔
nitrate of R	✔	✘	✘	✔
nitrate of S	✘	✘	✘	✘

Key: ✔ reaction ✘ no reaction

a) Arrange these four metals in order of **increasing** reactivity.

Least reactive S P R Q *(3 marks)* Q7a

b) Metal S reacts with steam to form a metal oxide and a colourless gas.

What is this gas?

Hydrogen *(1 mark)* Q7b

c) T is another metal more reactive than Q. A reaction takes place when a powdered mixture of T and the oxide of Q were heated together.

What type of reaction is this and what are the products?

A replacement reaction

Oxide of T and Q. *(2 marks)*

Q7c

d) T reacts when placed in a solution of the nitrate of R but does not react when placed in a solution of the nitrate of P.

What does this tell you about T?

T is ~~p~~ between P and

R in the series. *(2 marks)*

Q7d

(Total 8 marks)

8 A 'fizzy pop' maker uses artificial dyes to colour drinks. Only some dyes can be used.

Scientists in a drinks company test samples of two drinks, E and F, from rival firms. They compare the results with the results from their own brand G.

The diagram shows the apparatus they use.

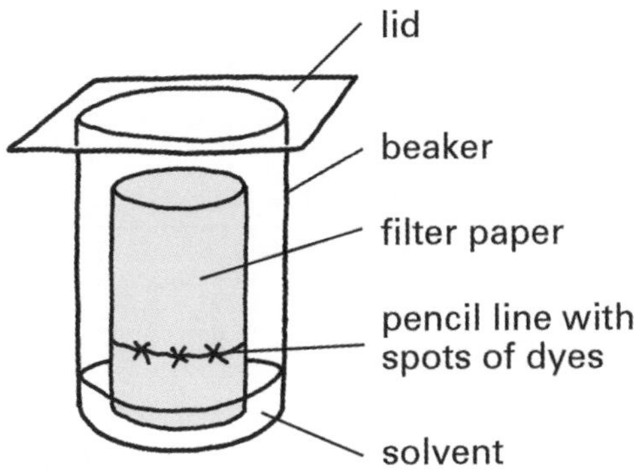

a) **What is the name of the method they are using?**

Chromotography *(1 mark)*

Q8a

subtotal

b) What happens during the experiment?

The solvent moves up the paper. (2 marks) Q8b

c) Why is it important that the spots on the filter paper are above the solvent at the start?

The dyes would just dissolve. (1 mark) Q8c

d) Why is it important that the line is a pencil line and not an ink line?

the dyes in the ink might start to separate (1 mark) Q8d

e) The chart shows the results of the experiment.

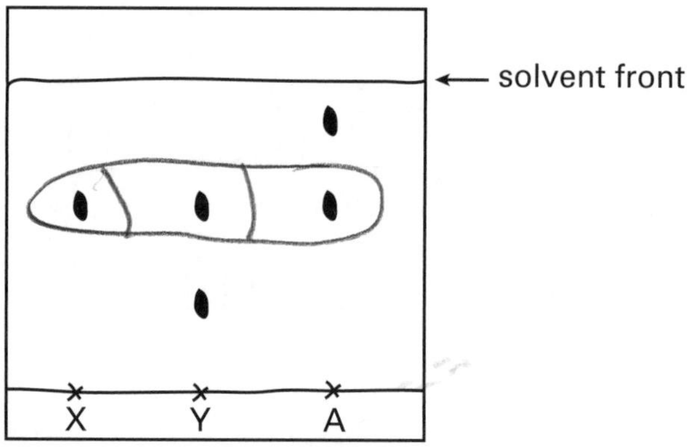

i Which drink contains only one dye?

X (1 mark) Q8ei

ii **On the chart** circle the dye which is in all the drinks. *(1 mark)* Q8eii

(Total 7 marks)

9 Grace investigated how the amount of light affects the number of bubbles given off by pondweed.

This is how she set up her apparatus.

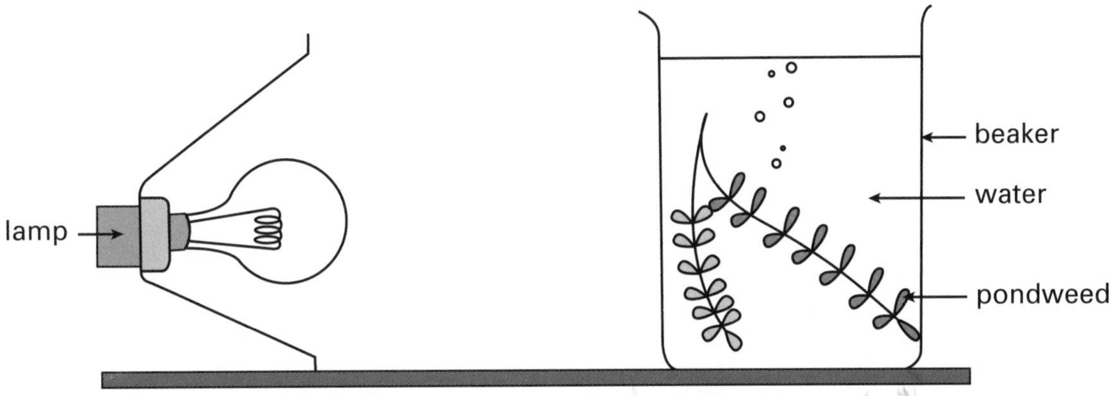

Grace left the apparatus set up for two minutes. She then started to count the number of bubbles formed in one minute intervals.

a) **Suggest why she left the apparatus for two minutes before starting to count the number of bubbles.**

Allow the plant to adapt to the light difference

(1 mark)

Q9a

Grace investigates the effect of increasing the amount of light by using extra lamps.

b) Grace wants to keep this a fair test.

i **Suggest two factors she will need to keep the same to make this a fair test.**

1 Temperature in water.

2 Colour of light

(2 marks)

Q9bi

subtotal

ii What is the **independent (input) variable** for this investigation?

light level. *(1 mark)* Q9bii

c) The table shows her results.

Number of lamps	Number of bubbles in one minute
0	2
1	8
2	16
3	20
4	22

i **On the grid below, plot the points of these results.**

The first one has been done for you. *(2 marks)* Q9ci

ii **Draw a smooth curve of best fit.** *(1 mark)* Q9cii

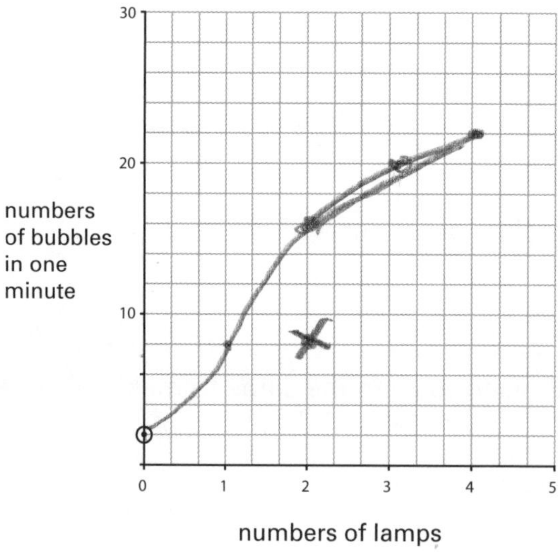

d) **From your graph, estimate the number of bubbles with 5 lamps.**

22 bubbles in one minute. *(1 mark)* Q9d

e) Describe and explain the pattern shown by your graph of results.

The more light, the more bubbles. the more light, the more photo synthesis takes place.

(2 marks) Q9e

(Total 10 marks)

10 The diagram shows the human digestive system.

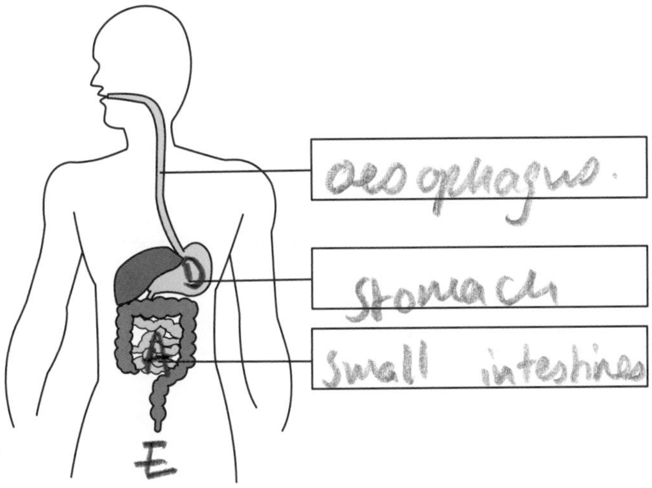

a) Finish labelling the diagram. *(3 marks)* Q10a

Choose words from this list.

large intestine **oesophagus (gullet)** **small intestine** **stomach** **liver**

b) **On the diagram:**

i Write a letter **D** to show where most digestion of food takes place. *(1 mark)* Q10bi

ii Write a letter **A** to show where most digested food is absorbed into the blood. *(1 mark)* Q10bii

iii Write a letter **E** to show where undigested food leaves the body. *(1 mark)* Q10biii

subtotal

c) Large molecules of food are digested (broken down) into smaller molecules.

Suggest why.

Large molecules cannot be absorbed into the intestines. *(1 mark)*

Q10c

d) The smaller molecules of digested food pass into the bloodstream through the walls of the small intestine. Describe how the small intestine is adapted for food absorption.

- Good blood supply.
- The villi increase the surface area.
- The walls are thin.

(3 marks)

Q10d

(Total 10 marks)

11 The diagram shows a plant cell which is found in a leaf. The main cell organelles are shown.

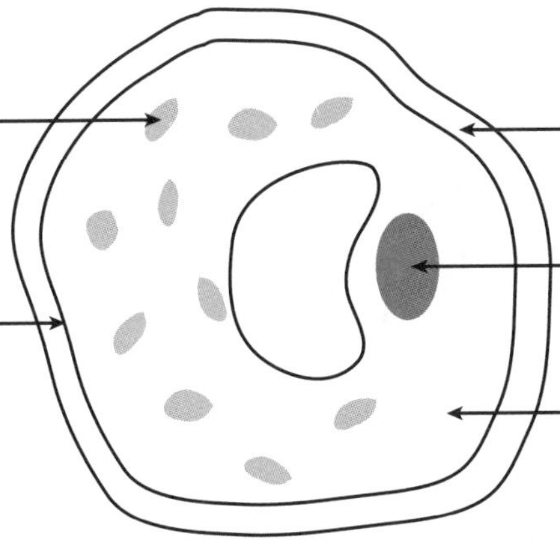

a) i **Which organelle, which is in this leaf cell, is not found in a plant root cell?**

chloroplast. *(1 mark)*

Q11ai

ii **Which two organelles shown on the diagram are not in animal cells?**

Cell wall and

chloroplast. *(2 marks)*

Q11aii

b) The five parts of the cell labelled on the diagram each have a different function.

In the table below, write the name of the cell organelle next to its function. One has been done for you. *(2 marks)*

Q11b

Organelle	**Function**
cytoplasm	Where chemical reactions take place
chloroplast	Site of photosynthesis
Nucleus	Control centre of the cell
cell wall	Helps to keep the cell shape
cell membrane	Controls which substances enter and leave the cells

(Total 5 marks)

END OF TEST

subtotal

Set **A**

KEY STAGE 3
Levels 5–7

Test Paper 2

Science

Test Paper 2

Test Paper 2

Instructions:

- find a quiet place where you can sit down and complete the test paper undisturbed
- make sure you have all the necessary equipment to complete the test paper
- read the questions carefully
- answer all the questions in this paper
- write your answers where you see this symbol
- show all your working as marks may be awarded for this
- go through and check your answers when you have finished the test paper
- check how you have done using pages 106–108 of the Answers and Mark Scheme

Time:

This test paper is **1 hour** long.

Page	25	27	29	31	33	35	37	39	Max. Mark	**Actual Mark**
Score	....	....	....	....	....	....	....	....	75	....

First name ....

Last name ....

1 Surinder pumps up a bicycle tyre.

When she has finished she notices that the pump has got warmer.

a) Describe where, and in what form, the energy was stored before it was transferred in pumping up the tyre.

____

_______________ *(1 mark)* Q1a

b) The gas particles inside the tyre exert a pressure on the inner walls of the tyre. Suggest how.

____

_______________ *(1 mark)* Q1b

c) When the air entering the tyres was warmed, the movement of the gas particles in the tyre changes. Suggest how.

____

_______________ *(1 mark)* Q1c

d) When the air in the tyre becomes hotter, the pressure rises. Give one reason why the pressure rises.

____

_______________ *(1 mark)* Q1d

e) The pressure in the tyre increases as Surinder forces more air into the tyre. Suggest why a larger amount of air increases the pressure in the tyre.

____

_______________ *(1 mark)* Q1e

(Total 5 marks)

subtotal

2 The diagram shows a food web.

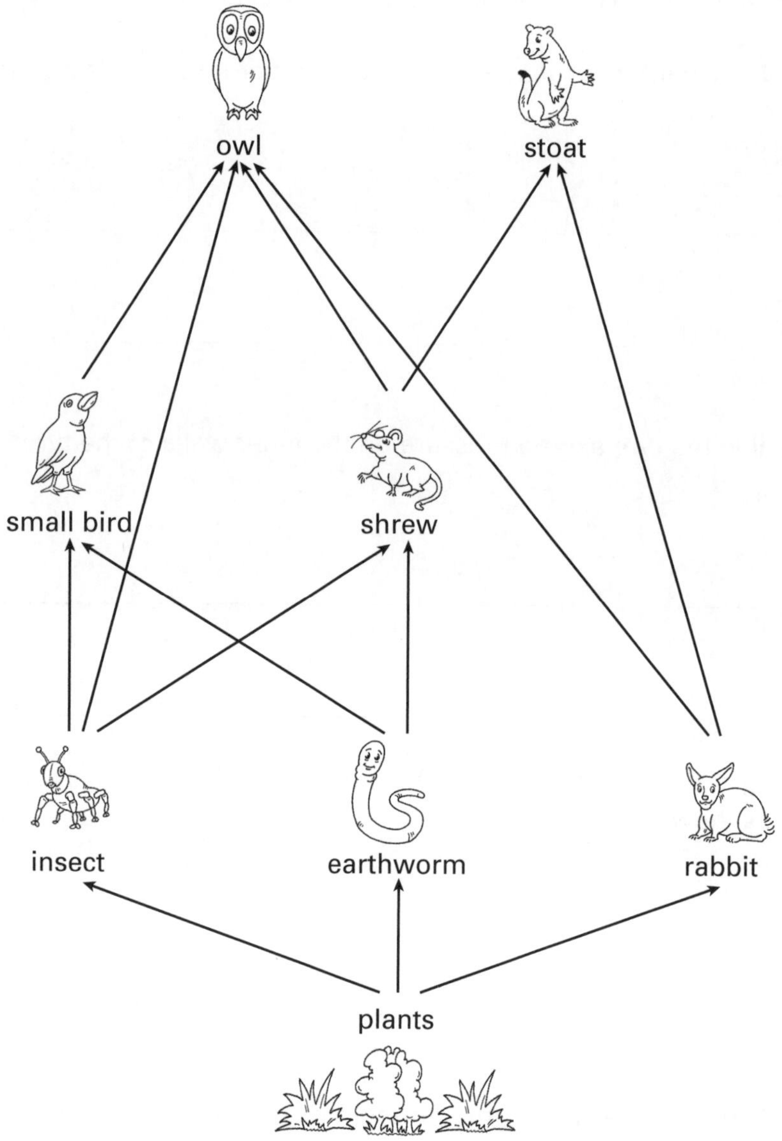

Use the information in the food web to help you answer the questions.

a) What **two** things do shrews eat?

____

____ *(2 marks)*

Q2a

b) Name the producer.

____ *(1 mark)*

Q2b

c) i The owl is a predator.

Name **one other** predator.

______________________________ *(1 mark)* Q2ci

ii Name an animal that is both prey and a predator.

______________________________ *(1 mark)* Q2cii

iii Give **two** ways in which the owl is adapted to be a predator.

____

____

______________________________ *(2 marks)* Q2ciii

d) Describe the effects on the food web if there were no shrews present.

____

____

____

____

______________________________ *(3 marks)* Q2d

(Total 10 marks)

subtotal

3 Class 9A were investigating the effects of burning different masses of magnesium metal in air. The diagram shows the apparatus they used.

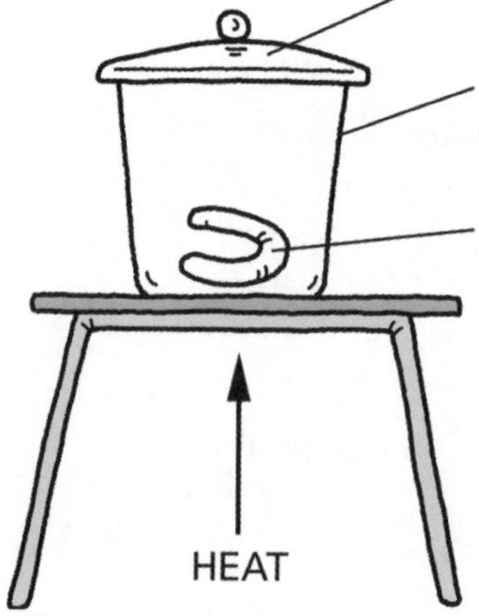

a) **Explain why it is important to keep the lid on the crucible during the experiment.**

____ *(1 mark)* Q3a

b) **Complete the word equation for this reaction.**

magnesium + ____________ → ____________ ____________ *(2 marks)* Q3b

There are five groups, A–E. The results of the five groups are shown on the grid.

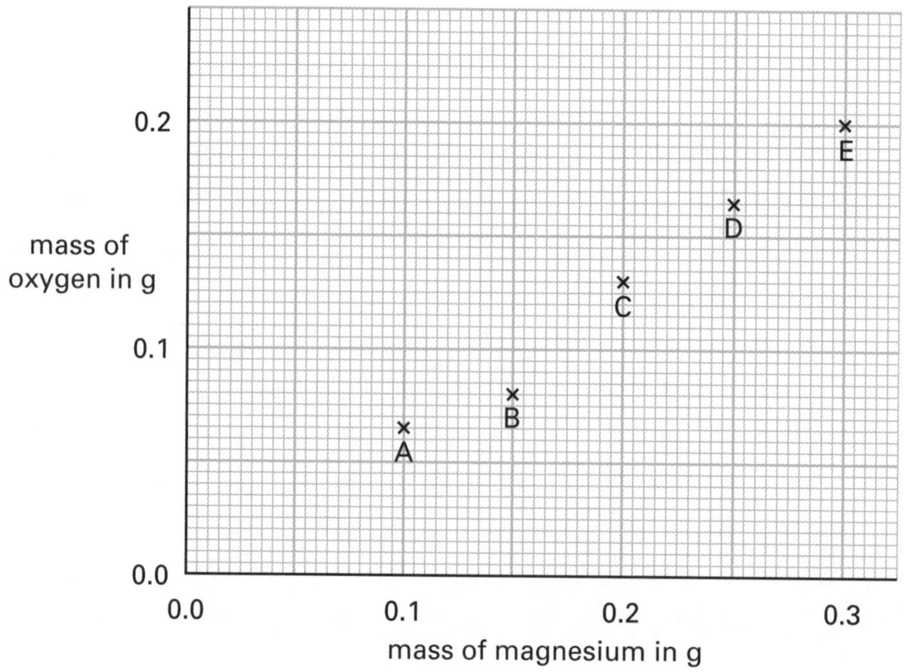

c) **Draw the best line through these points.** *(1 mark)* Q3c

d) i Which group seems to have produced a set of anomalous results?

______________________________ *(1 mark)* Q3di

ii Give two problems which might have occurred during this group's experiment.

____

______________________________ *(2 marks)* Q3dii

iii According to the graph, what mass of oxygen should have combined with this group's magnesium?

______________________________ *(1 mark)* Q3diii

e) Just over two hundred years ago, scientists believed that combustion of any substance resulted in a loss of mass.

Lavoisier carried out many experiments burning different substances and finding the mass of reactants and products. He showed that combustion results in an increase in mass.

Sam says: "I think that there is a mistake in the experiment. Surely when I burn the magnesium in the air it loses mass because the metal has gone?"

Use the theory of combustion and the results of the groups' experiments to explain to Sam why he is wrong.

____

____

______________________________ *(2 marks)* Q3e

(Total 10 marks)

subtotal

4 The three diagrams show the arrangement of particles in solids, liquids and gases.

A B C

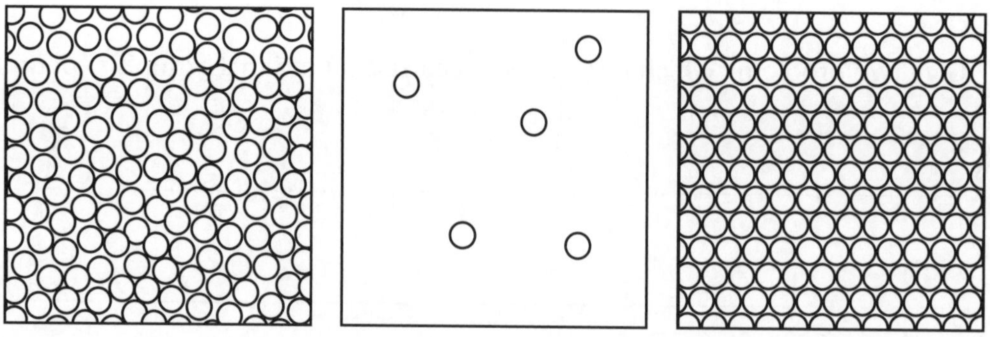

a) Which diagram shows a solid, which a liquid and which a gas?

solid ____________

liquid ____________

gas ____________ *(2 marks)* Q4a

b) Why does **C** have a higher density than **A** or **B**?

____

____ *(1 mark)* Q4b

c) Finish the table about changes of state.

From	To	Change of state	Is energy taken in or given out?
A	**B**	evaporation	taken in
C	**A**		
A	**C**		
B	**A**		

(4 marks) Q4c

(Total 7 marks)

5 Jane is out on a cycle ride.

In the diagram Jane is speeding up.

a) How can you tell Jane is speeding up?

____ *(1 mark)*

Q5a

b) Draw arrows to show the forces acting on Jane and her cycle when she travels at a constant speed. *(1 mark)*

Q5b

c) Jane pedals her bike along a level road. When she stops pedaling she slows down and then stops. Explain with reference to forces why the bike slows down and stops.

____

____ *(2 marks)*

Q5c

(Total 4 marks)

subtotal

6 The table shows the results of experiments to find the percentage of oxygen, nitrogen and carbon dioxide in three different places.

	Percentage in sample of air (%)		
Gas	**Centre of city**	**City suburb**	**In the country**
oxygen	17.5	18.0	19.8
nitrogen	79.9	79.9	79.9
carbon dioxide	0.05	0.03	0.02

a) One of the gases in the table is a compound.

Which gas is a compound and which elements make up this compound?

gas ______________________________

elements ______________________________ *(2 marks)* Q6a

b) **What can you conclude about the percentage of nitrogen in each place?**

______________________________ *(1 mark)* Q6b

c) **Why does the carbon dioxide concentration need to be measured more accurately than oxygen or nitrogen?**

______________________________ *(1 mark)* Q6c

d) i **Where is the oxygen concentration lowest?**

______________________________ *(1 mark)* Q6di

ii **Why is this?**

____

______________________________ *(1 mark)* Q6dii

e) Suggest another gas that might be found in the city centre in a higher concentration than in the country.

_______________________________________ *(1 mark)* Q6e

f) i Name the process that converts carbon dioxide into oxygen.

_______________________________________ *(1 mark)* Q6fi

ii In which of the three different places will more carbon dioxide be converted into oxygen? Explain your answer.

____

____

_______________________________________ *(2 marks)* Q6fii

(Total 10 marks)

7 The drawing shows a bulldozer.

a) **On the diagram** draw an arrow to show the weight of the bulldozer. *(1 mark)* Q7a

subtotal

b) The bulldozer weighs 180 000 N. It has large caterpillar tracks. The area of the track in contact with the ground is 10 m^2.

i Why does the bulldozer need large caterpillar tracks?

______________________________ *(1 mark)*

Q7bi

ii Calculate the pressure that the bulldozer exerts on the ground.

Use the equation Pressure = $\frac{\text{Force}}{\text{Area}}$. Use the correct units in your answer.

pressure ______________ *(3 marks)*

Q7bii

(Total 5 marks)

8 The graph shows a person's pulse rate before and after smoking a cigarette.

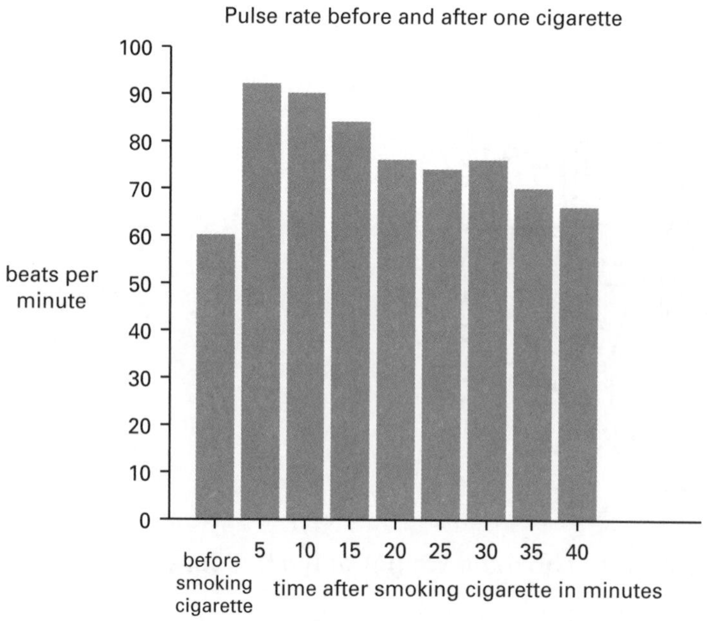

a) What was the pulse rate before smoking a cigarette?

______________ beats per minute *(1 mark)*

Q8a

b) By how beats per minute does the pulse rate increase in the first five minutes after smoking a cigarette?

Show how you worked out your answer.

_________________ beats per minute *(2 marks)*

Q8b

c) Explain why the pulse rate increases after smoking.

____

____

____ *(2 marks)*

Q8c

d) Describe **two other** effects that smoking has on the body.

____

____ *(2 marks)*

Q8d

(Total 7 marks)

subtotal

9 Becky is investigating electromagnets.

She winds insulated wire around an iron nail and connects the wire to a power pack.

She then counts how many paperclips the electromagnet will pick up.

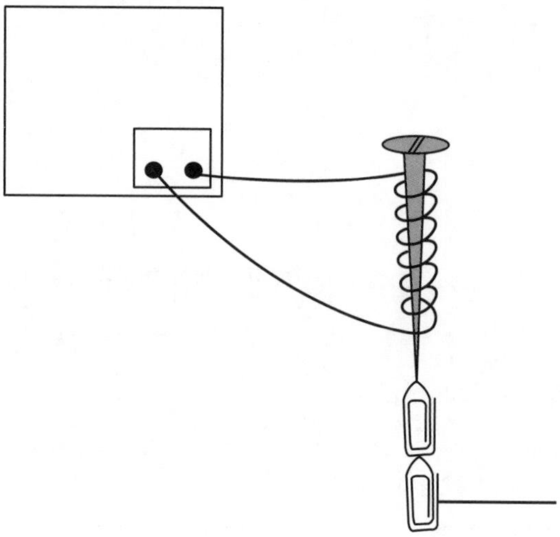

a) Becky wants to increase the strength of her electromagnet.

i **Suggest one factor she could change to increase the strength of her electromagnet.**

____

____ *(1 mark)*

Q9ai

ii Becky wants to make sure this is a fair test.

Write down two factors she should keep the same.

1 ____

2 ____ *(2 marks)*

Q9aii

iii **How will Becky know that the strength of her electromagnet has increased?**

____

____ *(1 mark)*

Q9aiii

b) Becky made this a fair test by controlling the other variables.

Explain why controlling the other variables makes it a fair test.

____

____

____ *(1 mark)*

Q9b

c) Becky's teacher tells her that she needs to make her results more **reliable**.

Describe what Becky must do to make her results more reliable.

____

____ *(1 mark)*

Q9c

d) **Write down one use for an electromagnet.**

____

____ *(1 mark)*

Q9d

(Total 7 marks)

10 Part of the reactivity series is shown below:

magnesium
zinc
iron
lead
copper
gold

a) **Why is gold found unreacted in the Earth but magnesium is not?**

____ *(1 mark)*

Q10a

subtotal

b) The word equation below is for a displacement reaction.

copper(II) sulphate + iron → iron(II) sulphate + copper

Why is the total mass unchanged during the reaction? Explain your answer.

____

____ *(1 mark)*

Q10b

c) **Which two of the following could be used to extract lead from lead(II) oxide?**

Put two ticks in the correct boxes.

carbon dioxide ☐

hydrogen ☐

gold ☐

oxygen ☐

zinc ☐

(2 marks)

Q10c

(Total 4 marks)

11 To help their customers choose the right plants, the Sunny Smile Garden Centre has added labels to them. The labels provide information about the best growing conditions for the plants.

The diagram shows the labels on two different plants.

Position: Partial shade
Humidity: Moist
Temperature: Keep warm

Position: Plenty of light
Humidity: Moist
Temperature: Keep warm

a) Plan an investigation to check if the labels were correct.

In your plan you must write about:
- the **one** factor you will change (the independent variable);
- **two** of the factors you will keep the same;
- the **one** factor you will observe (the dependent variable);

____

____

____

____

_______________ *(3 marks)* Q11a

b) The plant growing in the shade looks different from the plant growing in plenty of light.

i **Describe these differences.**

____

_______________ *(1 mark)* Q11bi

ii **Explain how these differences help these plants to survive.**

____

____

____

_______________ *(2 marks)* Q11bii

(Total 6 marks)

END OF TEST

subtotal

Set B

KEY STAGE 3
Levels 5–7

Test Paper 1

Science

Test Paper 1

Test Paper 1

Instructions:

- find a quiet place where you can sit down and complete the test paper undisturbed
- make sure you have all the necessary equipment to complete the test paper
- read the questions carefully
- answer all the questions in this paper
- write your answers where you see this symbol 
- show all your working as marks may be awarded for this
- go through and check your answers when you have finished the test paper
- check how you have done using pages 108–109 of the Answers and Mark Scheme

Time:

This test paper is **1 hour** long.

Page	41	43	45	47	49	51	53	55	Max. Mark	**Actual Mark**
Score	....	....	....	....	....	....	....	....	75	....

First name ....

Last name ....

1 The graph shows the solubilities of potassium nitrate and sodium chloride in water at different temperatures.

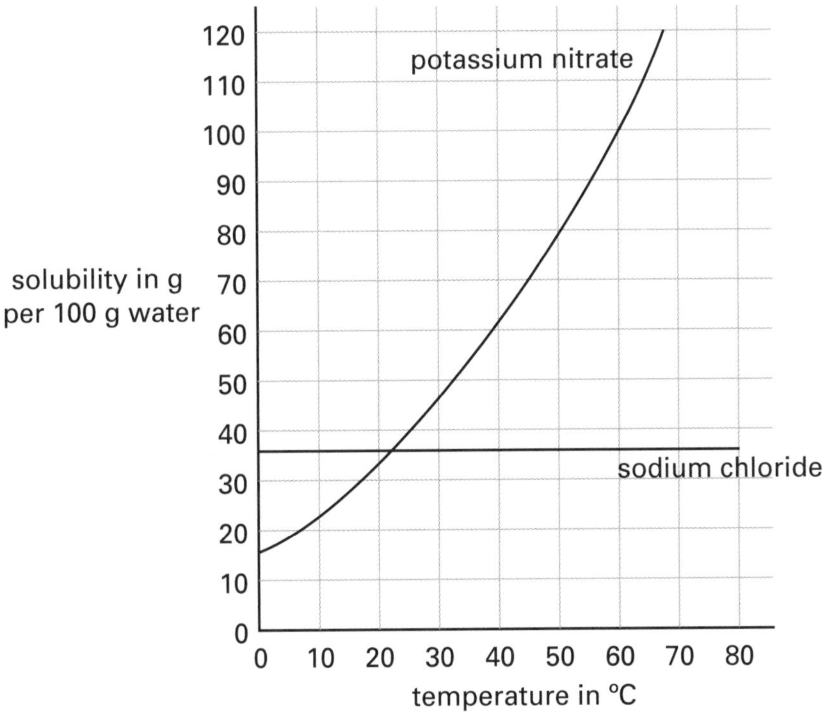

a) Use words from the list to complete the sentences.

insoluble **soluble** **solute** **solution** **solvent**

Sodium chloride dissolves in water and is said to be ____________________ in water.

A mixture of sodium chloride and water is a sodium chloride ____________________.

When sodium chloride is dissolved in water, sodium chloride is the

____________________ and water is the ____________________.

(4 marks) Q1a

b) **What is the maximum mass of potassium nitrate that would dissolve in 50 g of water at 40°C?**

____ *(1 mark)* Q1b

 subtotal

c) **How does the solubility of each substance change with temperature?**

potassium nitrate ______________________________

____

sodium chloride ______________________________

______________________________ *(2 marks)*

Q1c

d) Jim carries out an investigation to out find the solubility of sodium chloride at 30°C.

According to the graph the expected value is 37 g per 100 g of water. Jim's investigation gives a value of 45 g per 100 g of water. His friends suggest some reasons for the difference.

Polly says it is because he had the wrong temperature.

Rosie says it is because he spilt some of the solid before he weighed it.

Sadie says it is because he had not evaporated off all the water.

Tim says it is because he did not dissolve the maximum possible amount of sodium chloride.

i **Who is correct?**

______________________________ *(1 mark)*

Q1di

ii **Explain your answer.**

____

____

____

____

______________________________ *(3 marks)*

Q1dii

(Total 11 marks)

2 Jade looks across the fields and can see a man chopping down a tree.

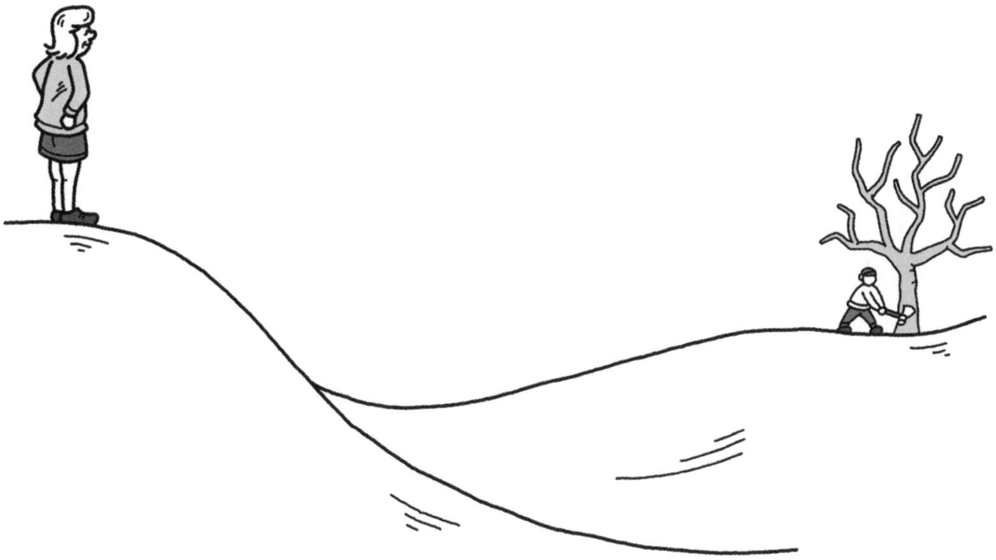

a) Jade can see the man chopping down the tree before she hears the sound of the axe. It is a clear day with no wind.

Suggest why.

____

____ *(1 mark)* ☐ Q2a

b) In the next swing, the man swings his axe higher to chop the tree.

What happens to the sound when the axe is moved from a higher distance?

Tick the correct box.

the sound cannot be heard ☐

the sound is louder ☐

the sound is quieter ☐

the sound is the same ☐

(1 mark) ☐ Q2b

subtotal

c) The diagram shows part of the human ear.

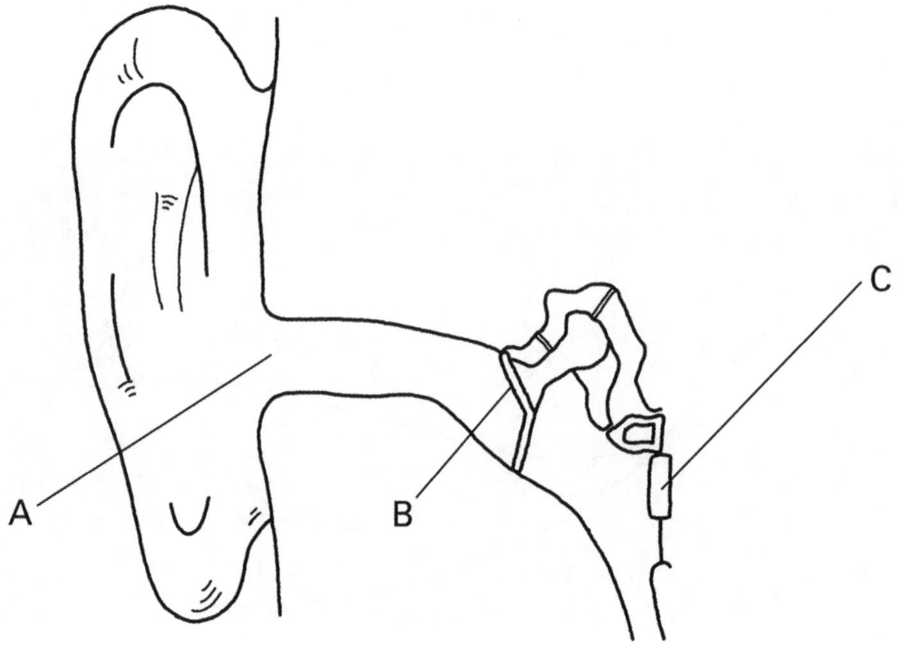

i **Which of the labels A, B or C shows the eardrum?**

Tick the correct box.

A ☐

B ☐

C ☐

(1 mark) ☐ Q2ci

ii **Describe what happens to our eardrums when sound reaches them.**

______________________________ *(1 mark)* ☐ Q2cii

d) Jade reads a leaflet that explains how some sounds can damage hearing.

Describe one type of sound that can affect hearing. State how it affects hearing.

type of sound ______________________________

affect on hearing ______________________________ *(2 marks)* ☐ Q2d

(Total 6 marks)

3 Tim carried out some experiments with four metals.

He wanted to put the metals in order of reactivity.

The results are shown in the table.

Metal salt solution	Add iron	Add zinc	Add magnesium	Add copper
iron(II) sulphate solution	no reaction	reaction	reaction	no reaction
zinc sulphate solution	no reaction	no reaction	reaction	no reaction
magnesium sulphate solution	no reaction	no reaction	no reaction	no reaction
copper(II) sulphate solution	reaction	reaction	reaction	no reaction

a) **Arrange the four metals in order of decreasing reactivity. Use the information in the table.**

_______________ _______________ _______________ _______________ *(3 marks)*

Q3a

b) i No reaction takes place when red-brown copper solid is added to colourless zinc sulphate solution.

Describe what you would see when zinc is added to copper(II) sulphate solution.

____

____ *(2 marks)*

Q3bi

subtotal

ii Write a word equation for this reaction.

[ ] + [ ] → [ ] + [ ]

(2 marks) Q3bii

iii What type of reaction is taking place?

Circle the correct answer.

combustion **displacement** **neutralisation** *(1 mark)* Q3biii

(Total 8 marks)

4 The diagram shows the female reproductive system.

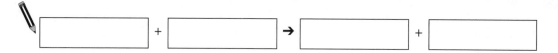

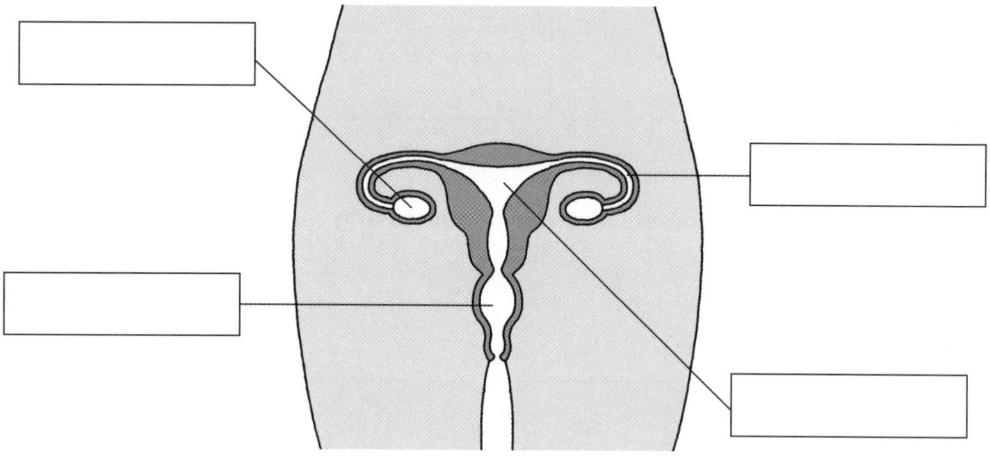

a) Label the diagram.

Choose words from the list.

ovary **oviduct** **uterus** **vagina** *(4 marks)* Q4a

b) On the diagram:

i Write an **X** to show where sperm are deposited. *(1 mark)* Q4bi

ii **Circle** the part where ovulation takes place. *(1 mark)* Q4bii

iii Write an **F** to show where fertilisation takes place. *(1 mark)* Q4biii

c) Sperm cells are adapted so they can move through the woman's reproductive system.

Describe two of these adaptations.

____

____ *(2 marks)* Q4c

(Total 9 marks)

5 Indigestion can be caused by too much hydrochloric acid in the stomach.

a) **What is the job of the hydrochloric acid in the stomach?**

____ *(1 mark)* Q5a

b) Indigestion can be controlled by chewing and swallowing an antacid tablet.

The antacid contains a carbonate.

Explain why the carbonate helps control the indigestion.

____

____

____ *(3 marks)* Q5b

c) Jo has three different makes of antacid tablets.

She has some hydrochloric acid.

Explain how she could find out which make of tablets contains the most carbonate.

____

____

subtotal

(4 marks) Q5c

(Total 8 marks)

6 Look at the different energy sources.

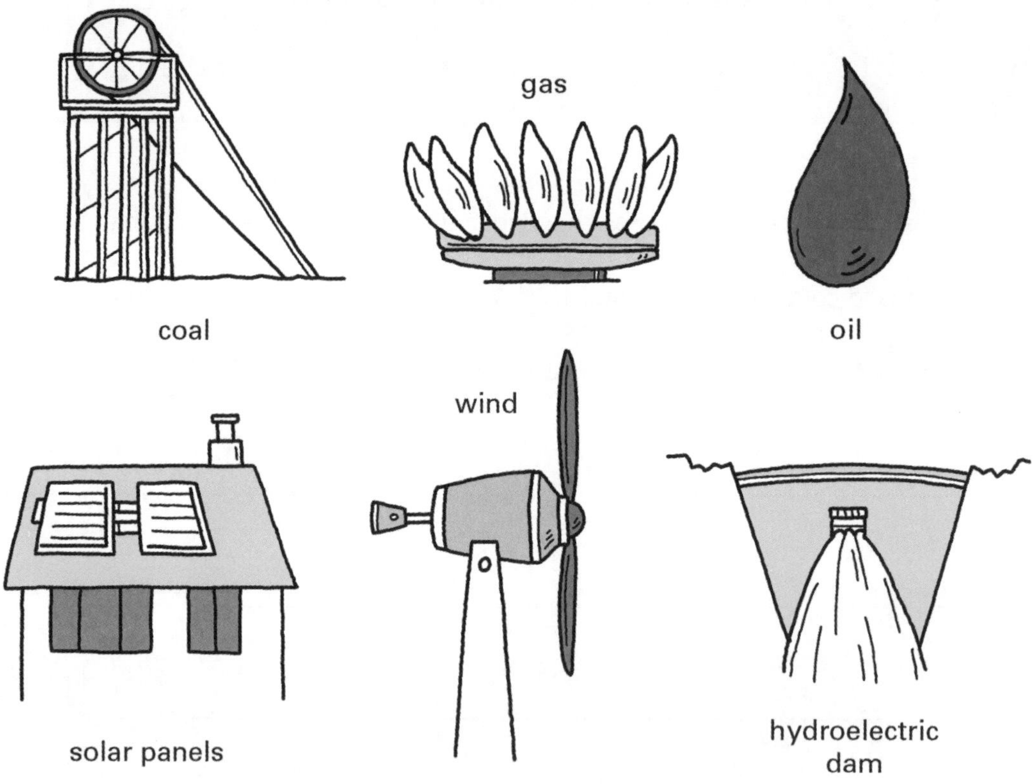

a) In many parts of the world fossil fuels are used to generate electricity. Give the names of three fossil fuels.

(2 marks) Q6a

b) Describe how fossil fuels were formed.

____

____

____

____ *(3 marks)*

Q6b

c) More than half of the total fuels used in the world are biomass fuels.

i What is a 'biomass' fuel?

____

____ *(1 mark)*

Q6ci

ii Biomass and fossil fuels are both energy resources. What is the original source of this energy?

____ *(1 mark)*

Q6cii

iii How is this energy transferred from the source to the Earth?

____ *(1 mark)*

Q6ciii

d) Fossil fuels are often described as non-renewable energy resources. Why are they called 'non-renewable'?

____

____ *(1 mark)*

Q6d

subtotal

e) There are advantages and disadvantages of burning different fuels.

i **Give one advantage of using biomass rather than fossil fuels as an energy resource.**

_______________________________________ *(1 mark)* Q6ei

ii **Give one advantage of using fossil fuels rather than biomass as an energy resource.**

_______________________________________ *(1 mark)* Q6eii

iii **Give one disadvantage of using both fossil fuels and biomass.**

_______________________________________ *(1 mark)* Q6eiii

(Total 12 marks)

7 Michael plays football.

He has injured the ligaments in his knee.

The diagram below shows the structure of a joint.

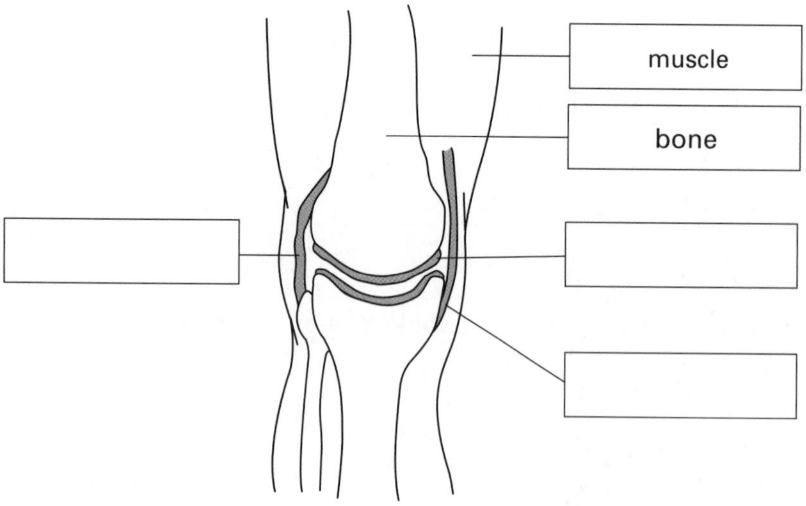

a) **Finish labelling the diagram. Choose words from the list:** *(3 marks)* Q7a

cartilage **ligament** **tendon** **synovial fluid**

b) Michael has damaged the ligaments in his knee joint.

i **Suggest one way this damage will affect his knee joint.**

____

____ *(1 mark)*

Q7bi

The doctor thinks there may also be damage to the cartilage.

ii **Why is cartilage needed in joints?**

____

____ *(1 mark)*

Q7bii

c) The diagram shows the muscles in Michael's leg.

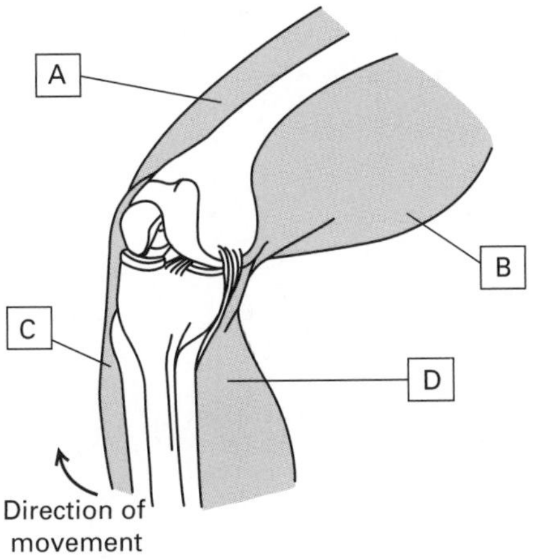

The doctor asks Michael to lift the lower part of his leg.

i **How do the muscles move the leg in the direction shown by the arrow?**

Write the letter in the box that describes how the muscles work to lift the lower part of the leg.

Choose from **A, B, C** or **D**.

This muscle contracts. ☐

This muscle relaxes. ☐ *(2 marks)*

Q7ci

subtotal

ii Explain why muscles need to work in pairs.

____

____ *(1 mark)*

Q7cii

(Total 8 marks)

8 Mollie and Ben sit on a seesaw and move about until it is balanced.

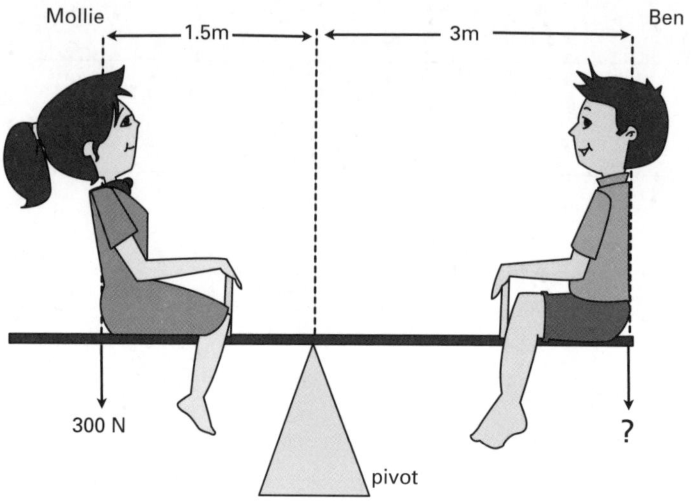

a) i Mollie weighs 300 N.

Calculate the turning moment produced by Mollie about the pivot.

_______________ Nm *(2 marks)*

Q8ai

ii The seesaw is balanced.

Write down the turning moment produced by Ben about the pivot.

_______________ Nm *(1 mark)*

Q8aii

b) **Calculate Ben's weight. Give the unit in your answer.**

Ben's weight is _______________ *(2 marks)*

Q8b

c) What is the size of the total force acting upon the pivot?

_______________ N

(1 mark) Q8c

(Total 6 marks)

9 Asif was asked to find out whether an acid or an alkali was a stronger solution.

He put 5cm^3 of alkali in a test tube.

He added acid 1cm^3 at a time.

Each time he added more acid, he measured the pH of the solution.

His results are in the table.

Volume of acid added (cm^3)	pH
Start (no acid)	10.5
1	10.5
2	10.0
3	9.5
4	7.5
5	5.0
6	4.0
7	3.5
8	3.5
9	3.0
10	3.0

a) **Suggest a way in which Asif could have measured the pH of the solution during the experiment.**

____

____ *(1 mark)* Q9a

subtotal

b) To make this a fair experiment, Asif needed to control the other variables in the experiment.

Suggest two variables that he would need to control.

____

____ *(1 mark)*

Q9b

c) Plot the results Asif obtained on the graph below.

Draw a suitable line of best fit. *(2 marks)*

Q9c

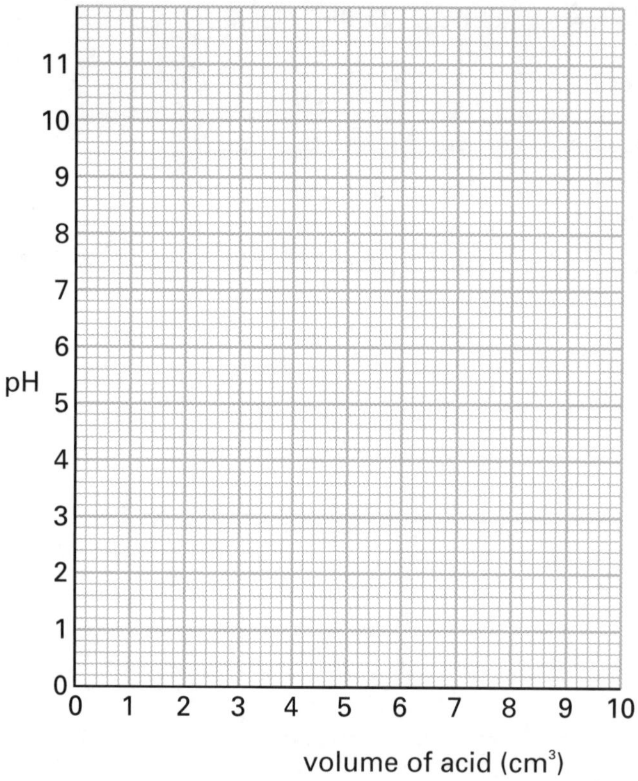

d) How much acid did Asif need to make the solution neutral?

Circle the best answer.

Exactly 4cm³ **Between 4 and 5cm³** **Exactly 5cm³** **More than 5cm³**

(1 mark)

Q9d

e) Which was stronger, the acid or the alkali?

Explain your answer.

____

____ *(2 marks)*

Q9e

(Total 7 marks)

END OF TEST

subtotal

Set
B

KEY STAGE 3
Levels 5–7

Test Paper 2

Science

Test Paper 2

Test Paper 2

Instructions:

- find a quiet place where you can sit down and complete the test paper undisturbed
- make sure you have all the necessary equipment to complete the test paper
- read the questions carefully
- answer all the questions in this paper
- write your answers where you see this symbol
- show all your working as marks may be awarded for this
- go through and check your answers when you have finished the test paper
- check how you have done using pages 110–111 of the Answers and Mark Scheme

Time:

This test paper is **1 hour** long.

Page	57	59	61	63	65	67	69	71	Max. Mark	**Actual Mark**
Score	....	....	....	....	....	....	....	....	75	....

First name ....

Last name ....

1 Class 7B are investigating inherited variation.

Lisa and Jane record the eye colour of everyone in the class.

Here are their results.

Eye colour	brown	blue	grey	green	mixed
Number of pupils	7	14	0	3	4

a) **Draw a bar chart to show the different eye colours in class 7B.** *(2 marks)* Q1a

One has been done for you.

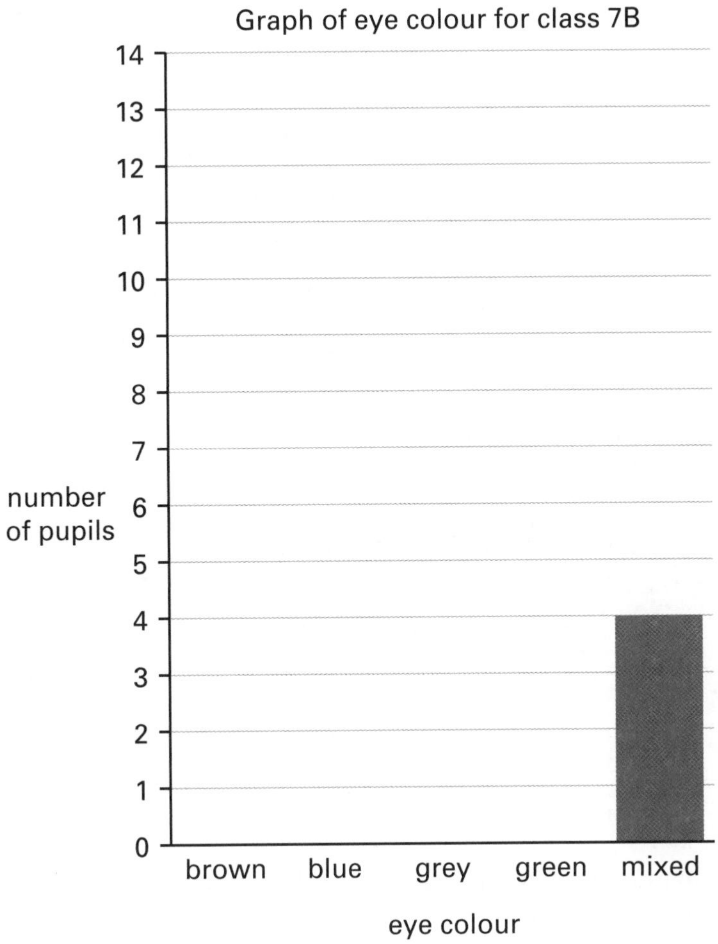

b) **What is the most common eye colour?**

_______________________________ *(1 mark)* Q1b

subtotal

c) Lisa and Jane have different ideas about their results.

Their teacher says not all of their ideas are correct.

Circle the correct letter for each idea.

Comment	Idea		
This idea is correct.	A	B	C
This idea is incorrect.	A	B	C
There are not enough results for this idea.	A	B	C

(2 marks) Q1c

d) i **What is meant by the term 'inherited'?**

____

____ *(2 marks)* Q1di

Their teacher tells them to investigate one other variation that is inherited.

ii **Suggest one other variation they could investigate.**

____ *(1 mark)* Q1dii

(Total 8 marks)

2 The headstones in a cemetery are made from different rocks.

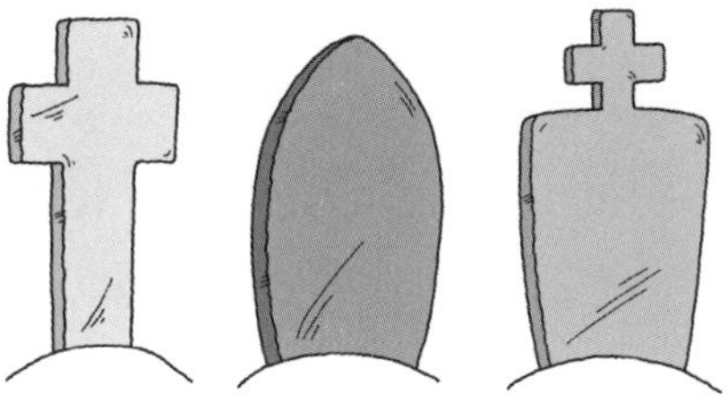

At one time, local rocks would be used. Today there is a wider choice including marble, granite and limestone.

a) **Why were local rocks usually used?**

____ *(1 mark)* Q2a

b) **Why was stone chosen rather than wood or metals?**

____ *(1 mark)* Q2b

c) **Complete the table by using words from the list.**

igneous **metamorphic** **sedimentary**

You may use the words once, more than once or not at all.

Rock	**Type of rock**
granite	
limestone	
marble	

(3 marks) Q2c

d) Sometimes, traces of ancient plants and animals can be found in certain types of rocks. These can be used to help date certain rocks.

i **What are these traces of ancient plants and animals called?**

____ *(1 mark)* Q2di

subtotal

ii In which rock in the table would these traces **not** be found?

____ *(1 mark)*

Q2dii

e) The detail on a headstone wears down over a period of time. This occurs even when there is no atmospheric pollution.

i **Why is this?**

____ *(1 mark)*

Q2ei

ii **Explain why the carbon dioxide which is found in the atmosphere can have long-term effects on limestone.**

____

____

____ *(2 marks)*

Q2eii

f) A headstone made of limestone has some cracks in it.

Explain fully how this headstone breaks down more quickly.

Diagrams may help your answer.

____

____

____ *(3 marks)*

Q2f

(Total 13 marks)

3 The diagram shows three circuits.

In each circuit there is a lamp and a motor.

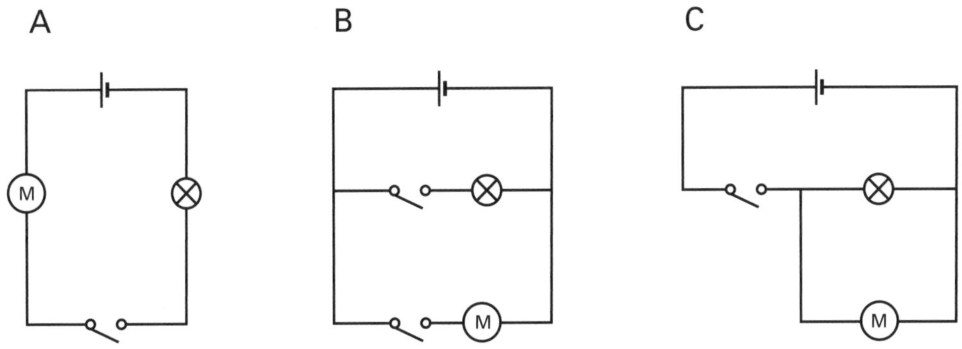

a) In which circuit are the lamp and motor in series?

____ *(1 mark)* Q3a

b) In which circuit can the lamp be switched on without switching on the motor?

____ *(1 mark)* Q3b

c) Use the same components to draw a circuit where the lamp is on all of the time but the motor can be switched on and off.

(1 mark) Q3c

d) In Circuit A, the current passing through the motor is 0.5 A.

i What instrument is used to measure the current?

____ *(1 mark)* Q3di

subtotal

ii **On the diagram** mark with an **X** where this instrument should be connected.

(1 mark) Q3dii

iii What current would be passing through the lamp?

_______________ *(1 mark)* Q3diii

e) In Circuit C, the current passing through the lamp and the motor is the same.

What information does this give?

_______________ *(1 mark)* Q3e

(Total 7 marks)

4 Alex is calculating the volume of different objects.

a) Alex has a block 4 cm long, 3 cm wide and 2 cm high.

What is the volume of the block?

Use the correct unit in your answer.

_______________ *(2 marks)* Q4a

b) Alex needs to use a measuring cylinder to calculate the volume of the pebble.

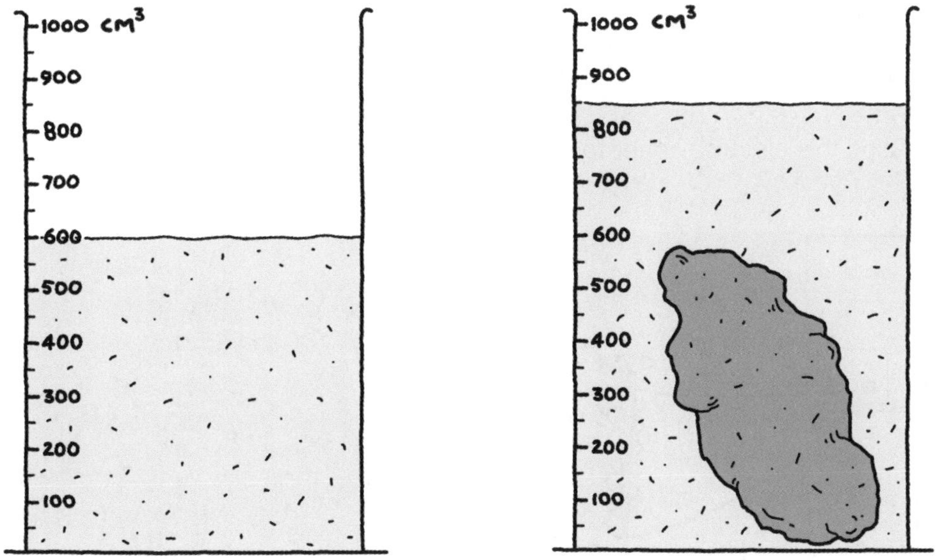

i What is the volume of the pebble?

_____________ *(1 mark)*

Q4bi

ii Explain how you found the volume of the pebble.

____

____

____ *(2 marks)*

Q4bii

(Total 5 marks)

subtotal

5 Annette is making an electromagnet.

She uses an iron nail as the core and wraps insulated copper wire around it. She then connects a power supply to the two ends of the wire.

She then uses this electromagnet to pick up some steel paper-clips.

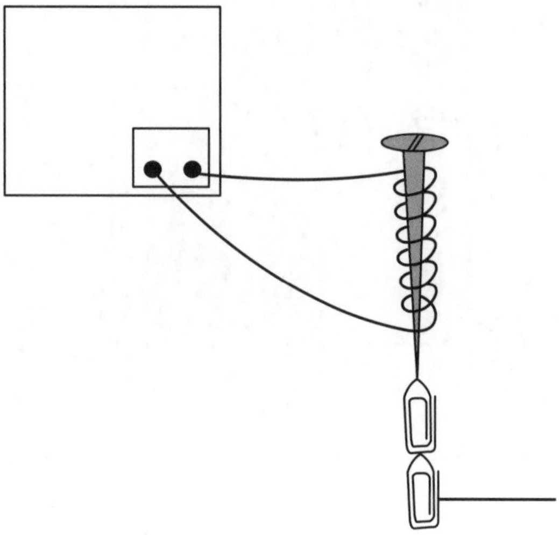

Annette makes a prediction about the strength of her electromagnet. She predicts that:

Reducing the number of turns of wire around the iron nail will reduce the strength of the electromagnet.

a) i **What variable should she change to investigate her prediction?**

____ *(1 mark)* Q5ai

ii **Give one variable that she should keep the same.**

____ *(1 mark)* Q5aii

iii **How could she use the paper-clips to measure the strength of her electromagnet?**

____ *(1 mark)* Q5aiii

b) i Which size of paper-clips should Annette use to get the most accurate results?

Tick the correct box.

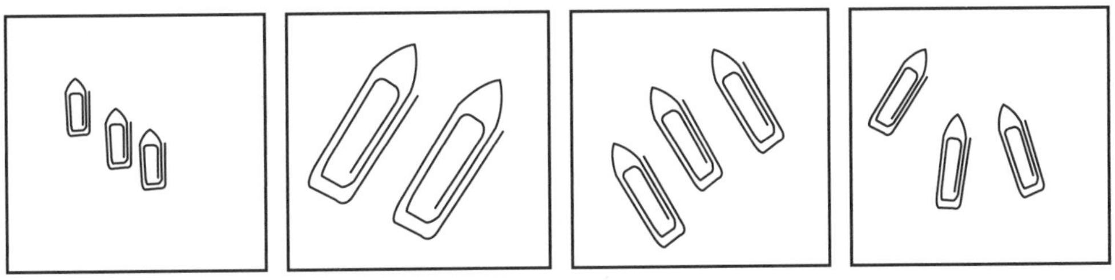

☐ ☐ ☐ ☐ *(1 mark)*

Q5bi

b) ii Why would this size provide the most accurate results?

____ *(1 mark)*

Q5bii

(Total 5 marks)

6 Jack sits on a mat at the top of a helter-skelter and then slides down a chute around the outside.

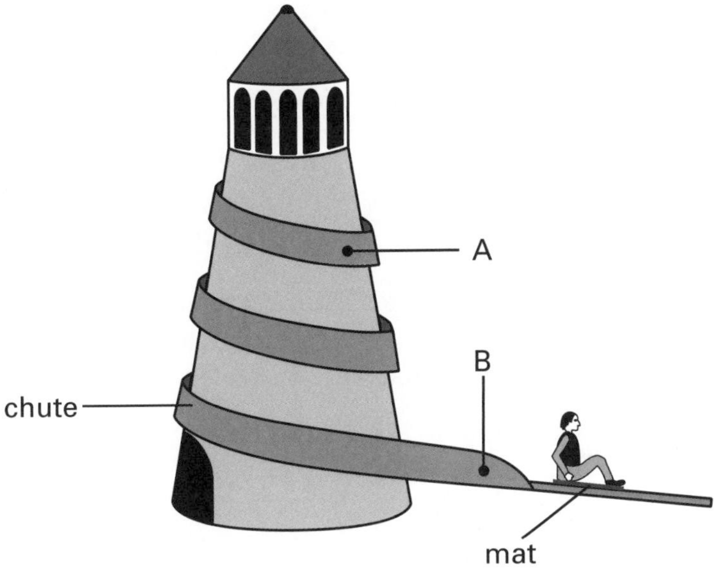

a) i Name **two** of the forces acting on Jack as he moves between point A and point B.

____

____ *(2 marks)*

Q6ai

subtotal

ii As Jack slides from point A to point B, the forces acting on him are balanced.

Describe what happens to Jack's speed when the forces acting on him are balanced.

____

____ *(1 mark)*

Q6aii

b) Jack goes back for a second go. This time he sits on a smooth cushion instead of a mat. He goes much faster.

Explain why he goes much faster on the cushion than on the mat.

____ *(1 mark)*

Q6b

c) On his next go Jack lies back on the cushion with his arms by his sides.

What happens to his speed? Explain why.

____

____ *(2 marks)*

Q6c

(Total 6 marks)

7 Emily's friends are concerned that she smokes cigarettes. They carry out an experiment to show Emily the effect that smoking has on her body. They find Emily's average pulse rate, then Emily smokes a cigarette. They record Emily's pulse rate after smoking the cigarette.

The graph shows the effect that smoking one cigarette has on Emily's pulse rate.

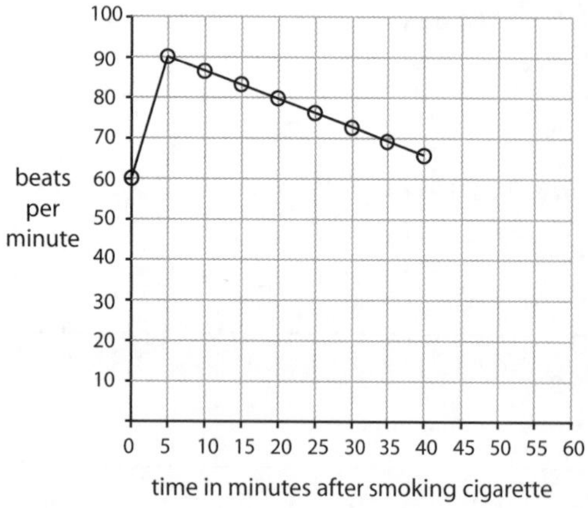

a) What was Emily's average pulse rate before smoking a cigarette?

_______________ beats per minute (1 mark) Q7a

b) Use the graph to estimate how many minutes it will take for Emily's pulse rate to return to normal.

_______________ minutes (1 mark) Q7b

c) Explain why this effect on pulse rate is dangerous for Emily's health.

____

____

____ *(2 marks)* Q7c

d) It is the nicotine in cigarettes that affects pulse rate.

i Write down **one other** effect of nicotine.

____

____ *(1 mark)* Q7di

ii Write down the name of **one other** chemical produced when cigarettes are smoked and explain why it is dangerous to health.

Name of chemical _______________________

Why it is dangerous to health _______________________

____

____ *(2 marks)* Q7dii

subtotal

e) At the start of the experiment, Emily's friends find her average pulse rate.

i **Describe how you would find the average pulse rate for a person.**

____

____

____

____

____

____ *(3 marks)*

Q7ei

ii **Explain why it is better to find an average reading.**

____

____ *(1 mark)*

Q7eii

(Total 11 marks)

8 Many farmers spray chemicals on their fields. These chemicals are useful because they help crops to grow, but they can poison animals.

Sometimes these chemicals can enter a food chain. The diagram shows how these chemicals can be passed through an aquatic food chain.

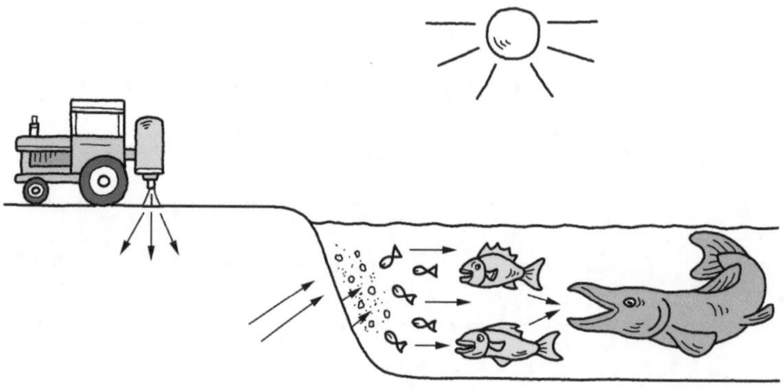

a) What name is given to the chemicals that farmers use to help their crops grow?

____ *(1 mark)* Q8a

b) Explain how the chemicals can get into the river.

____

____ *(2 marks)* Q8b

c) After a few years, the number of large fish in the river has gone down.

i Explain why the toxic chemicals did not kill the smaller fish.

____

____ *(2 marks)* Q8ci

ii Suggest why the larger fish died from the toxic chemicals.

____

____ *(1 mark)* Q8cii

iii Explain why the larger fish do not start to die until a few years after the toxic chemicals have been used.

____

____ *(2 marks)* Q8ciii

(Total 8 marks)

subtotal

9 The table shows information about some planets in our Solar System and the length of their year.

Planet	Length of planet's year
Mercury	88 Earth days
Earth	365.25 Earth days
Jupiter	12 Earth years
Saturn	30 Earth years

a) Explain why the length of a year is different on each planet.

____

____ *(2 marks)* Q9a

b) Which of the planets in the table will have the **coldest** climate?

Explain why.

Planet: ____________________

Explanation: ____

____ *(2 marks)* Q9b

c) Not all of the planets are listed in the table.

i Write down the name of the planet that is positioned between Mercury and Earth.

____ *(1 mark)* Q9ci

ii The length of year for Neptune is 165 Earth years.

After which planet on the table would you list Neptune?

____ *(1 mark)* Q9cii

d) The length of a day is different on each of the planets. Explain why.

____

____ *(1 mark)* Q9d

(Total 7 marks)

10 There are a number of different organ systems in the human body. Some of these organ systems are shown on the diagrams.

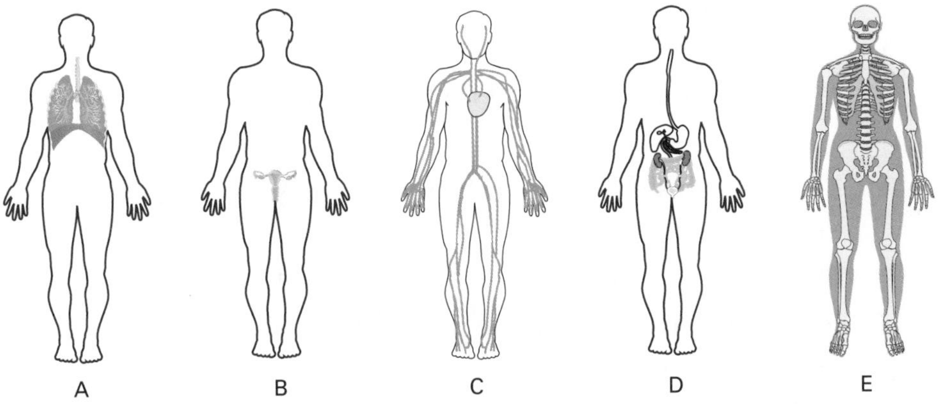

The names of the five organ systems are given in the table. Next to each name, write the letter of the diagram which shows the organ system.

Name of organ system	Letter of diagram showing organ system
Circulatory system	
Digestive system	
Reproductive system	
Respiratory system	
Skeleton	

(5 marks) Q10

(Total 5 marks)

END OF TEST

subtotal

Set C

KEY STAGE 3
Levels 5–7

Test Paper 1

Science

Test Paper 1

Test Paper 1

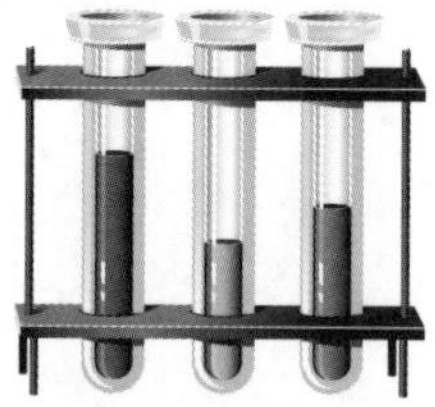

Instructions:

- find a quiet place where you can sit down and complete the test paper undisturbed
- make sure you have all the necessary equipment to complete the test paper
- read the questions carefully
- answer all the questions in this paper
- write your answers where you see this symbol
- show all your working as marks may be awarded for this
- go through and check your answers when you have finished the test paper
- check how you have done using pages 112–113 of the Answers and Mark Scheme

Time:

This test paper is **1 hour** long.

Page	73	75	77	79	81	83	85	87	Max. Mark	**Actual Mark**
Score	....	....	....	....	....	....	....	....	75	....

First name ....

Last name ....

1 The diagram shows a cross-section through a flower.

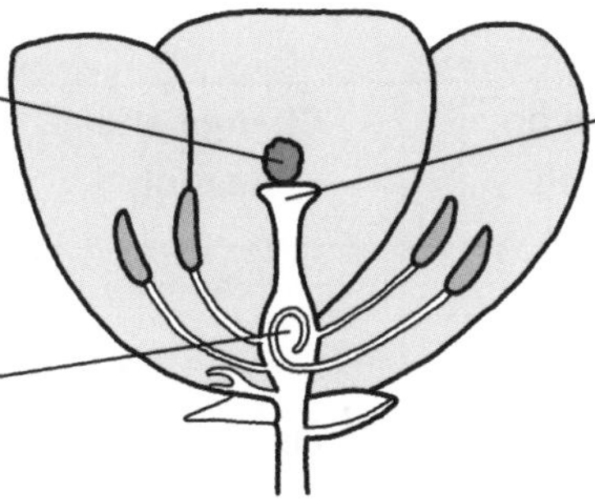

a) The plant is reproducing.
A pollen grain has landed on the stigma of the flower.
The pollen and the egg cell need to join together.

Below are five stages that lead to this process. They are in the wrong order.

A The nucleus of the pollen cell travels down the pollen tube and into the ovary.

B The pollen cell grows a pollen tube.

C The pollen cell nucleus and the egg cell nucleus join together.

D This forms the first cell of a new plant.

E The pollen tube grows down through the stigma and into the ovary.

Fill in the boxes to show the right order.
The first one has been done for you.

B				

(3 marks) Q1a

b) **What is the name given to the process at stage C?**

Circle the correct answer.

fertilisation **germination** **pollination**

(1 mark) Q1b

c) The first cell that is formed at stage D continues to divide.

What do the dividing cells form into before a new plant can be produced?

______________________________ *(1 mark)* Q1c

(Total 5 marks)

subtotal

2 Three solids, X, Y and Z, were heated.

Each solid was weighed before heating and after cooling to room temperature.

Solid	Appearance	Change on heating	Change after heating	Mass change
X	white solid	turns yellow	white solid	none
Y	purple crystals	black crystals	black crystals	decrease in mass
Z	red-brown solid	turns red	red-brown solid with a black coating	slight increase in mass

a) For each solid, decide if there is a physical change or a chemical change when it is heated. Put a ring around the correct answer each time.

Solid X: Physical / Chemical

Solid Y: Physical / Chemical

Solid Z: Physical / Chemical *(2 marks)* Q2a

b) In one case oxygen is produced.

i Which of the three solids produces oxygen gas when it is heated?

______________________________ *(1 mark)* Q2bi

ii Describe how you would test to see if oxygen gas was produced in this case.

____

______________________________ *(2 marks)* Q2bii

c) Suggest why there is only a small increase in mass when Z is heated.

______________________________ *(1 mark)* Q2c

(Total 6 marks)

3 Kelly and Becky are investigating friction.

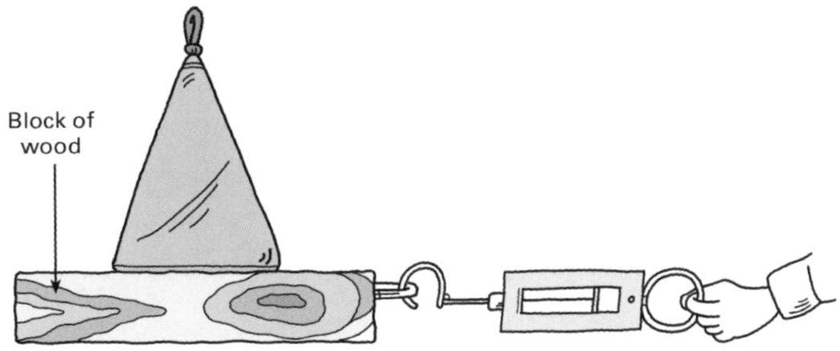

Kelly predicts that the weight on top of the block of wood will affect the friction.

To investigate this prediction, the girls measure the force needed to pull the wood when different weights are placed on top of the block of wood.

a) **State two factors they should keep the same to make their investigation fair.**

1 ______________________________

2 ______________________________

(2 marks) Q3a

The table shows their results.

weight (N)	0	5	10	15	20	25
friction force (N)	15	21	26	30	37	42

b) i **Use the data in the table to plot the points on the grid.** *(2 marks)* Q3bi

The first two points have been done for you.

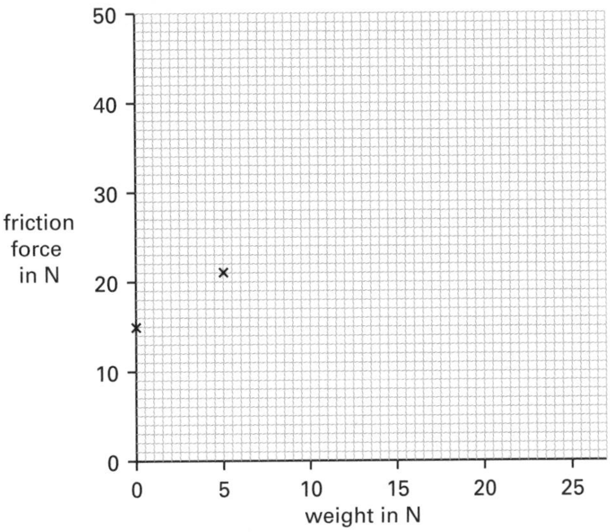

ii **Draw the best line through the points.** *(1 mark)* Q3bii

subtotal

c) **Describe the relationship between the weight on the block and the friction.**

___

___

___ *(1 mark)*

Q3c

d) Friction and weight are both types of force; they both use the symbol N.

What does the symbol N stand for?

Tick the correct box.

Neutral ☐ Nigel ☐

Newton ☐ Nought ☐ *(1 mark)*

Q3d

(Total 7 marks)

4 Kate is trying to find out which disinfectant is the best to destroy microbes. She does the following:

- She leaves the agar plates open for 10 minutes to allow microbes to settle on the agar.
- She adds a different disinfectant to each agar plate.
- The plates are sealed, then left in a warm place for a few days.

a) i **Give one reason why we need to kill microbes.**

___

___ *(1 mark)*

Q4ai

ii **Sometimes it may be a disadvantage to kill microbes. Give one reason why.**

___

___ *(1 mark)*

Q4aii

b) Describe **two** factors Kate must control to make this a fair test.

1 ____

____

2 ____

____ *(2 marks)*

Q4b

Here are Kate's results.

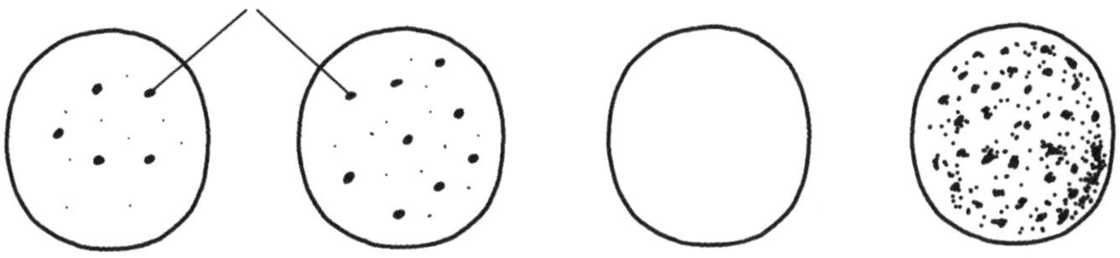

c) Why did Kate leave one agar plate without disinfectant?

____

____ *(1 mark)*

Q4c

d) Which disinfectant is the best to destroy microbes?

i disinfectant ____________________ *(1 mark)*

Q4di

ii Give a reason for your choice.

____

____ *(1 mark)*

Q4dii

subtotal

e) Kate's results are different from the class results.

Suggest how Kate could improve her experiment.

____

____ *(1 mark)* Q4e

f) In 1928, a famous scientist carried out a similar experiment and discovered antibiotics.

Circle the correct name of the scientist who discovered antibiotics.

Darwin **Fleming** **Pasteur** *(1 mark)* Q4f

(Total 9 marks)

5 All electrical devices work because they convert electrical energy into other forms of energy.

a) **For each of the devices below, state what forms of energy we want it to produce.**

i Electric lamp ______________________________

ii Loudspeaker ______________________________

iii Electric motor ______________________________ *(2 marks)* Q5a

b) An electric lamp produces 5J of light energy for every 100J of electrical energy which is supplied to it.

i **What does the letter J stand for?**

____ *(1 mark)* Q5bi

ii **How much heat energy does the lamp produce at the same time?**

____ *(1 mark)* Q5bii iii What is the efficiency of the lamp? Underline the correct value.

0.05%   5%   50%   95%   100%   *(1 mark)*

Q5biii

(Total 5 marks)

6 Limestone and marble are two different types of rock. They both contain calcium carbonate. Calcium carbonate has the chemical formula $CaCO_3$.

a) Write down the names of the three elements found in calcium carbonate.

____

____ *(2 marks)*

Q6a

Limestone is an example of a sedimentary rock and marble is a metamorphic rock.

b) Describe how sedimentary rocks are formed from existing rocks.

____

____

____

____ *(3 marks)*

Q6b

c) Marble is an example of a metamorphic rock.

Describe how limestone is turned into marble.

____

____ *(2 marks)*

Q6c

(Total 7 marks)

subtotal

7 The diagram below shows an outline of part of the Periodic Table of Elements.

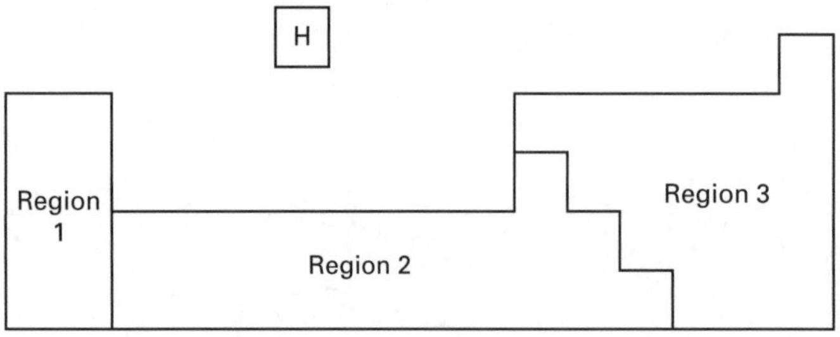

a) **Which element has the symbol H?** ________________ *(1 mark)* Q7a

b) **Different elements are found in different parts of the Periodic Table. In which of the regions in the diagram of the Periodic Table are the following types of element found?**

i Non-metals ________________ *(1 mark)* Q7bi

ii Very reactive metals ________________ *(1 mark)* Q7bii

iii Less reactive metals ________________ *(1 mark)* Q7biii

c) **Suggest why aluminium sulphate is not found in the Periodic Table.**

____

________________ *(1 mark)* Q7c

d) An iron nail is placed into some blue copper(II) sulphate solution. A reaction takes place between the iron and the copper(II) sulphate and the nail changes colour.

i **Suggest why the nail changes colour.**

________________ *(1 mark)* Q7di

ii **Complete the word equation for the reaction.**

iron + copper(II) sulphate → [ ] + [ ] *(1 mark)* Q7dii

(Total 7 marks)

8 Butane is a chemical compound which is often used as a fuel. Butane belongs to a group of compounds called hydrocarbons. The formula for butane is C_4H_{10}.

a) **Write down the names of the two elements in butane.**

_______________ and _______________ *(1 mark)* Q8a

b) Butane is used as a fuel in a patio heater. Butane burns using oxygen in the air to form carbon dioxide and water.

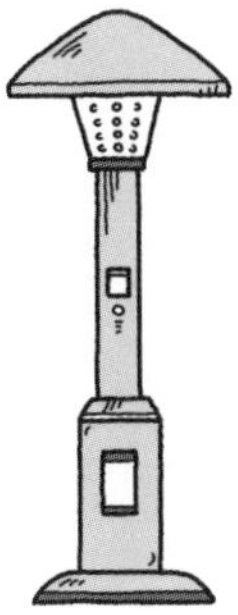

i **Write a word equation for the combustion of butane.**

[ ] + [ ] → [ ] + [ ]

(2 marks) Q8bi

ii **What environmental problem is caused by burning butane?**

_______________ *(1 mark)* Q8bii

c) The melting point and boiling point of butane are shown on the scale below.

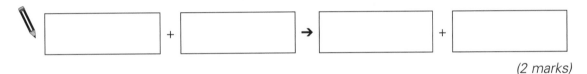

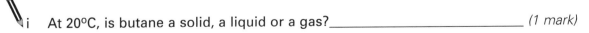

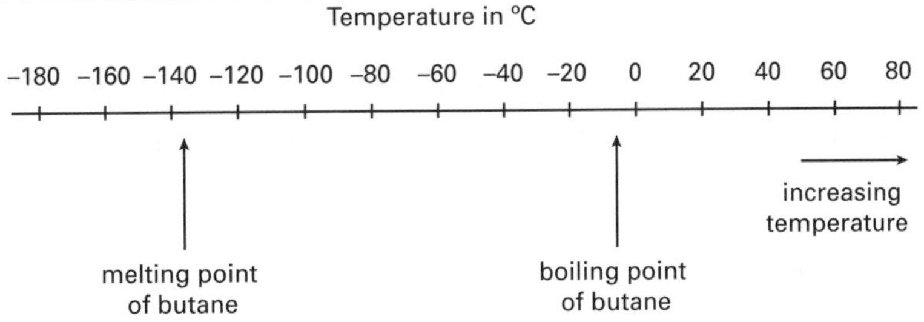

i **At 20°C, is butane a solid, a liquid or a gas?** _______________ *(1 mark)* Q8ci

ii **At –10°C, is butane a solid, a liquid or a gas?** _______________ *(1 mark)* Q8cii

subtotal

d) Butane is usually stored as a liquid rather than a gas. Give one advantage of storing butane as a liquid rather than a gas.

____

____ *(1 mark)* Q8d

(Total 7 marks)

9 The diagram shows the human breathing system.

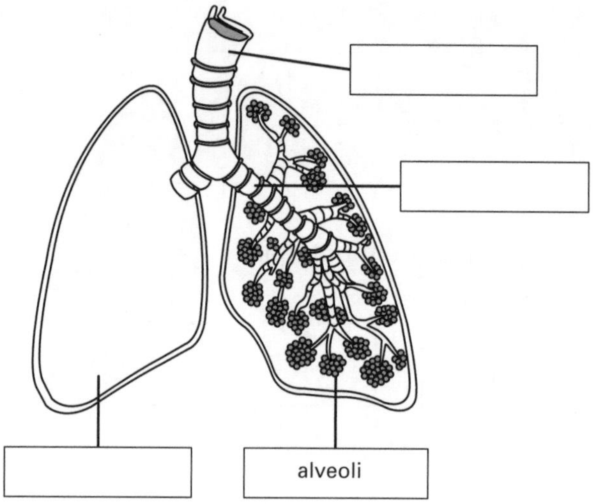

a) **Finish labelling the diagram.** *(2 marks)* Q9a

Choose words from this list.

bronchioles **bronchus** **lung** **rib cage** **trachea**

b) Oxygen passes from the lungs into the blood.

Describe **one feature** of the alveoli that allows the efficient movement of gases to take place.

____

____ *(1 mark)* Q9b

c) Why does the oxygen need to pass into the blood?

____

____ *(1 mark)*

Q9c

d) Breathing and respiration are two different processes.

Describe some of the differences between them.

____

____ *(2 marks)*

Q9d

(Total 6 marks)

10 Joss is investigating electric circuits.

Joss uses identical batteries and bulbs to set up two different circuits, as shown in the diagrams below.

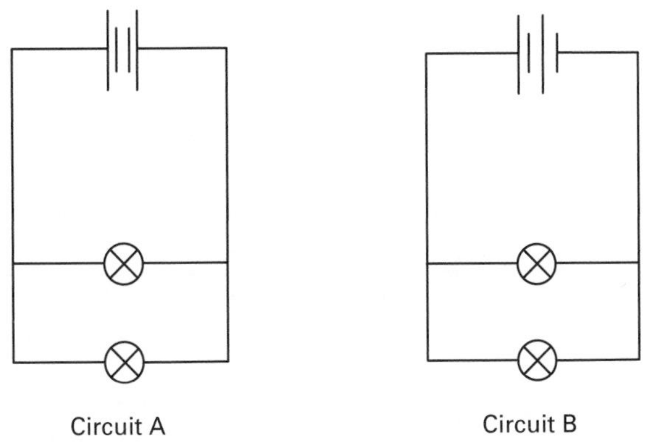

a) The lamps in circuit A will not light.

Give a reason.

____

____ *(1 mark)*

Q10a

subtotal

b) When Joss sets up circuit B, both of the lamps light up. Joss unscrews one of the lamps.

Describe what happens to the other lamp.

____

____ *(1 mark)*

Q10b

c) **What is the name given to this type of electric circuit?**

____ *(1 mark)*

Q10c

d) Joss adds two ammeters to the circuit.

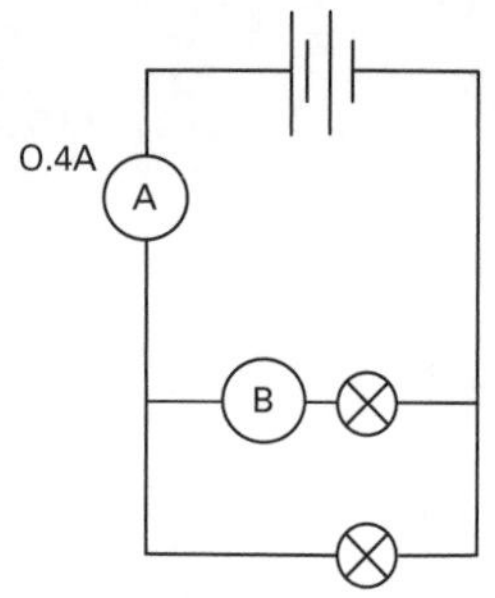

i **What is the reading for Meter B?**

________________ amps *(1 mark)*

Q10di

ii **Why is this?**

____

____ *(1 mark)*

Q10dii

e) The ammeter gives a reading in amps.

Describe what it is that the ammeter measures.

____

____ *(1 mark)*

Q10e

(Total 6 marks)

11 Tom is investigating sound.

He makes an instrument by stretching different-sized rubber bands around a wooden box.

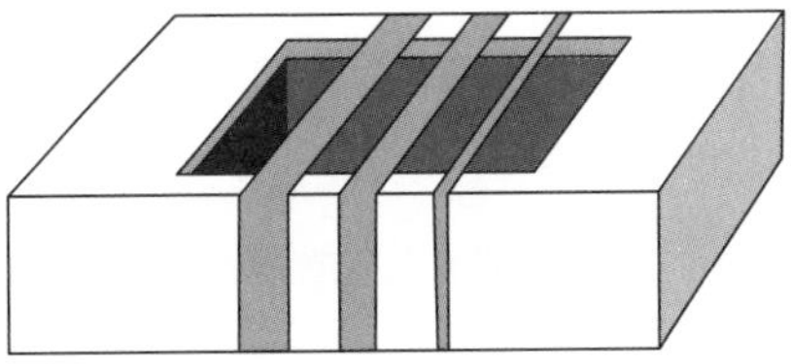

a) Tom plays the instrument by plucking the rubber bands. It makes a loud sound.

Describe what Tom must do to make a quiet sound.

____

____ *(1 mark)* Q11a

b) Tom has used different thicknesses of rubber bands for his instrument. As he plucks each rubber band, they each make a different sound.

The thick rubber band vibrates and produces a sound with a lower pitch.

Why does the thick rubber band have a lower pitch?

Tick the correct box.

- The thick rubber band is a red colour. ☐
- The thick rubber band vibrates more slowly. ☐
- The thick rubber band does not vibrate. ☐
- The thick rubber band vibrates more quickly. ☐

(1 mark) Q11b

c) Tom plays his instrument near to a microphone that is connected to an oscilloscope.

The diagram shows the pattern made when he plucks the thick rubber band. The sound shown in this pattern is:

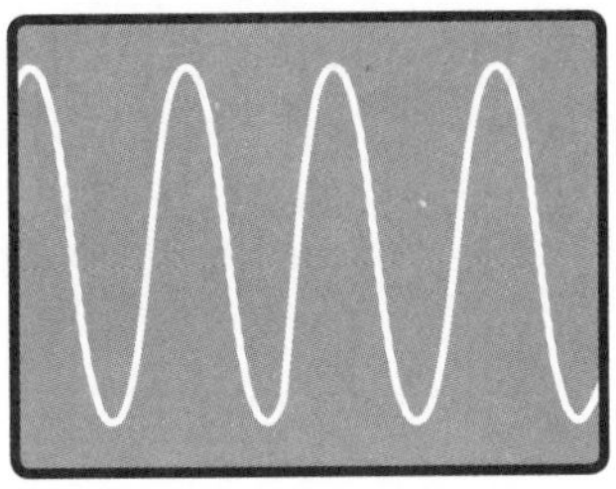

Tick the correct box.

- high pitch and loud ☐
- low pitch and quiet ☐
- high pitch and quiet ☐
- low pitch and loud ☐

(1 mark) Q11c

subtotal

d) Tom changes the rubber bands.
He puts two rubber bands of the same thickness onto the box.
They are a different length.

One rubber band is tight and one is loose.

Describe how the sound made by the tight rubber band is different from the sound made by the loose rubber band.

____

____ *(1 mark)*

Q11d

(Total 4 marks)

12 In the 18th century, the disease smallpox was killing many people.

There was no cure for the disease.

A doctor named Edward Jenner wanted to prevent smallpox.

These notes describe how Edward Jenner developed a vaccine for smallpox.

A Jenner noticed that milkmaids often caught cowpox but did not get smallpox.

B Jenner had the idea that the cowpox prevented the milkmaids catching smallpox.

C Jenner took pus from a cowpox sore of a milkmaid. He then made a small cut into the arm of a young boy. Jenner then rubbed the cowpox pus into the wound.

D The young boy became ill with cowpox, but soon recovered.

E Jenner then took some pus from the spots of a smallpox victim.

F He made another small cut into the arm of the young boy and rubbed in the smallpox pus.

G The young boy did not catch smallpox.

H Jenner decided that having cowpox would stop you getting smallpox.

a) Write down the letter of the correct statement to answer these questions. Choose your answers from **A, B, C, D, E, F, G** or **H**.

Which of the statements show:

i Edward Jenner makes an **observation**. ☐

ii Edward Jenner makes a **hypothesis**. ☐

iii Edward Jenner makes a **conclusion**. ☐ *(3 marks)* ☐ Q12a

b) Describe how Jenner infected the young boy with cowpox.

____

____ *(1 mark)* ☐ Q12b

c) Jenner carried out his experiment on a young boy.

Suggest why.

____

____

____ *(1 mark)* ☐ Q12c

d) This method of **vaccination** has been so successful that doctors have managed to wipe out smallpox throughout the world.

Name **one other** disease that you can be vaccinated for.

____ *(1 mark)* ☐ Q12d

(Total 6 marks)

END OF TEST

subtotal

Set
C

KEY STAGE 3
Levels 5–7

Test Paper 2

Science

Test Paper 2

Test Paper 2

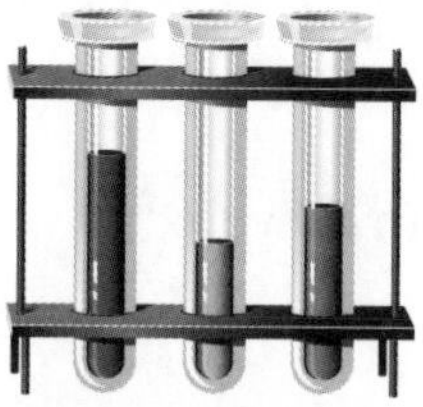

Instructions:

- find a quiet place where you can sit down and complete the test paper undisturbed
- make sure you have all the necessary equipment to complete the test paper
- read the questions carefully
- answer all the questions in this paper
- write your answers where you see this symbol ✎
- show all your working as marks may be awarded for this
- go through and check your answers when you have finished the test paper
- check how you have done using pages 113–115 of the Answers and Mark Scheme

Time:

This test paper is **1 hour** long.

Page	89	91	93	95	97	99	101	Max. Mark	**Actual Mark**
Score	....	....	....	....	....	....	....	75	....

First name ....

Last name ....

1 The table shows information about the amount of air breathed in during different activities.

Activity	**Litres of air breathed in per minute**
sitting	
standing	7.8
slow walking	12.8
fast walking	23.0
running	45.0

a) i **Plot the information on to the bar chart.**

One has been done for you.

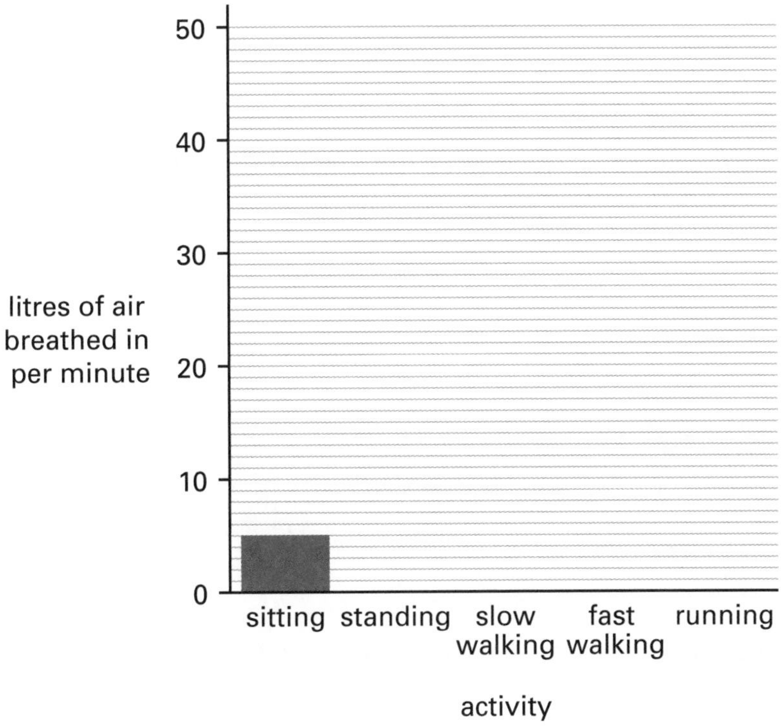

(2 marks) Q1ai

ii **How much air was breathed in whilst sitting?**

Use the bar chart to find out the answer.

________________ litres per minute *(1 mark)* Q1aii

subtotal

b) Describe the relationship between the type of activity and the amount of air breathed in.

____

____

____ *(2 marks)*

Q1b

c) The air is used in the cells for respiration.

Finish the word equation for respiration.

Choose your words from the list.

carbon dioxide **carbon monoxide** **nitrogen** **oxygen**

[ ] + glucose → [ ] + water

(2 marks)

Q1c

d) i **Describe how oxygen is transported from inside the lungs to other cells in the body.**

____

____

____ *(2 marks)*

Q1di

ii **Explain why oxygen has to be transported to all body cells.**

____

____

____ *(2 marks)*

Q1dii

(Total 11 marks)

2 The following diagram represents part of a wave.

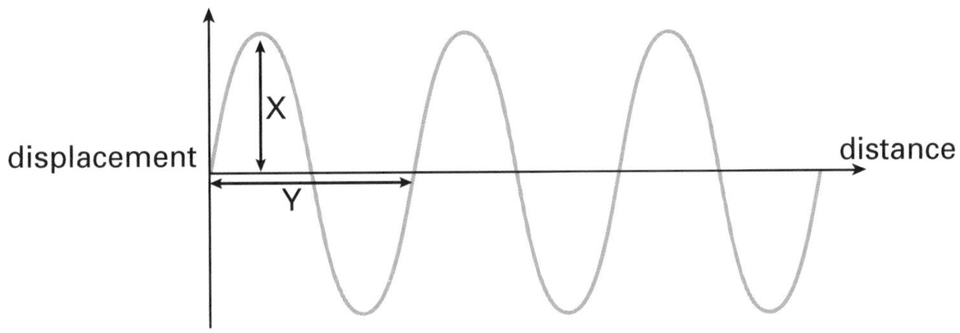

a) Choose words from the following list to name features X and Y on the diagram.

amplitude frequency velocity wavelength

X ______________________

Y ______________________ *(2 marks)*

Q2a

b) X-rays and light rays are two types of electromagnetic radiation. Complete the following table by naming the missing radiations shown by letter P and letter Q.

Gamma rays	**X-rays**	**P**	**Light waves**	**Infra-red radiation**	**Microwaves**	**Q**

P ______________________

Q ______________________ *(2 marks)*

Q2b

c) All electromagnetic waves have properties in common. State **two** properties which are common to all electromagnetic waves.

1 ____

2 ____ *(2 marks)*

Q2c

subtotal

d) Ultrasound waves are used in hospitals for examining unborn babies while they are in the uterus.

i Describe what is meant by 'ultrasound'.

____ *(1 mark)* Q2di

ii Give one advantage of using ultrasound instead of X-rays for examining an unborn baby.

____ *(1 mark)* Q2dii

iii Give one way in which an ultrasound wave is different from a light wave.

____ *(1 mark)* Q2diii

iv Give one way in which an ultrasound wave is similar to a light wave.

____ *(1 mark)* Q2div

e) X-rays can be used by doctors to look at broken bones inside our bodies.

Explain how X-rays are able to produce pictures of bones inside the body.

____

____

____ *(2 marks)* Q2e

(Total 12 marks)

3 The table shows the times taken by some children to run 80 metres in a race.

Runner	Time taken
Becky	22 seconds
Chris	17 seconds
Faiza	20 seconds
Richard	25 seconds
Shaun	28 seconds

a) **Who won the race?**

________________________________ *(1 mark)* Q3a

b) **Calculate Richard's average speed. Include the unit in your answer.**

Average speed = ____________ *(3 marks)* Q3b

c) **Which runner was running at a speed of 2.9 m/s?**

Show how you worked out your answer.

Runner ____________ *(2 marks)* Q3c

(Total 6 marks)

subtotal

4 Farmers breed animals to improve their usefulness. This is called selective breeding.

a) **Suggest two features a farmer would want to breed into his animals.**

1 ____

____

2 ____

____ *(2 marks)* Q4a

b) Here are four sentences about the selective breeding process.
They are in the wrong order.

A Farmers breed from these parents.

B The process is repeated for many years.

C When the offspring are grown, the farmers again select those with the best features.

D Farmers choose the parents with the most useful features.

Fill in the boxes to show the right order.

The first one has been done for you.

D			

(3 marks) Q4b

c) **Sometimes selective breeding is a process which takes many years. Explain why.**

____

____ *(2 marks)* Q4c

(Total 7 marks)

5 a) State **two** ways in which a mixture is different from a compound.

1 ____

2 ____ *(2 marks)*

Q5a

Ali draws five sketches of methods of separating mixtures.

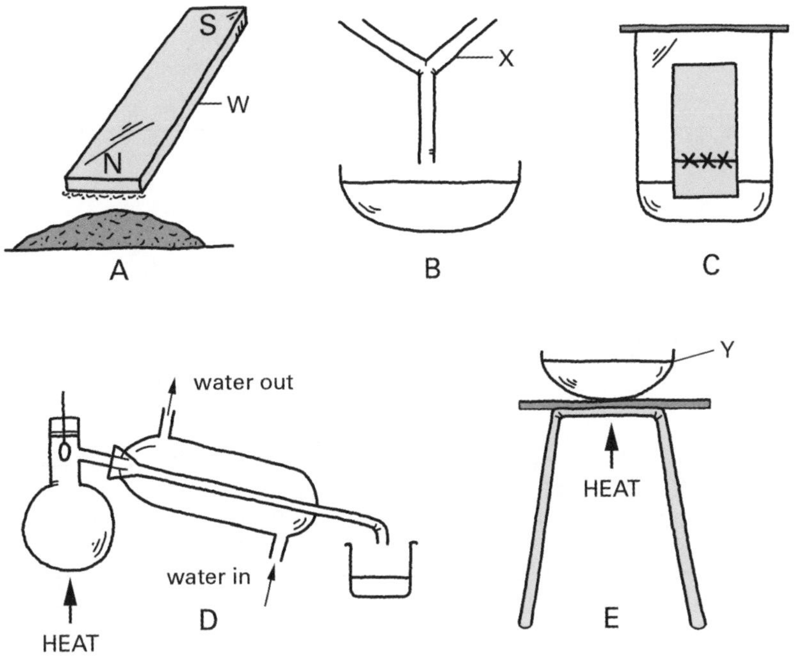

b) Three pieces of equipment, W, X and Y, are labelled on the diagrams.

Write down the names of the three pieces of apparatus.

W ____

X ____

Y ____ *(3 marks)*

Q5b

subtotal

c) **Which method, A, B, C, D or E, could be used for each of the following separations? In each case give a reason why the method can be used.**

i Sand from a mixture of sand and salt solution.

____

______________________________________ *(2 marks)* Q5ci

ii Iron from a mixture of iron and sulphur powders.

____

______________________________________ *(2 marks)* Q5cii

iii Water from salt solution.

____

______________________________________ *(2 marks)* Q5ciii

(Total 11 marks)

6 Steve enjoys winter sports.

He has a snowboard and ice skates.

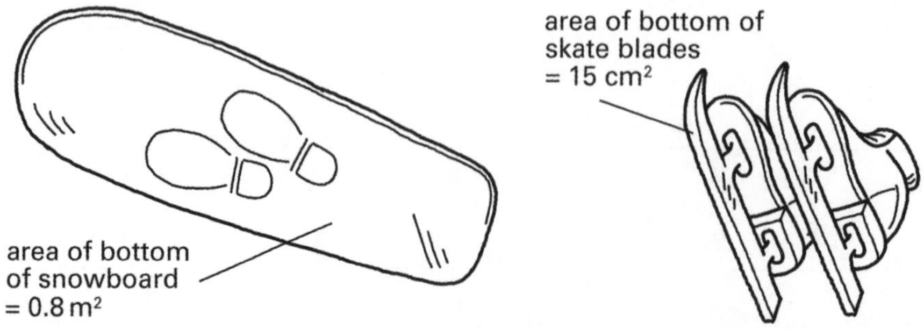

a) When Steve walks on snow, his feet sink into the snow.

When Steve uses his snowboard, he does not sink into the snow.

Explain why.

____

____ *(1 mark)* Q6a

b) Steve's ice skates are very useful for moving around on ice.

Explain why.

____

____ *(2 marks)* Q6b

c) Steve weighs 600 N.

i **Calculate the pressure on the ground when Steve is on his snowboard.**

Use the equation $\text{Pressure} = \frac{\text{Force}}{\text{Area}}$. Give the unit in your answer.

pressure = ____________ *(2 marks)* Q6ci

ii **Calculate the pressure on the ground when Steve is on his ice skates.**

Give the unit in your answer.

pressure = ____________ *(3 marks)* Q6cii

(Total 8 marks)

subtotal

7 Jamie is trying to float some different materials.

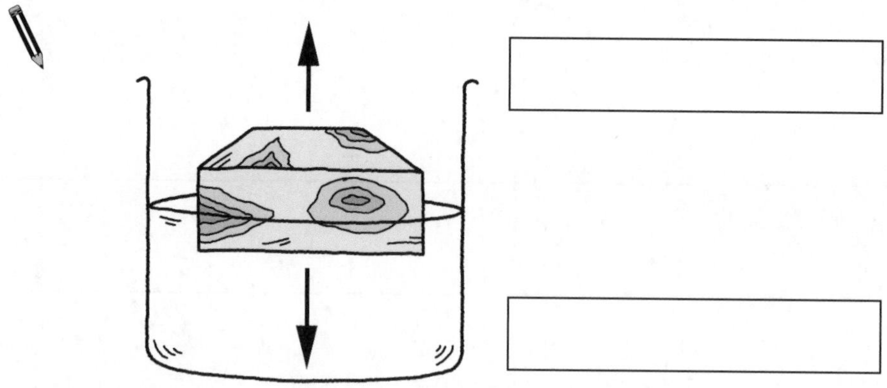

Jamie floats a block of wood on the water.
The arrows show the directions of two forces acting on the block of wood.

a) **On the diagram** label the forces. *(2 marks)* Q7a

b) The wood is floating on the water.

What does this tell you about the forces acting on the wood?

______________________________ *(1 mark)* Q7b

c) Jamie thinks that whether a substance sinks or floats depends on its density.

The density of water is 1.0 g/cm^3.

The density of the wood is 0.6 g/cm^3.

The density of polystyrene foam is 0.03 g/cm^3.

Predict whether the polystyrene will float or sink.

The polystyrene will ______________

Give a reason for your answer.

____

______________________________ *(1 mark)* Q7c

(Total 4 marks)

8 The diagrams represent the arrangement of the particles in a solid, a liquid and a gas.

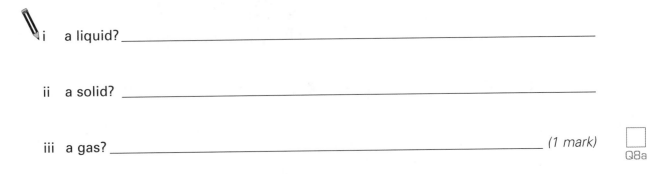

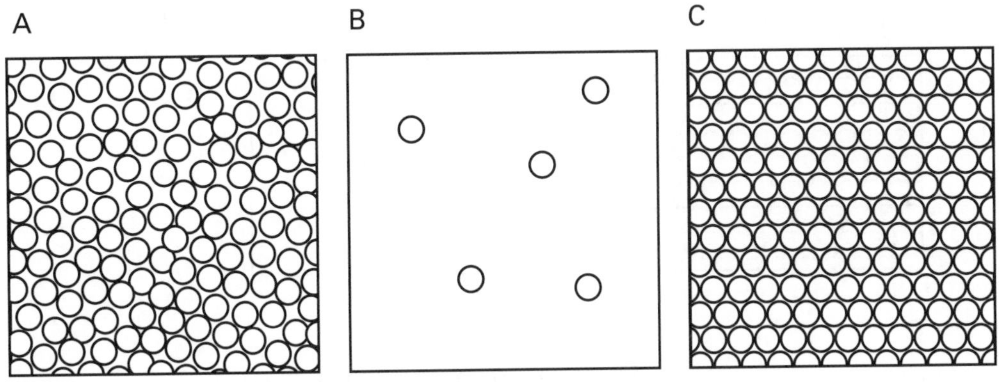

a) Which diagram represents the particle arrangement in...

i a liquid? ____________________

ii a solid? ____________________

iii a gas? ____________________ *(1 mark)*

Q8a

b) Describe what happens to the arrangement of the particles when...

i solid is turned to a liquid.

____

____________________ *(2 marks)*

Q8bi

ii a liquid turns to a gas.

____

____________________ *(2 marks)*

Q8bii

c) Do the two changes in b) require energy or give out energy?

____________________ *(1 mark)*

Q8c

subtotal

d) The diagrams below show how the particles are arranged in four substances, A, B, C and D.

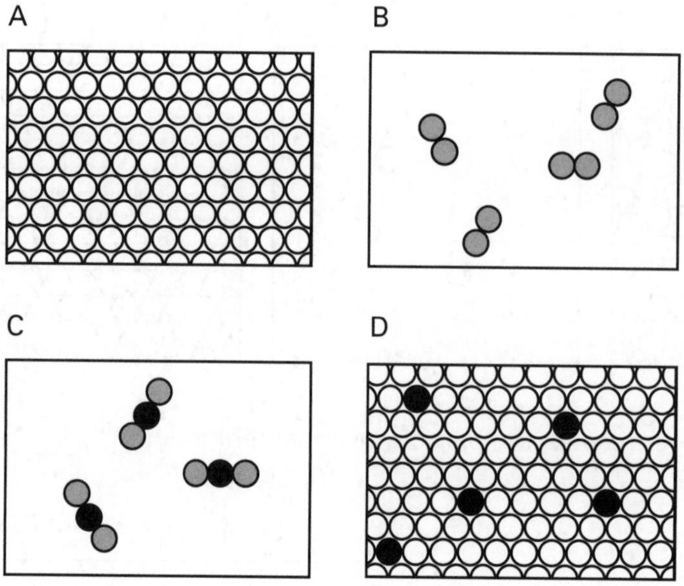

Each of the circles, ○ , ◍ and ●, shows an atom of a different element.

i Which substance is a compound? ____________________ *(1 mark)* Q8di

ii Which substance is a mixture? ____________________ *(1 mark)* Q8dii

iii Which two substances are elements? ____________________

____________________ *(1 mark)* Q8diii

iv Which two substances could be good conductors of heat?

____________________ *(1 mark)* Q8div

v Which substance could be carbon dioxide? ____________________ *(1 mark)* Q8dv

(Total 11 marks)

9 The table shows the pH values of some substances.

pH value	example
1	dilute hydrochloric acid
2	
3	
4	
5	vinegar
6	
7	ethanol
8	
9	sodium hydrogencarbonate
10	
11	
12	
13	sodium hydroxide solution

a) Choose from this list.

copper(II) sulphate solution litmus solution limewater universal indicator

The pH value of a solution can be found using ______________________ *(1 mark)*

Q9a

b) Choose from the table.

i A neutral substance ______________________

ii A strong alkali ______________________

iii A weak acid ______________________ *(3 marks)*

Q9b

c) Phenolpthalein is an indicator which is used in acid-alkali neutralisation. It is pink above pH8 and colourless below pH8.

Some phenolpthalein is added to a solution of sodium hydroxide. Vinegar is added slowly until the solution changes colour.

What is the colour change?

From ____________ to ____________ . *(1 mark)*

Q9c

(Total 5 marks)

END OF TEST

subtotal

Notes

Notes

Notes

Answers and Mark Scheme

Science Set A Test Paper 1 Answers

1) a) Arrows clearly marked and in correct direction from object into eye. *(1 mark)*
Continuous straight line from object to mirror reflection at both mirror surfaces and entry into eye *(2 marks)*
b) Light travels in straight lines.
OR
The mirror is not pointing towards Shaun. *(1 mark)*
c) reflection *(1 mark)*

2) a) Between 10 and 16 years *(1 mark)*
b) i 5 *(1 mark)*
ii Blood from the uterus wall is lost. *(1 mark)*
c) i Between 12 and 16 days *(1 mark)*
ii An egg is released. *(1 mark)*
d) i An egg is released from the ovary. *(1 mark)*
And is travelling along the narrow fallopian tube (egg tube). *(1 mark)*
ii The sperm die **and** pass out of the woman's body. *(1 mark)*
Examiner's tip *Your answer must not concentrate on fertilisation. You must consider what happens to the other sperm. Both points are needed in your answer.*
iii Any **one** from:
Menstruation stops occurring / Positive pregnancy test / There is an increase in weight or size. *(1 mark)*
iv 9 months or 40 weeks *(1 mark)*

3) a) Correct order: Jamil, John, Jay, Jimmy *(1 mark)*
b) Speed = distance ÷ time *(1 mark)*
Speed = 90 ÷ 18 = 5 *(1 mark)*
m/s *(1 mark)*
Examiner's tip *In this question it is important to write down the relationship you are going to use. This gains the first mark. The second mark is for the calculation and not forgetting that Jimmy has a 10 metre start. The final mark is for the unit.*

4) a) The poles of the right-hand magnet should read NS. *(1 mark)*
b) The arrow shows force direction from left to right. *(1 mark)*
c) Any **one** from:
Iron / Steel / Cobalt / Nickel *(1 mark)*
d) hairdryer *(1 mark)*
Examiner's tip *Any device containing an electric motor will contain a magnet.*

5) a) Refraction *(1 mark)*
*(**Accept:** dispersion)*
b) yellow, green, blue *(1 mark in correct order)*
Examiner's tip *If you need help remembering the order of colours in the spectrum, remember Richard Of York Gained Battles In Vain, where each first letter is the first letter of the colour.*
c) Different components (colours) travel at different speeds *(1 mark)*
So are refracted by differing amounts. *(1 mark)*
Red light is refracted least as it is travelling fastest
OR
Violet light is refracted most as it is travelling slowest. *(1 mark)*

6) a) Natural gas *(1 mark)*
As a gas it needs to be stored in a sealed container under pressure. *(1 mark)*
b) oxygen *(1 mark)*
c) Carbon dioxide is a greenhouse gas. *(1 mark)*
Which absorbs heat energy in the atmosphere. *(1 mark)*
Examiner's tip *The question talks about environmental problems. Students often confuse these different environmental problems.*
d) i Wood is renewable as fresh supplies can be grown. *(1 mark)*
Examiner's tip *Answer must recognise that wood is a renewable resource.*
ii Shortage of supply as use exceeds replanting. *(1 mark)*

7) a) S P R Q *(3 marks)*
(One mark if Q is anywhere after R. One mark if R is anywhere after P. One mark if P is anywhere after S.)
b) Hydrogen *(1 mark)*
c) A displacement (or replacement) reaction. *(1 mark)*
Oxide of T and Q. *(1 mark)*
d) T is between P and R in the reactivity series. *(2 marks)*
(T is above R – 1 mark; and below P – 1 mark)

8) a) Chromatography *(1 mark)*
b) The solvent moves up the paper. *(1 mark)*
*(**Allow:** Water moves up paper.)*
Different dyes move up different amounts or they move at different rates. *(1 mark)*
*(**Allow:** At different rates.)*
Examiner's tip *It is important that you make two points here.*
c) Otherwise the dyes would just dissolve in the solvent. *(1 mark)*
d) Ink contains dyes and these might start to separate. *(1 mark)*
e) i X *(1 mark)*
ii A circle or circles (which appears in each) around the dye half way up. *(1 mark)*

9) a) To allow the plant to adjust to the difference in light *(1 mark)*
   b) i Any **two** from:
   Distance of lamp from beaker / Type of pondweed / Amount of pondweed / Volume of water / Temperature of water / Length of time to count bubbles / Two minutes at the start of each experiment / Colour of light / Background light *(2 marks)*
   ii Amount of light *(1 mark)*
   ***(Accept:** light level)*
   c) i 4 points plotted correctly *(2 marks)*
   3 or 2 points plotted correctly *(1 mark)*
   ii smooth curve *(1 mark)*
   d) answer between 22 and 24 *(1 mark)*
   e) Increasing the number of lamps (or the amount of light) increases the number of bubbles. *(1 mark)*
   The more light or lamps, the more photosynthesis takes place. *(1 mark)*

10) a) oesophagus (gullet), *(1 mark)*
   stomach, *(1 mark)*
   small intestine *(1 mark)*
   ***(Do not accept:** intestine)*
   b) i D on stomach *(1 mark)*
   ii A on small intestine *(1 mark)*
   iii E on anus (end of large intestine) *(1 mark)*
   c) Large molecules cannot be easily absorbed (into the blood or intestines) *(1 mark)*
   d) Any **three** from:
   It is very long so there is a large surface area / Presence of villi increase surface area / Walls thin and permeable / Good blood supply. *(3 marks)*

11) a) i Chloroplast *(1 mark)*
   ii Chloroplast *(1 mark)*
   Cell wall *(1 mark)*
   b) Cytoplasm
   Chloroplast
   Cell wall
   Cell membrane
   (All 4 correct for 2 marks; 2 or 3 correct for 1 mark)

Science Set A Test Paper 2 Answers

1) a) As chemical energy in Surinder
   OR
   As chemical energy in her muscles. *(1 mark)*
   ***(Accept:** As chemical energy in glucose **OR** named chemicals)*
   b) Any **one** from:
   Particles collide with the walls of the tyre / They hit the walls / Bounce off the walls / The particles exert a force acts on the area of the tyre walls. *(1 mark)*
   c) They speed up.
   OR
   They get faster. *(1 mark)*
   d) Any **one** from:
   Particles hit tyre wall more frequently / With more force / More collisions with tyre. *(1 mark)*
   ***(Do not accept:** More collisions / The particles move faster.)*
   e) There will be more frequent collisions with the tyre wall. *(1 mark)*
   ***(Accept:** More collisions with the tyre / The force applied by the particles increases.)*
   ***(Do not accept:** More collisions / Less space for the particles / There are more air particles to hit the tyre wall.)*

2) a) earthworms, *(1 mark)*
   insects *(1 mark)*
   b) plants *(1 mark)*
   c) i Any **one** of the following:
   stoats, small birds, or shrews *(1 mark)*
   ii **Either** of the following:
   small bird, shrew *(1 mark)*
   iii Good eyesight to see prey moving on the ground
   OR
   Fast dive in flight to catch prey *(2 marks)*
   ***Examiner's tip** A mark can be gained for either one explained adaptation or two adaptations stated. Remember to check the number of marks available and ensure you have written the same number of facts to match the mark.*
   d) Any **three** from:
   There would be more earthworms and insects.
   There would be more for the small birds to eat.
   There would be fewer plants for the rabbits.
   There would be fewer rabbits for the owls and stoats to eat, owls would need to eat more small birds, insects and rabbits, stoats would need to eat more rabbits, owls and stoats may leave the area to hunt somewhere else. *(3 marks)*
   ***Examiner's tip** A common mistake is to only describe effects from below the removed organism. To gain full credit, mention must be made about the effects above and below the position of missing shrews.*

3) a) To prevent any gases from moving in or out. *(1 mark)*
b) oxygen *(1 mark)*
magnesium oxide *(1 mark)*
c) Straight line through origin **and** all points except B *(1 mark)*
d) i B *(1 mark)*
ii Any **two** from:
Removing of the lid during the experiment / Incomplete burning of magnesium / Insufficient heating *(2 marks)*
iii 0.1g *(Number **and** unit needed)* *(1 mark)*
e) Any **two** from:
The magnesium uses oxygen as it burns / Combined mass of magnesium oxide / Greater than mass of magnesium *(2 marks)*

4) a) solid – C liquid – A gas – B
(All correct – 2 marks, 1 or 2 correct – 1 mark)
b) The particles are closer together. *(1 mark)*
c)

From	To	Change of state	Is energy taken in or given out?
A	B	evaporation	taken in
C	A	**melting** *(1)*	**taken in**
A	C	**freezing** *(1)*	**given out**
B	A	**condensing** *(1)*	**given out** *(1)*

(One mark for three energy changes in bold. The mark in the right-hand column is scored only if all three answers in this column are correct) (4 marks)

5) a) The driving force is greater than the resistive force. *(1 mark)*
b) Equal in size and opposite in direction *(1 mark)*
c) Friction *(1 mark)*
Any **one** from:
Between the tyres and the road / Arising from air resistance / Or moving parts of the bike rubbing against each other. *(1 mark)*

6) a) carbon dioxide *(1 mark)*
carbon and oxygen (both required) *(1 mark)*
b) It is the same. *(1 mark)*
c) There is little of it.
OR
The changes in concentration are very small. *(1 mark)*
d) i In the city centre. *(1 mark)*
ii More people, vehicles etc. using oxygen up.
OR
There is no way the oxygen used can be replaced. *(1 mark)*
e) Any **one** from:
Sulphur dioxide / Carbon monoxide / Nitrogen oxides *(1 mark)*
f) i photosynthesis *(1 mark)*
ii In the country *(1 mark)*
More green plants. *(1 mark)*

7) a) vertical downward arrow from the centre of the bulldozer *(1 mark)*
b) i Any **one** from:
To spread the weight over a larger area / To reduce the pressure acting on the ground / To prevent it sinking into the ground. *(1 mark)*
ii 180 000 ÷ 10 = 18 000 *(2 marks)*
N/m^2 *(**Accept:** pascals)* *(1 mark)*
Examiner's tip *Remember – relationship, calculation and then unit.*

8) a) 60 *(1 mark)*
b) Beats per minute after smoking = 92
92 – 60 *(1 mark)*
= 32 *(1 mark)*
Examiner's tip *It is always important to show working out. If a simple error is made during the calculation, some credit can be awarded for evidence of working out.*
c) Less oxygen is reaching the cells, *(1 mark)* so the body breathes faster to compensate (or the heart pumps faster to compensate). *(1 mark)*
d) Any **two** from:
Heart disease / Bronchitis / Emphysema / Cancer. *(2 marks)*

9) a) i Any **one** from:
Increase number of coils / Increase size of core / Use soft iron core / Increase voltage/current *(1 mark)*
ii Any **two** from:
Voltage *(if not used as answer to part a) i)* / Type of core *(if not used as answer to part a) i)* / Length of wire / Size of paperclips *(2 marks)*
iii A greater number of paperclips will be picked up. *(1 mark)*
b) Only looking at the effect of the variable that has been changed. *(1 mark)*
c) Increase number of readings
OR
Calculate an average reading *(1 mark)*
d) Any **one** from:
To move cars at a scrap yard / Used in surgery to remove small pieces of iron / Inside electric bells / relays / inside speakers *(1 mark)*
Examiner's tip *An electromagnet is only magnetic when the electric current is passing around the circuit.*

10) a) Gold is unreactive and does not react with air, water etc., but magnesium is reactive. *(1 mark)*

b) No substances are gained or lost during the reaction *(1 mark)*

c) hydrogen and zinc *(2 marks)*

11) a) One set of plants in the shade and one set in plenty of light. *(1 mark)*

Any **two** from:

Keep the same / Size of pots / Material of pots / Type of soil / Volume of water given each day / Temperature / Humidity *(1 mark)*

Observe growth of plant *(1 mark)*

b) i The plant in the shade has leaves with a larger surface area.

*(**Accept:** plant in shade has larger leaves, accept the reverse: plant in light has smaller leaves)* *(1 mark)*

ii Any **two** from:

The plant in the shade has larger leaves to allow more sunlight to be absorbed /

To ensure photosynthesis can take place /

The plant in the light has smaller leaves to reduce water loss (transpiration) *(2 marks)*

Examiner's tip *Any question about plants and light will be expecting answers relating to photosynthesis.*

Science Set B Test Paper 1 Answers

1) a) i soluble *(1 mark)*

ii solution *(1 mark)*

iii solute; solvent *(2 marks)*

Examiner's tip *It is important to know and understand the meanings of the words in the list.*

b) 31 g *(1 mark)*

c) The solubility of potassium nitrate increases as temperature increases. *(1 mark)*

The solubility of sodium chloride is the same at all temperatures. *(1 mark)*

Examiner's tip *It is not enough to say the solubility of potassium nitrate increases. You must link it to temperature.*

d) i Sadie *(1 mark)*

ii Solubility of sodium chloride in water is not temperature dependent. *(1 mark)*

Rosie and Tim's suggestions would result in a higher value for solubility. *(1 mark)*

Sadie's suggestion leads to a lower result. *(1 mark)*

2) a) Light travels faster than sound. *(1 mark)*

Examiner's tip *Think about fireworks. You can see the firework explode in the sky before you hear the 'bang'.*

b) the sound is louder *(1 mark)*

c) i B *(1 mark)*

ii The eardrum vibrates. *(1 mark)*

Examiner's tip *'Vibrations' is a key word. Remember that sounds are made as a result of vibrations.*

d) Loud **OR** high pitch/frequency *(1 mark)*

can cause (temporary) deafness *(1 mark)*

3) a) magnesium, zinc, iron, copper *(3 marks)*

Examiner's tip *One mark if magnesium is anywhere before zinc. One mark if zinc is anywhere before iron. One mark if iron is anywhere before copper. You are not expected to learn the order of metals in the reactivity series but to work it out from the information given.*

b) i Blue copper(II) sulphate solution turns colourless. *(1 mark)*

Red-brown solid forms. *(1 mark)*

ii copper(II) sulphate + zinc → zinc sulphate *(**Allow** zinc(II) sulphate)* + copper *(2 marks)*

(One mark for left-hand side and one for right-hand side.)

iii displacement *(1 mark)*

4) a) *(4 marks)*

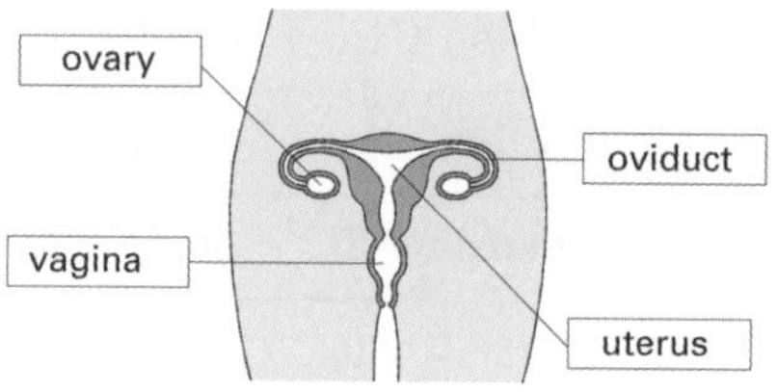

b) i X inside vagina *(1 mark)*

ii circle around an ovary *(1 mark)*

iii F on an oviduct *(1 mark)*

c) Any **two** from:

Sperm have a tail to propel them / Sperm are streamlined to help them move easily through the reproductive system / Sperm are small to help them move easily through the reproductive system *(2 marks)*

Examiner's tip *An easy way to remember the adaptations of sperm cells is to think of them as: 'many, minute and mobile'.*

5) a) Any **one** from:

To break down or digest food / To destroy bacteria (that enter the stomach with the food) *(1 mark)*

b) Carbonate reacts with acid *(1 mark)*

forming carbon dioxide *(1 mark)*

less acid reduces indigestion. *(1 mark)*

c) Measure out known quantity of acid or known quantity of tablet – mass used not number used. *(1 mark)*

Add tablets until stops fizzing / is neutralised or add acid until reaction stops. *(1 mark)*

Repeat with equal volumes of fresh acid for each tablet brand. *(1 mark)*
Smallest number used / smallest mass used / greatest amount of acid neutralised contains most carbonate. *(1 mark)*

6) a) Any order: coal, gas, oil
(All 3 for 2 marks, 2 correct for 1 mark)
*(**Accept:** peat / methane)*

b) Any **three** from:
Dead plants and animals became covered in mud (or sand, or clay) / Oxygen could not reach the dead plants and animals / So decomposition could not take place / Pressure from overlying material forms fossils / Over millions of years. *(3 marks)*
Examiner's tip *It is important that you realise that the dead remains were covered and oxygen could not reach them for decomposition. If oxygen was available the dead remains would decompose rather than fossilise.*

c) i Material from living things or plant matter. *(1 mark)*
ii The Sun / sunlight *(1 mark)*
iii (Electromagnetic) Radiation *(1 mark)*

d) They cannot be replaced / no more can be produced. *(1 mark)*

e) i Any **one** from:
It is renewable / It is widely available / You can grow more of it / It will conserve fossil fuels. *(1 mark)*
*(**Do not accept:** It is cheaper to produce)*
ii Any **one** from:
It takes up less space / More suitable for use in vehicles / More energy per unit mass. *(1 mark)*
*(**Accept:** It is more concentrated / It can be transported more easily)*
iii Any **one** from:
Atmospheric pollution / Sulphur dioxide or carbon dioxide released / They release greenhouse gases. *(1 mark)*

7) a) ligament (left-hand box), cartilage (top right-hand box), tendon (bottom right-hand box), *(3 marks)*

b) i Bones will move out of position as knee joint is bent *(1 mark)*
ii Reduces friction
OR
Stops bones rubbing together *(1 mark)*

c) i A *(1 mark)*
B *(1 mark)*
ii Muscles can only pull the bone
OR
As one muscle pulls the other relaxes and becomes longer *(1 mark)*
Examiner's tip *Muscles can only pull bones, they cannot push bones. This is why they need to work in pairs. One muscle pulls the bone one way and the other muscle will pull it back.*

8) a) i weight x distance from pivot,
300×1.5 *(1 mark)*
450 *(1 mark)*
ii 450 *(1 mark)*

b) turning moment ÷ distance from pivot
$450 \div 3$
150N *(1 mark for number, 1 mark for unit)*

c) $450 + 150 = 600$ *(1 mark)*
Examiner's tip *When asked to carry out a calculation, you must write out the formula and show all of your working out.*

9) a) Meter *(1 mark)*
*(**Accept:** data logger)*
*(**Do not accept:** colour change)*

b) Any **two** from:
Temperature / Amount of stirring / Agitation / Time needed *(1 mark)*

c) All points correctly plotted: see graph. *(1 mark)*
Smooth curve of best fit through all points: see graph. *(1 mark)*

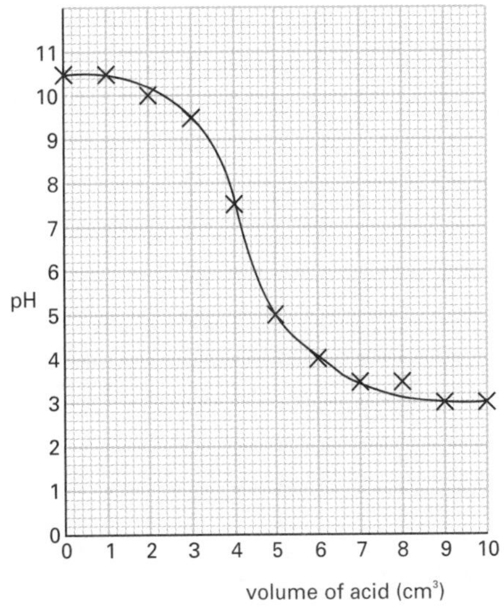

d) Between 4 and 5cm³ *(1 mark)*

e) Acid *(1 mark)*
Any **one** from:
Less than 5cm³ of acid needed to neutralise 5cm³ of alkali / When equal volumes of acid and alkali had been mixed the pH was less than 7 *(1 mark)*

Science Set B Test Paper 2 Answers

1) a) *(All 4 bars correct – 2 marks, 2 or 3 bars correct – 1 mark)*
b) blue *(1 mark)*
c) C
B
A
(All 3 correct – 2 marks, 1 or 2 correct – 1 mark)
Examiner's tip *It is important to understand that a lack of results can prevent a definite conclusion. The more results, the more reliable the conclusion.*
d) i Passed on from parents, *(1 mark)*
by genes. *(1 mark)*
ii Any **one** from: Hair colour / Height / Shoe size / Length of finger / Ear lobes attached or unattached / Can roll tongue / Left handed or right handed etc. *(1 mark)*

2) a) Any **one** from:
To minimise costs of transport / Difficult to travel with heavy rocks / Availability. *(1 mark)*
b) Rocks do not rot or corrode away like wood or metals. *(1 mark)*
*(**Accept:** stronger / last longer)*
*(**Do not accept:** it looks good)*
c) igneous *(1 mark)*
sedimentary *(1 mark)*
metamorphic *(1 mark)*
d) i Fossils *(1 mark)*
ii Granite or igneous rock *(1 mark)*
e) i Weathering and/or erosion of rocks. *(1 mark)*
ii Any **two** from:
Carbon dioxide is soluble / Dissolves in water / To produce carbonic acid or acid rain / Acid reacts with the limestone rocks / Wearing them away. *(2 marks)*
Examiner's tip *The action of carbonic acid on limestone is an example of chemical weathering.*
f)

water gets into crack *(1 mark)*
water expands when it freezes *(1 mark)*
splits rock apart *(1 mark)*
Examiner's tip *Full marks are possible for a good diagram clearly labelled.*

3) a) A *(1 mark)*
b) B *(1 mark)*
c) *(1 mark)*

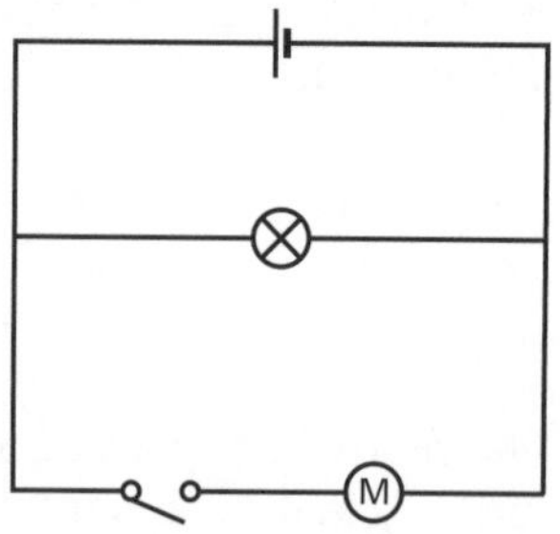

d) i Ammeter *(1 mark)*
ii X can be marked anywhere in the circuit. *(1 mark)*
iii 0.5 A *(1 mark)*
Examiner's tip *The current in a series circuit is the same all round the circuit.*
e) The lamp and the motor must have the same resistance. *(1 mark)*
Examiner's tip *If the resistance of the motor was greater than the lamp, the current passing through the motor would be less than the lamp.*

4) a) $4 \times 3 \times 2$ *(1 mark)*
24 cm^3 *(1 mark)*
b) i 250 (cm^3) *(1 mark)*
ii The pebble displaced the water; *(1 mark)*
the volume of the pebble is equal to the amount of water displaced. *(1 mark)*
(the difference between the second reading and the first)

5) a) i The number of turns **or** coils of wire *(1 mark)*
ii Any **one** from:
The current / The length **or** thickness **or** material of the wire **or** coil *(1 mark)*
*(**Accept:** the voltage **or** power, the circumference of the coil.)*
*(**Do not accept:** the number of paper-clips.)*
iii Any **one** from:
Count the number of paper-clips picked up / Measure their mass (weigh them) *(1 mark)*
*(**Accept:** the more clips the stronger the magnet)*
b) i

(1 mark)
(if more than one box is ticked, award no mark)
ii Greater precision is possible with smaller increases in (mass) increments *(1 mark)*
*(**Do not accept:** they are smaller)*

6) a) i Any **two** from:
Gravity or weight / Friction / Reaction / Air resistance *(2 marks)*
*(**Accept:** upthrust or drag)*
*(**Do not accept:** centrifugal force **or** centripetal force **or** g-force)*

ii Any **one** from:
Constant speed / Steady speed / It stays the same *(1 mark)*
*(**Accept:** it is the same **or** it does not change)*

b) Friction is less *(1 mark)*
*(**Do not accept:** it is smoother **or** it is slippery)*

c) It increases *(1 mark)*
*(**Accept:** he goes more quickly)*
Because there is less air resistance **or** friction *(1 mark)*
*(**Accept:** he is streamlined **or** aerodynamic)*

7) a) 60 *(1 mark)*
b) Accept answer between 45 and 50 minutes *(1 mark)*
c) The increase in pulse rate is due to the heart beating faster; *(1 mark)*
this puts a strain on the heart. *(1 mark)*
d) i Nicotine is addictive *(1 mark)*
ii Tar *(1 mark)*
clogs lungs and causes lung disease / cancer *(1 mark)*
OR
Carbon monoxide *(1 mark)*
stops the red blood cells supplying oxygen to the body *(1 mark)*
e) i Any **three** from:
Use your fingers at a point where an artery comes close to the surface of the skin (wrist, neck) / Count the number of ripples (pulse beats) for one minute (or part of a minute and multiply to make up to one minute) / Repeat (usually three times) / Add the total of readings together / Divide the total by the number of times a reading taken (usually three) *(3 marks)*

Examiner's tip *If an answer is worth 3 marks, you must check that you have included 3 important points. It is often useful to write down your 3 important points before you start to write your answer. Cross them out as you write about each one. This way you will not forget an important point.*

ii An average is more reliable than just one reading. *(1 mark)*

8) a) Fertilisers *(1 mark)*
*(**Accept:** manure or named chemicals in fertilisers, e.g. N,P,K)*
b) Any **two** from:
Chemicals sprayed onto fields / Chemicals soluble in water / Chemicals washed off land into river *(2 marks)*
c) i The smaller fish only take in small amounts of toxic chemcials; *(1 mark)*
this is not sufficient to kill the smaller fish. *(1 mark)*

Examiner's tip *It is easier to remember the rule that the concentration of toxic substances increases as it moves through the food chain.*

ii Larger fish eat the smaller fish and take in more toxic chemicals.
OR
Larger amounts of chemicals accumulate inside the body of the fish, causing it to die. *(1 mark)*
iii The larger fish eat lots of smaller fish over a few years. *(1 mark)*
It takes time for the chemicals to accumulate inside the fish to a high enough level to cause death. *(1 mark)*

9) a) Any **two** from:
A year is the time taken for the planet to orbit once around the Sun / Different planets take different times to orbit the Sun / The longer the orbital line, the longer the year. *(2 marks)*
b) Saturn *(1 mark)*
It is furthest away from the Sun. *(1 mark)*
c) i Venus *(1 mark)*
ii After Saturn *(1 mark)*
d) Any **one** from:
A day is the time taken for the planet to rotate/spin once on its axis / Different planets take different amounts of time to rotate on their axis. *(1 mark)*

Examiner's tip *Make sure you understand the difference between 'orbit' and 'rotate'. When a planet orbits the Sun it moves around the Sun. When a planet rotates it spins on its axis.*

10)

Name of organ system	Letter of diagram showing organ system
Circulatory system	C
Digestive system	D
Reproductive system	B
Respiratory system	A
Skeleton	E

(5 marks)

Science Set C Test Paper 1 Answers

1) a) B E A C D *(3 marks)*
(E anywhere before A – 1 mark; A anywhere before C – 1 mark; C anywhere before D – 1 mark)
b) fertilisation *(1 mark)*
c) A seed *(1 mark)*

2) a) Solid X – Physical
Solid Y – Chemical
Solid Z – Chemical *(All 3 for 2 marks; any 2 for 1 mark)*
b) i Y *(1 mark)*
ii Glowing splint *(1 mark)*
relights *(1 mark)*
c) Reaction only takes place on surface of red-brown solid. *(1 mark)*
Examiner's tip *You are not expected to try to identify these solids.*

3) a) Any **two** from:
Surface being pulled over / Size of wood block / Type of wood / Same force meter. *(2 marks)*
b) i

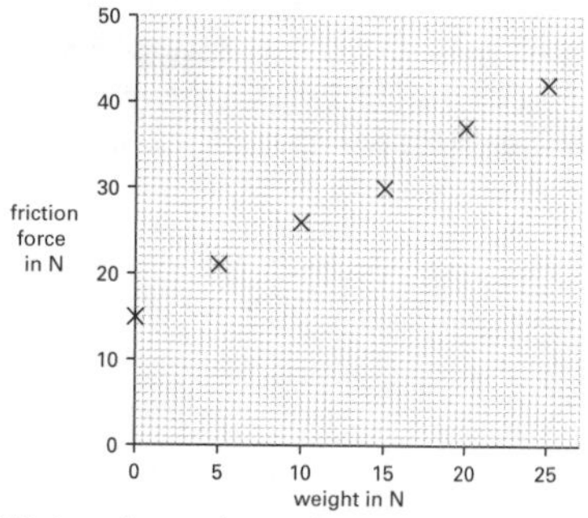

All 4 points plotted correctly *(2 marks)*
3 or 2 points plotted correctly *(1 mark)*
ii Straight line through most of the points. *(1 mark)*
Examiner's tip *Don't just join all the points. This is not acceptable. The line is to show the pattern or trend. Some of the points may not be correct, so an incorrect trend would be shown if points were joined up.*
c) Increasing the weight increases the friction OR vice versa *(1 mark)*
d) Newton *(1 mark)*

4) a) i Some microbes cause disease and illness. *(1 mark)*
ii Microbes can be useful (to humans). *(1 mark)*
*(**Accept:** Any specific example, e.g. they help digestion / sewage treatment / decay)*
b) Any **two** from:
Left open in same place / Left open for the same amount of time / Same amount of disinfectant / Same temperature / Same length of time to incubate. *(2 marks)*
Examiner's tip *Questions asking about controlling factors to ensure a fair test are common in tests.*
c) As a control
OR
To check that microbes would grow on the agar *(1 mark)*
d) i C *(1 mark)*
ii No microbes were growing on the agar. *(1 mark)*
e) By adding microbes to the agar at the start *(1 mark)*
(by taking a swab of soil and wiping it onto the agar).
f) Fleming *(1 mark)*

5) a) i Light
ii Sound
iii Kinetic or movement
(All 3 for 2 marks; 2 correct for 1 mark)
b) i Joule(s) *(1 mark)*
ii 95 Joules *(**Accept:** 95)* *(1 mark)*
iii 5% *(1 mark)*

6) a) Calcium, carbon and oxygen
(Two marks for all three correct. One mark for two correct)
b) Any **three** from:
Existing rocks are broken down by weathering and/or erosion / Into small particles/sediments / Sediments are transported by rivers / Sediments are deposited / Sediments are compressed / Sediments are buried. *(3 marks)*
c) Any **two** from:
By the action of heat and pressure / Under the Earth's surface / When the limestone is subducted. *(2 marks)*

7) a) Hydrogen *(1 mark)*
b) i Region 3 *(1 mark)*
ii Region 2 *(1 mark)*
iii Region 1 *(1 mark)*
c) Ammonium sulphate is a compound (and the Periodic Table contains only elements) *(1 mark)*
Examiner's tip *The word compound must be used to gain the mark.*
d) i Copper is deposited on the surface of the nail. *(1 mark)*
ii iron(II) sulphate + copper *(1 mark)*
Examiner's tip *The order of these chemicals is not important but both are needed to gain the mark.*

8) a) carbon and hydrogen *(both required)* *(1 mark)*
b) i butane + oxygen → carbon dioxide + water *(2 marks)*
(One mark for left-hand side and one mark for right-hand side)
ii Global warming *(1 mark)*

c) i gas (1 mark)
ii liquid (1 mark)
d) Much more can be stored in the same volume
OR
There are risks of explosion with high pressure storage. *(1 mark)*

9) a) trachea (top),
bronchus (2nd from top),
lung (bottom left)
(2 marks for all 3 correct; 1 mark if 2 correct)
b) Any **one** from:
Wall of alveoli only one cell thick / Alveoli surrounded by network of capillaries (good blood supply) / Shape of alveoli increases surface area / Inside wall of alveoli moist *(1 mark)*
c) So blood can carry oxygen around the body/to all of the cells. *(1 mark)*
d) *1 mark for* breathing:
– Breathing moves air into the lungs
– Breathing moves air out of the lungs
1 mark for respiration:
– Takes place in cells
– Reaction between oxygen and glucose
– Releases energy
– Produces water and carbon dioxide
(2 marks)

Examiner's tip *The processes of breathing and respiration are often confused. It is easier to remember that breathing gets the air into the body and respiration takes place inside every cell in your body. B comes before R.*

10) a) Cells are facing each other. *(1 mark)*
b) Stays light *(1 mark)*
c) Parallel *(1 mark)*
d) i 0.2 *(1 mark)*
ii The current is shared between each route in a parallel circuit. *(1 mark)*
e) The passage of electric current *(1 mark)*

Examiner's tip *In a parallel circuit the electric current is divided equally as it passes through each route. If there had been four routes in this circuit the current in each route would be 0.1 A.*

11) a) Pluck the rubber bands more gently
OR
Not pluck the rubber bands so hard *(1 mark)*
b) The thick rubber band vibrates more slowly. *(1 mark)*
c) low pitch and loud *(1 mark)*
d) The tight rubber band will be a higher pitch. *(1 mark)*

Examiner's tip *When looking at the patterns formed by oscilloscopes you need to remember the louder the sound the higher the wave pattern, the higher the pitch the closer together the wave pattern.*

12) a) i A *(1 mark)*
ii B *(1 mark)*
iii H *(1 mark)*
b) He took pus from a cowpox sore and rubbed it into a wound. *(1 mark)*
c) The young boy had less chance of already having smallpox.
OR
The young boy was less likely to have had any diseases. *(1 mark)*
d) Any **one** from:
Polio / Mumps / Measles / Rubella / T.B. *(1 mark)*

Examiner's tip *There is a lot of reading for this question. It is often a good idea to have a quick look through the questions first before you start reading the text. This way you know what information you are looking for.*

Science Set C Test Paper 2 Answers

1) a) i

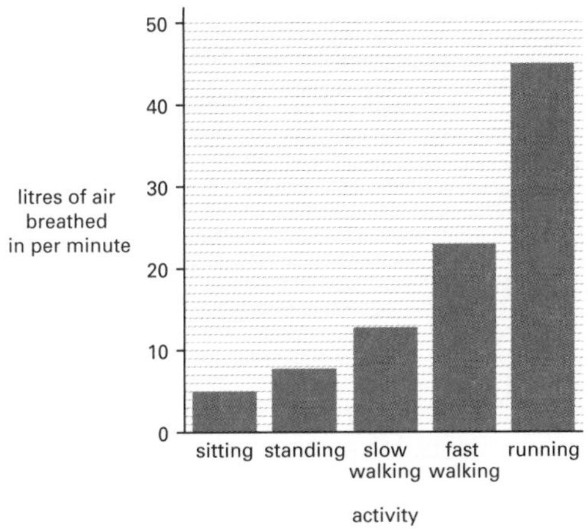

All four plotted correctly – 2 marks.
2 or 3 plotted correctly – 1 mark.

ii 5 *(1 mark)*
b) The greater the activity, *(1 mark)*
the greater the amount of air breathed in. *(1 mark)*

Examiner's tip *When asked to describe a relationship it is a good idea to think of relationships as "er–er relationships." This helps to reinforce the idea that you need to consider two factors. The factors are usually greater, slower, stronger, faster, etc.*

c) oxygen *(1 mark)*
carbon dioxide *(1 mark)*
d) i Any **two** from:
Oxygen diffuses through the alveoli (air sacs/lungs) / Into the bloodstream / The bloodstream transports the oxygen around the body. *(2 marks)*

ii Any **two** from:
Oxygen needed for respiration / To release energy from food / Respiration happens in all body cells. *(2 marks)*

2) a) X= amplitude *(1 mark)*
Y = wavelength *(1 mark)*
b) P = Ultra violet *(1 mark)*
***(Accept**: UV)*
Q = Radiowaves *(1 mark)*
***(Do not accept:** TV or UHF)*
c) Any **two** from:
Travel at same speed / Travel at speed of light / Can be reflected / Can be refracted *(2 marks)*
d) i Any **one** from:
High frequency sound waves / Waves with frequency higher than 20KHz / Waves with frequency above threshold of human hearing *(1 mark)*
***Examiner's tip** Your answer must refer to frequency to get the mark*
ii Any **one** from:
X-rays can cause cancer/mutations/birth defects / Ultrasound is safe *(1 mark)*
iii Any **one** from:
Travels slower / Lower frequency / Shorter wavelength / Longitudinal not transverse wave *(1 mark)*
iv Can be reflected *(1 mark)*
e) Any **two** from:
Pass through skin and muscle / Absorbed by bone / Produces shadow picture of bones / X-rays cause film to be exposed *(2 marks)*

3) a) Chris *(1 mark)*
b) Speed = distance ÷ time *(1 mark)*
= 80 ÷ 25 = 3.2 *(1 mark)*
m/s *(1 mark)*
c) Shaun (must be slower than Richard) *(1 mark)*
80 ÷ 28 = 2.9 m/s *(1 mark)*
***(Accept** 2.8)*
***Examiner's tip** You need to compare the results and estimate which runner it might be. The second mark can only be awarded if the answer is supported with the calculation.*

4) a) Any **two** from:
Increase in milk yield / Thicker fleece / Disease resistance / Greater muscles / Increase in egg yield *(2 marks)*
(Accept other reasonable answers)
b) D A C B *(3 marks)*
c) With any generation there is a slight change *(1 mark)*
It takes many generations before the required features are consistently reproduced in the offspring. *(1 mark)*

5) a) Any **two** from:
Compounds are produced in chemical reactions / Compounds need a chemical reaction to separate them / Mixtures can be separated by physical means / Compounds have fixed compositions (mixtures do not) *(2 marks)*
b W – magnet *(1 mark)*
X – (filter) funnel *(1 mark)*
Y – evaporating basin *(1 mark)*
c) i B *(1 mark)*
Sand remains in filter paper.
OR
Salt solution goes through filter paper.
OR
Salt dissolves in water and sand does not. *(1 mark)*
ii A *(1 mark)*
Iron is attracted to a magnet.
OR
Sulphur is not attracted to a magnet. *(1 mark)*
iii D *(1 mark)*
Water boils off when heated, and steam is condensed.
OR
Salt remains in flask. *(1 mark)*

6) a) The snowboard has a larger surface area. *(1 mark)*
b) The ice skates have a small area; *(1 mark)*
OR high pressure;
that causes a groove in the ice. *(1 mark)*
c) i Pressure = force ÷ area
600 ÷ 0.8 = 750 N/m^2
(1 mark for correct answer, 1 mark for unit)
***Examiner's tip** Make sure you have a calculator that works and that you know how to use it.*
ii 600 ÷ 30 *(1 mark)*
= 20 *(1 mark)*
N/cm^2 *(1 mark)*
***Examiner's tip** Be careful to work in the correct units.*

7) a) upthrust *(top box)* *(1 mark)*
weight *(bottom box)* *(1 mark)*
b) The forces are balanced. *(1 mark)*
c) float *(no mark)*
The density of polystyrene is less than the density of water. *(1 mark)*

8) a) i A
ii C
iii B *(All correct for 1 mark)*
b) i Particles gain energy; *(1 mark)*
regular arrangement breaks down *(1 mark)*
ii Particles gain more energy; *(1 mark)*
structure breaks down and moves apart *(1 mark)*

c) Both require energy *(1 mark)*

d) i C *(1 mark)*

ii D *(1 mark)*

iii A and B *(1 mark)*

Examiner's tip *Answers may be in either order, but* ***both*** *answers are required for the mark.*

iv A and D *(1 mark)*

Examiner's tip *Answers may be in either order, but* ***both*** *answers are required for the mark.*

v C *(1 mark)*

9) a) universal indicator *(1 mark)*

b) i ethanol *(1 mark)*

ii sodium hydroxide solution *(1 mark)*

iii vinegar *(1 mark)*

c) pink to colourless *(1 mark)*

Notes

Notes

Notes